THE EARLY NORMAN CASTLES OF
THE BRITISH ISLES

DOL.

RENNES.

DINAN.

BAYEUX.

HASTINGS.

MOTTE-CASTLES FROM THE BAYEUX TAPESTRY.

THE EARLY NORMAN CASTLES
OF THE BRITISH ISLES

BY ELLA S. ARMITAGE

HONORARY FELLOW OF THE SOCIETY OF ANTIQUARIES OF SCOTLAND

AUTHOR OF "THE CHILDHOOD OF THE ENGLISH NATION"; "THE CONNECTION
OF ENGLAND AND SCOTLAND"; "AN INTRODUCTION TO ENGLISH ANTIQUITIES,"
ETC., ETC.

WITH PLANS BY D. H. MONTGOMERIE, F.S.A.

LONDON
JOHN MURRAY, ALBEMARLE STREET, W.
1912

ISBN 0 576 19207 4

Republished in 1971 by Gregg International Publishers Limited
Westmead, Farnborough, Hants, England

Printed in England

ERRATA

Page 34, *note* 1.—*For* "construerat" *read* "construxerat."

Page 40, line 9.—*For* "there was only one motte, the site of the castle of the Norman Giffards is now almost obliterated," *read* "there was only one motte, site of the castle of the Norman Giffards, now almost obliterated."

Page 133, line 16.—*For* "1282" *read* "1182."

Page 145, *note* 1.—*For* "Legercestria" *read* "Legecestria."

Page 147, line 15.—Delete comma after "castle."

Page 216, *note* 2.—*For* "instalment" *read* "statement."

Page 304, *note* 3.—*For* "Galloway, Wigton, Kirkcudbright, and Dumfries," *read* "Galloway (Wigton, Kirkcudbright, and Dumfries)."

PREFACE

SOME portions of this book have already appeared in print. Of these, the most important is the *catalogue raisonné* of early Norman castles in England which will be found in Chapter VII., and which was originally published in the *English Historical Review* (vol. xix., 1904). It has, however, been enlarged by the inclusion of five fresh castles, and by notes upon thirty-four others, of which the article in the *Review* gave only the names ; the historical notes in that essay being confined to the castles mentioned in Domesday Book.

The chapter on Irish mottes appeared in the *Antiquary* (vol. xlii., 1906), but it has been revised, corrected, and added to. Portions of a still earlier paper, read before the Society of Antiquaries of Scotland in March 1900, are incorporated in various parts of the book, but these have been recast in the fuller treatment of the subject which is aimed at here.

The rest of the work is entirely new. No serious attempt had been made to ascertain the exact nature of Saxon and Danish fortifications by a comparison of the existing remains with the historical records which have come down to us, until the publication of Mr Allcroft's valuable book on *Earthwork of England*.

The chapters on Saxon and Danish earthworks in the present volume were written before the appearance of his book, though the results arrived at are only slightly different.

In Chapter V. an effort is made to trace the first appearance of the private castle in European history. The private castle is an institution which is often carelessly supposed to have existed from time immemorial. The writer contends that it only appears after the establishment of the feudal system.

The favourable reception given by archæologists to the paper read before the Scottish Society led the writer to follow up this interesting subject, and to make a closer study of the motte-castles of Wales, Scotland, and Ireland. The book now offered is the fruit of eleven years of further research. The result of the inquiry is to establish the theory advanced in that earlier paper, that these castles, in the British Islands, are in every case of Norman origin.

The writer does not claim to have originated this theory. Dr Round was the first to attack (in the *Quarterly Review*, 1894) the assertion of the late Mr G. T. Clark that the moated mound was a Saxon castle. Mr George Neilson continued the same line of argument in his illuminating paper on " The Motes in Norman Scotland " (*Scottish Review*, vol. xxxii., 1898).[1] All that the writer claims is to have carried the contention a stage further, and to have shown that the private castle did not exist at all in Britain until it was brought here by the Normans.

[1] Mr W. H. St John Hope arrived independently at similar conclusions.

The author feels that some apology is necessary for the enormous length of Chapter VII., containing the catalogue of Early English castles. It may be urged in extenuation that much of the information it contains has never before appeared in print, seeing that it has been taken from unpublished portions of the Pipe Rolls; further, that contemporary authorities have in all cases been used, and that the chapter contains a mass of material, previously scattered and almost inaccessible, which is here for the first time collated, and placed, as the author thinks, in its right setting. It is hoped that the chapter will prove a useful storehouse to those who are working at the history of any particular castle mentioned in the list.

To many it may seem a waste of labour to devote a whole book to the establishment of a proposition which is now generally adopted by the best English archæologists; but the subject is an important one, and there is no book which deals with it in detail, and in the light of the evidence which has recently been accumulated. The writer hopes that such fuller statement of the case as is here attempted may help not only to a right ascription of British castle-mounds, and of the stone castles built upon many of them, but may also furnish material to the historian who seeks to trace the progress of the Norman occupation.

Students of the architecture of castles are aware that this subject presents much more difficult questions than does the architecture of churches. Those who are seriously working on castle architecture are very few in number, and are as yet little known to the world at large. From time to time, books on castles are issued from the press, which show that the writers have not even an idea of the preliminary studies without which their work has no value at all. It is hoped that the sketch of castle architecture from the 10th century to the 13th, which is given in the last chapter, may prove a useful contribution to the subject, at any rate in its lists of dated castles. The Pipe Rolls have been too little used hitherto for the general history of castle architecture, and no list has ever been published before of the keeps built by Henry II. But without the evidence of the Pipe Rolls we are in the land of guesswork, unsupported, as a rule, by the decorative details which render it easy to read the structural history of most churches.

My warmest thanks are due to Mr Duncan H. Montgomerie, F.S.A., for his generous labour on the plans and illustrations of this book, and for effective assistance in the course of the work, especially in many toilsome pilgrimages for the purpose of comparing the Ordnance Survey with the actual remains. I also owe grateful thanks to Mr Goddard H. Orpen, R.I.A., for most kindly revising the chapter on Irish mottes; to Mr W. St John Hope (late Assistant Secretary of the Society of Antiquaries), for information on many difficult points; to Mr Harold Sands, F.S.A., whose readiness to lay his great stores of knowledge at my disposal has been always unfailing; to Mr George Neilson, F.S.A.Scot., for most valuable help towards my chapter on Scottish mottes; to Mr Charles Dawson, F.S.A., for granting the use of his admirable photographs from the Bayeux Tapestry; to Mr Cooper, author of the

History of York Castle, for important facts and documents relating to his subject ; to the Rev. Herbert White, M.A., and to Mr Basil Stallybrass, for reports of visits to castles ; and to correspondents too numerous to mention who have kindly, and often very fully, answered my inquiries.

ELLA S. ARMITAGE.

WESTHOLM,
RAWDON, LEEDS.

CONTENTS

xiii

CONTENTS

LIST OF ILLUSTRATIONS
AND PLANS

xv

THE EARLY NORMAN CASTLES OF
THE BRITISH ISLES

CHAPTER I

INTRODUCTORY

THE study of earthworks has been one of the most
neglected subjects in English archæology until quite
recent years. It may even be said that during the first
half of the 19th century, less attention was paid to
earthworks than by our older topographical writers.
Leland, in the reign of Henry VIII., never failed to
notice the "Dikes and Hilles, which were Campes of
Men of Warre," nor the "Hilles of Yerth cast up like
the Dungeon of sum olde Castelle," which he saw in
his pilgrimages through England. And many of our
17th- and 18th-century topographers have left us invaluable notices of earthworks which were extant in their
time. But if we turn over the archæological journals
of some fifty years ago, we shall be struck by the
paucity of papers on earthworks, and especially by the
complete ignoring, in most cases, of those connected
with castles.

The misfortune attending this neglect, was that it
left the ground open to individual fancy, and each
observer formed his own theory of the earthworks
which he happened to have seen, and as often as not,

stated that theory as a fact. We need not be surprised
to find Camden doing this, as he wrote before the dawn
of scientific observation; but that such methods should
have been carried on until late in the 19th century is
little to the credit of English archæology. Mr Clark's
work on *Mediæval Military Architecture* (published in
1884), which has the merit of being one of the first to
pay due attention to castle earthworks, counterbalances
that merit by enunciating as a fact a mere guess of his
own, which, as we shall afterwards show, was absolutely
devoid of solid foundation.

The scientific study of English earthworks may be
said to have been begun by General Pitt-Rivers in the
last quarter of the 19th century; but we must not
forget that he described himself as a pupil of Canon
Greenwell, whose careful investigations of British
barrows form such an important chapter of prehistoric
archæology. General Pitt-Rivers applied the lessons
he had thus learned to the excavation of camps and
dykes, and his labours opened a new era in that branch
of research. By accumulating an immense body of
observations, and by recording those observations with
a minuteness intended to forestall future questions, he
built up a storehouse of facts which will furnish
materials to all future workers in prehistoric antiquities.
He was too cautious ever to dogmatise, and if he
arrived at conclusions, he was careful to state them
merely as suggestions. But his work destroyed many
favourite antiquarian delusions, even some which had
been cherished by very learned writers, such as Dr
Guest's theory of the "Belgic ditches" of Wiltshire.

A further important step in the study of earthworks
was taken by the late Mr I. Chalkley Gould, when he
founded the Committee for Ancient Earthworks, and

drew up the classification of earthworks which is now being generally adopted by archæological writers. This classification may be abridged into (*a*) promontory or cliff forts, (*b*) hill forts, (*c*) rectangular forts, (*d*) moated hillocks, (*e*) moated hillocks with courts attached, (*f*) banks and ditches surrounding homesteads, (*g*) manorial works, (*h*) fortified villages.

We venture to think that still further divisions are needed, to include (1) boundary earthworks; (2) sepulchral or religious circles or squares; (3) enclosures clearly non-military, intended to protect sheep and cattle from wolves, or to aid in the capture of wild animals.[1]

This classification, it will be observed, makes no attempt to decide the dates of the different types of earthworks enumerated. But a great step forward was taken when these different types were separated from one another. There had been no greater source of confusion in the writings of our older antiquaries, than the unscientific idea that one earthwork was as good as another; that is to say, that one type of earthwork would do as well as another for any date or any circumstances. When it is recognised that large classes of earthworks show similar features, it becomes probable that even if they were not thrown up in the same historic period, they were at any rate raised to meet similar sets of circumstances. We may be quite sure that a camp which contains an area of 60 or 80 acres was not constructed for the same purpose as one which only contains an area of three.

We are not concerned here, however, with the

---

[1] In the paper on Earthworks in the second volume of the *Victoria County History of Yorkshire*, this subdivision of the promiscuous class X., is used.

attempt to disentangle the dates of the various classes of prehistoric earthworks.[1] Such generalisations are for the most part premature ; and although some advance is being made in this direction, it is still impossible to decide without excavation whether a camp of class (*a*) or (*b*) belongs to the Stone Age, the Bronze Age, or the Iron Age. Our business is with classes (*d*) and (*e*) of Mr Gould's list, that is, with the moated hillocks. We shall only treat of the other classes to the extent which is necessary to bring out the special character of classes (*d*) and (*e*).

Let us look more closely into these earthworks in their perfect form, the class (*e*) of the Earthwork Committee's list. They consist, when fully preserved, of an artificial hillock, 20, 30, 40, or in some rare instances 100 feet high. The hillock carried a breastwork of earth round the top, which in many cases is still preserved ; this breastwork enclosed a small court, sometimes only 30 feet in diameter, in rare cases as large as half an acre ; it must have been crowned by a stockade of timber, and the representations in the Bayeux Tapestry would lead us to think that it always enclosed a wooden tower.[2] As a rule the hillock is round, but it is not unfrequently oval, and occasionally square. The base of the hillock is surrounded by a ditch. Below the hillock is a court, much larger than the small space enclosed on the top of the mount. It also has been surrounded by a ditch, which joins the ditch of the mount, and thus encloses the whole fortification. The court is defended by earthen banks, both on the scarp and counterscarp of the ditch, and these banks

---

[1] Since the above was written, Mr Hadrian Allcroft's work on *Earthwork of England* has furnished an admirable text-book of this subject.

[2] See Frontispiece.

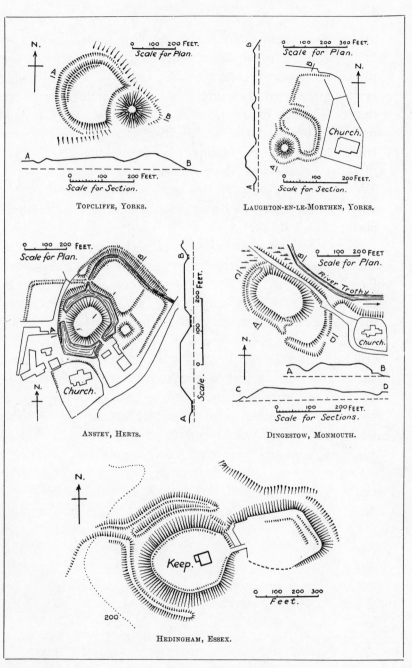

TOPCLIFFE, YORKS.

LAUGHTON-EN-LE-MORTHEN, YORKS.

ANSTEY, HERTS.

DINGESTOW, MONMOUTH.

HEDINGHAM, ESSEX.

FIG. 1.—TYPICAL MOTTE-CASTLES.

[To face p. 4.

of course had also their timber stockades, the remains of
which have sometimes been found on excavation.[1]

These are the main features of the earthworks in
question. Some variations may be noticed. The
ditch is not invariably carried all round the hillock,
occasionally it is not continued between the hillock and
the court.[2] Sometimes the length of the ditch separating the hillock from the court is at a higher level than
the main ditch.[3] Often the ditches were evidently dry
from the first, but not infrequently they are wet, and
sometimes vestiges of the arrangements for feeding
them are still apparent. The hillock is not invariably
artificial; often it is a natural hill scarped into a conical
shape; sometimes an isolated rock is made use of to
serve as a citadel, which saved much spade-work. The
shape of the court is very variable: it may be square or
oblong, with greatly rounded corners, or it may be oval,
or semilunar, or triangular; a very common form is the
bean-shaped. The area covered by these fortifications
is much more uniform; one of the features contrasting
them most strongly with the great prehistoric "camps"
of southern England is their comparatively small size.
We know of only one (Skipsea) in which the bailey
covers as much as eight acres; in by far the greater
number the whole area included in the hillock, court,
and ditches does not exceed three acres, and often it is
not more than one and a half.[4]

Now this type of fort will tell us a good deal about

[1] See Fig. 1.

[2] For instance, at Berkeley, Ewias Harold, Yelden, and Tomen y
Roddwy.

[3] As at Rayleigh and Downpatrick.

[4] In some of these castles there is no gap in the bailey banks for an
entrance. They must have been entered by a movable wooden stair, such
as horses can be taught to climb. See the plan of Topcliffe Castle, Yorks
(Fig. 1).

itself if we examine it carefully. In the first place, its character is more pronounced than that of any other class of earthwork. It differs entirely from the great camps which belong to the tribal period. It was evidently not designed to accommodate a mass of people with their flocks and herds. It is small in area, and its citadel, as a rule, is very small indeed. Dr Sophus Müller, the eminent Danish archæologist, when dealing with the specimens of this class of fortification which are to be found in Denmark, made the luminous remark that "the fortresses of prehistoric times are the defences of the *community*, north of the Alps as in the old classical lands. Small castles for an individual and his warrior-band belong to the Middle Ages."[1] These words give the true direction to which we must turn for the interpretation of these earthworks.

In the second place, this type presents a peculiar development of plan, such as we do not expect to find in the earliest times in these islands. It has a citadel of a most pronounced type. This alone differentiates it from the prehistoric or Keltic camps which are so abundant in Great Britain. It might be too hasty a generalisation to say that no prehistoric camps have citadels, but as a rule the traverses by which some of these camps are divided appear to have been made for the purpose of separating the cattle from the people, rather than as ultimate retreats in time of war. The early German camps, according to Köhler, have inner enclosures which he thinks were intended for the residence of the chief; but he calls attention to the great difference between these camps and the class we are now considering, in that the inner enclosure is of much greater size.[2] It would appear that some of the fortifica-

---

[1] *Vor Oldtid*, p. 629.   [2] *Entwickelung des Kriegswesens*, iii., 379.

tions in England which are known or suspected to be Saxon have also these inner enclosures of considerable size (6 acres in the case of Witham), but without any vestige of the hillock which is the principal feature of class (*e*).

It is clear, in the third place, that the man who threw up earthworks of this latter class was not only suspicious of his neighbours, but was even suspicious of his own garrison. For the hillock in the great majority of cases is so constructed as to be capable of complete isolation, and capable of defending itself, if necessary, against its own court. Thus it is probable that the force which followed this chieftain was not composed of men of his own blood, in whom he could repose absolute trust ; and the earthworks themselves suggest that they are the work of an invader who came to settle in these islands, who employed mercenaries instead of tribesmen, and who had to maintain his settlement by force.

When on further inquiry we find that earthworks of this type are exceedingly common in France, and are generally found in connection with feudal castles,[1] and when we consider the area of their distribution in the United Kingdom, and see that they are to be found in every county in England, as well as in Wales and in the Normanised parts of Ireland and Scotland, we see that the Norman invader is the one to whom they seem to point. We see also that small forts of this kind, easily and cheaply constructed, and defensible by a small number of men, exactly correspond to the needs of the Norman invader, both during the period of the Conquest and for a long time after his first settlement here.

But it will at once occur to an objector that there have been other invaders of Britain before the Normans,

---

[1] See Chapter VII.

and it may be asked why these earthworks were not
equally suited to the needs of the Saxon or the Danish
conquerors, and why they may not with equal reason be
attributed to them.   To answer this question we will try
to discover what kind of fortifications actually were
constructed by the Saxons and Danes, and to this
inquiry we will address ourselves in the succeeding
chapters.

It will clear the ground greatly if it is recognised at
the outset that these earthworks are *castles*, in the
usual sense of the word ; that is, the private fortified
residences of great landowners.   It was the chief merit
of Mr G. T. Clark's work on *Mediæval Military
Architecture*, that he showed the perfect correspondence
in plan of these earthen and timber structures with
the stone castles which immediately succeeded them,
so that it was only necessary to add a stone tower
and stone walls to these works to convert them into
a Norman castle of the popularly accepted type.   We
regard the military character of these works as so
fully established that we have not thought it necessary to
discuss the theory that they were temples, which was
suggested by some of our older writers, nor even the
more modern idea that they were moot-hills, which
has been defended with considerable learning by Mr
G. L. Gomme.[1]   Dr Christison remarks in his valuable
work on Scottish fortifications that an overweening
importance has been attached to moot-hills, without
historical evidence.[2]   And Mr George Neilson, in his
essay on " The Motes in Norman Scotland "[3] (to which
we shall often have occasion to refer hereafter), shows that

[1] *Primitive Folkmoots.*   See Appendix A.
[2] *Early Fortifications in Scotland,* p. 13.   He adds an instance showing
that Moot Hill is sometimes a mistake for Moot Hall.
[3] *Scottish Review,* vol. xxxii.

moot-hill in Scotland means nothing but mote-hill, the hill of the mote or *motte ;* but that *moots* or courts were held there, just because it had formerly been the site of a castle, and consequently a seat of jurisdiction.[1]

That some of these hillocks have anciently been sepulchral, we do not attempt to deny. The Norman seems to have been free from any superstitious fear which might have hindered him from utilising the sepulchres of the dead for his personal defence ; or else he was unaware that they were burial-places. There are some very few recorded instances of prehistoric burials found under the hillocks of castles ; but in ordinary cases, these hillocks would not be large enough for the *mottes* of castles.[2] There are, however, some sepulchral barrows of such great size that it is difficult to distinguish them from mottes ; the absence of a court attached is not sufficient evidence, as there are some mottes which stand alone, without any accompanying court. Excavation or documentary evidence can alone decide in these cases, though the presence of

---

[1] Some writers give the name of moot-hill to places in Yorkshire and elsewhere where the older ordnance maps give moat-hill. *Moat* in this connection is the same as *motte*, the Scotch and Irish *mote*, i.e., the hillock of a castle, derived from the Norman-French word *motte*. As this word is by far the most convenient name to give to these hillocks, being the only specific name which they have ever had, we shall henceforth use it in these pages. We prefer it to *mote*, which is the Anglicised form of the word, because of its confusion with *moat*, a ditch. Some writers advocate the word *mount*, but this appears to us too vague. As the word *motte* is French in origin, it appropriately describes a thing which was very un-English when first introduced here.

[2] At York, a prehistoric crouching skeleton was found by Messrs Benson and Platnauer when excavating the castle hill in 1903, 4 feet 6 inches below the level of the ground. The motte at York appears to have been raised after the destruction of the first castle, but whether the first hillock belonged to the ancient burial is not decided by the account, " Notes on Clifford's Tower," by the above authors. *Trans. York. Philosoph. Soc.*, 1902. Another instance is recorded in the *Revue Archæologique*, to which we have unfortunately lost the reference.

an earthen breastwork on top of the mount furnishes a strong presumption of a military origin. But the undoubtedly sepulchral barrows of New Grange and Dowth in Ireland show signs of having been utilised as castles, having remains of breastworks on their summits.[1]

[1] From the report of a competent witness, Mr Basil Stallybrass.

CHAPTER II

ANGLO-SAXON FORTIFICATIONS

WE have pointed out in the preceding chapter that when it is asked whether the earthworks of the moated mound-and-court type were the work of the Anglo-Saxons, the question resolves itself into another, namely, Did the Anglo-Saxons build castles?

As far as we know, they did not; and although to prove a negative we can only bring negative evidence, that evidence appears to us to be very conclusive. But before we deal with it, we will try to find out what sort of fortifications the Anglo-Saxons actually did construct.

The first fortification which we read of in the *Anglo-Saxon Chronicle* is that of Bamborough, in Northumberland. The *Anglo-Saxon Chronicle* tells us that in 547 Ida began to reign in Northumberland, and adds that he built " Bebbanburh," which was first enclosed with a hedge, and afterwards with a wall. Unfortunately this celebrated passage is merely the interpolation of a 12th-century scribe, and is consequently of no authority whatever,[1] though there is nothing improbable in the statement, and it is supported by Nennius.[2]

[1] Earle, *Two Saxon Chronicles Parallel*, Introd., xxiii.

[2] Nennius says that Ida "*unxit* (read cinxit) Dynguayrdi Guerth-Berneich"=a strength or fort of Bernicia. *Mon. Hist. Brit.*, 75. Elsewhere he calls Bamborough Dinguo Aroy. It is quite possible that there might have been a Keltic *din* in a place so well fitted for one as Bamborough.

11

Ida's grandson Ethelfrith gave this fortress to his wife Bebba, from whom it received the name of Bebbanburh, now Bamborough. It was built without doubt on the same lofty insulated rock where the castle now stands; for when it was attacked by Penda in 633, he found the situation so strong that it was impossible to storm it, and it was only by heaping up wood on the most accessible side that he was able to set fire to the wooden stockade.[1]   Modern historians talk of this fort as a castle, but all the older authorities call it a town;[2] nor is there any mention of a castle at Bamborough till the reign of William II.   The area of the basaltic headland of Bamborough covers $4\frac{3}{4}$ acres, a site large enough for a city of Ida's day.   The church of St Peter was placed on the highest point.   The castle which was built there in Norman times does not seem to have occupied at first more than a portion of this site,[3] though it is probable that eventually the townsmen were expelled from the rock, and that thus the modern town of Bamborough arose in the levels below.   Although $4\frac{3}{4}$ acres may seem a small size for an *urbs*, it was certainly regarded as such, and was large enough to protect a considerable body of invaders.

Strange to say, this is the only record which we have of any fortress-building by the invading Saxons. Until we come to the time of Alfred, there is hardly an allusion to any fortification in use in Saxon times.[4]   It

[1] Bede, H. E., iii., 16.

[2] See Bede, as above, and Symeon, ii., 45 (R.S.).

[3] We infer this from the strong defences of what is now the middle ward.

[4] The fact, however, that the *Trinoda Necessitas*, the duty of landholders to contribute to the repair of boroughs and bridges, and to serve in the fyrd, is occasionally mentioned in charters earlier than the Danish wars, shows that there were town walls to be kept up even at that date.   See Baldwin Brown, *The Arts in Early England*, i., 82.

is mentioned in 571 that the Saxons took four towns (*tunas*) of the Britons, and the apparent allusion to sieges seems to show that these British towns had some kind of fortification. The three *chesters*, which were taken by the Saxons in 577, Gloucester, Cirencester, and Bath, prove that some Roman cities still kept their defences. In 755 the slaughter of Cynewulf, king of the West Saxons, by the etheling Cyneard, is told with unusual detail by the *Chronicle*. The king was slain in a *bur* (bower, or isolated women's chamber [1]), the door of which he attempted to defend; but this *bur* was itself enclosed in a *burh*, the gates of which were locked by the etheling who had killed the king, and were defended until they were forced by the king's avengers. Here it seems to be doubtful whether the *burh* was a town or a private enclosure resembling a stable-yard of modern times. The description of the storming of York by the Danes in 867 shows that the Roman walls of that city were still preserved. These passages are the solitary instances of fortifications in England mentioned by the *Chronicle* before the time of Alfred. [2] The invasions of the Danes led at last to a great fortifying epoch, which preserved our country from being totally overwhelmed by those northern immigrants.

The little Saxon kingdom of Wessex was the germ of the British Empire. When Alfred came to the throne it had already absorbed the neighbouring kingdoms of Kent, Sussex, and Surrey, and the issue hanging in the balance was whether this small English state would survive the desolating flood of pagan barbarism which had already overwhelmed the sister kingdoms of the

[1] See Wright, *History of Domestic Manners*, p. 13.
[2] The Danish fortress of Nottingham is mentioned by the *Chronicle* in 868, but we are speaking now of purely Anglo-Saxon fortresses.

Midlands and the North. It was given to Alfred to raise again the fallen standard of Christendom and civilisation, and to establish an English kingdom on so sound a basis that when, in later centuries, it successively became the prey of the Dane and the Norman, the English polity survived both conquests. The wisdom, energy, and steadfastness of King Alfred and his children and grandchildren were amongst the most important of the many factors which have helped to build up the great empire of Britain.

We are concerned here with only one of the measures by which Alfred and his family secured the triumph of Wessex in her mortal struggle with the Danes, the fortifications which they raised for the protection of their subjects. From the pages of the *Anglo-Saxon Chronicle* we might be led to think that Alfred's son and daughter, Edward and Ethelfleda, were the chief builders of fortifications. But there is ample evidence that they only carried out a systematic purpose which had been initiated by Alfred. We know that Alfred was a great builder. "What shall I say," cries Asser, "of the cities and towns which he restored, and of others which he built which had never existed before! Of the royal halls and chambers, wonderfully built of stone and wood by his command!"[1] The *Anglo-Saxon Chronicle* notices the restoration of London (886),[2] about which two extant charters are more precise.[3] It also mentions the building of a work (geweorc) at Athelney,

[1] Asser, ch. 91, Stevenson's edition.

[2] "That same year King Alfred repaired London; and all the English submitted to him, except those who were under the bondage of the Danish men; and then he committed the city (*burh*) to the keeping of Ethelred the ealdorman." *A.-S. C.*, 886. The word used for London is *Londonburh*. Asser says: "Londoniam civitatem honorifice restauravit et habitabilem fecit," p. 489.

[3] Birch's *Cartularium*, ii., 220, 221.

and another at Limene-muthan (doubtless a repair of the Roman fort at Lympne), and two works built by Alfred on the banks of the river Lea.[1] William of Malmesbury tells us that in his boyhood there was a stone in the nunnery of Shaftesbury which had been taken out of the walls of the town, which bore this inscription : "Anno dominicæ incarnationis Alfredus rex fecit hanc urbem, DCCCLXXX, regni sui VIII."[2] Ethelred, Alfred's son-in-law, built the *burh* at Worcester in Alfred's lifetime, as a most interesting charter tells us.[3]

It may be safely assumed, then, that when Edward came to the throne he found Wessex well provided with defensive places, and that when he and his sister signalised their conquests in the Midlands by building strongholds at every fresh step of their advance, they were only carrying out the policy of their father.

At the time of Alfred's death, and the succession of Edward the Elder to the crown (901), Ethelfleda, daughter of Alfred, was the wife of Ethelred, ealdorman of Mercia, who appears to have been a sort of under-king of that province.[4] On the death of Ethelred in 912,[5] Edward took possession of London and Oxford and "of all the lands which owed obedience thereto"— in other words, of that small portion of Eastern Mercia which was still in English hands ; that is, not only the present Oxfordshire and Middlesex, but part of Herts,

[1] *Anglo-Saxon Chronicle*, 878, 893, 896. According to Henry of Huntingdon, the work on the Lea was the splitting of that river into two channels ; but I am informed that no trace of such a division remains.

[2] *Gesta Pontificum*, 186. See Appendix C.

[3] Birch's *Cartularium*, ii., 222 ; Kemble's *Codex Diplomaticus*, v., 142.

[4] He signs a charter in 889 as "subregulus et patricius Merciorum," Kemble's *Codex Diplomaticus*. See Freeman, *N. C.*, i., 564 ; and Plummer, *A.-S. C.*, i., 118.

[5] The dates in this chapter are taken from Florence of Worcester, who is generally believed to have used a more correct copy of the *Anglo-Saxon Chronicle* than those which have come down to us.

part of Bedfordshire, all Buckinghamshire, and the southern part of Northants. The Watling Street, which runs north-west from London to Shrewsbury, and thence north to Chester and Manchester, formed at that time the dividing line between the English and Danish rule.[1] It would seem from the course of the story that after Ethelred's death there was some arrangement between Ethelfleda and her brother, possibly due to the surrender of the territory mentioned above, which enabled her to rule English Mercia in greater independence than her husband had enjoyed. Up to this date we find Edward disposing of the *fyrd* of Mercia ;[2] this is not mentioned again in Ethelfleda's lifetime. Nothing is clearer, both from the *Chronicle* and from Florence, than that the brother and sister each "did their own," to use an expressive provincial phrase. Ethelfleda goes her own way, subduing Western Mercia, while Edward pushes up through Eastern Mercia and Essex to complete the conquest of East Anglia. A certain concert may be observed in their movements, but they did not work in company.

The work of fortification begun in Alfred's reign had been continued by the restoration of the Roman walls of Chester in 908, by Ethelred and his wife ; and Ethelfleda herself (possibly during the lingering illness which later chroniclers give to her husband) had built a *burh* at Bremesbyrig. During the twelve years which elapsed between Ethelred's death and that of Edward in 924, the brother and sister built no less than twenty-seven *burhs*, giving a total of thirty, if we add Chester and Bremesbyrig, and Worcester, which was built in Alfred's reign. Now what was the nature of these fortifications, which the *Anglo-Saxon Chronicle* uniformly calls *burhs* ?

[1] See Appendix B.   [2] *A.-S. C.*, 910, 911.

There is really not the slightest difficulty in answering this question. The word is with us still; it is our word *borough*. It is true we have altered the meaning somewhat, because a borough means now an enfranchised town; but we must remember that it got that meaning because the fortified towns, the only ones which were called *burhs* or *burgi*, were the first to be enfranchised, and while the fortifications have become less and less important, the franchise has become of supreme importance.

Bede, in the earliest times of our history, equated *burh* with *urbs*, a city; Alfred in his *Orosius* translates *civitas* by *burh;*[1] the Anglo-Saxon gospels of the 11th century do the same;[1] and the confederacy of five Danish towns which existed in Mercia in the 10th century is called in contemporary records *fif burga*, the five boroughs.[2]

Burh is a noun derived from the word *beorgan*, to protect. Undoubtedly its primitive meaning was that of a *protective enclosure*. As in the case of the words *tun*, *yard*, or *garth*, and *worth* or *ward*, the sense of the word became extended from the protecting bulwark to the place protected. In this sense of a *fortified enclosure*, the word was naturally applied by the Anglo-Saxons to the prehistoric and British "camps" which they found in Britain, such as Cissbury. Moreover, it is clear that some kind of enclosure must have existed round every farmstead in Saxon times, if only as a protection against wolves. The illustrated Saxon manuscripts show that the hall in which the thane dwelt, the

---

[1] *New English Dictionary*, Borough.

[2] *Anglo-Saxon Chronicle*, 942. The *Anglo-Saxon Chronicle* has three words for fortifications, *burh, faesten*, and *geweorc*. Burh is always used for those of Edward and Ethelfleda, faesten (fastness) or geweorc (work) for those of the Danes.

ladies' bower, the chapel and other buildings dependent
on the hall, were enclosed in a stockade, and had gates
which without doubt were closed at night.[1] This
enclosure may have been called a *burh*, and the innumerable place-names in England ending in *borough* or *bury*[2]
seem to suggest that the *burh* was often nothing more
than a stockade, as in so many of these sites not a
vestige of defensive works remains.[3] We may concede
that the original meaning of an *enclosure* was never
entirely lost, and that it appears to be preserved in a few
passages in the Anglo-Saxon laws. Thus Edmund
speaks of *mine burh* as an asylum, the violation of which
brings its special punishment ; and Ethelred II. ordains
that every compurgation shall take place in *thaes
kyninges byrig;* and the *Rectitudines Singularum
Personum* tells us that one of the duties of the geneat
was to build for his lord, and to hedge his *burh*.[4] But
it is absolutely clear that even in these cases a *burh* was
an enclosure and not a tump; and it is equally clear
from the general use of the word that its main meaning
was a *fortified town.* Athelstan ordains that there shall
be a mint in every *burh ;* and his laws show that already
the *burh* has its *gemot* or meeting, and its *reeve* or
mayor.[5] He ordains that all *burhs* are to be repaired

---

[1] See the illustrations in Wright, *History of Domestic Manners.*

[2] *Bury* is formed from *byrig*, the dative of *burh.*

[3] Professor Maitland observed : "To say nothing of hamlets, we have
full 250 parishes whose names end in burgh, bury, or borough, and in many
cases we see no sign in them of an ancient camp or of an exceptionally
dense population." *Domesday Book and Beyond,* 184.

[4] Schmid, *Gesetze der Angelsachsen,* pp. 176, 214, 372. It is not
absolutely certain that the *burh* in these three cases does not mean a town.

[5] Schmid, 138. Professor Maitland says : "In Athelstan's day it
seems to be supposed by the legislator that a *moot* will usually be held in a
burh. If a man neglect three summonses to a moot, the oldest men of the
burh are to ride to his place and seize his goods." *Domesday Book and
Beyond,* 185. "All my reeves," are mentioned in the Preface to *Athelstan's
Laws,* Schmid, 126.

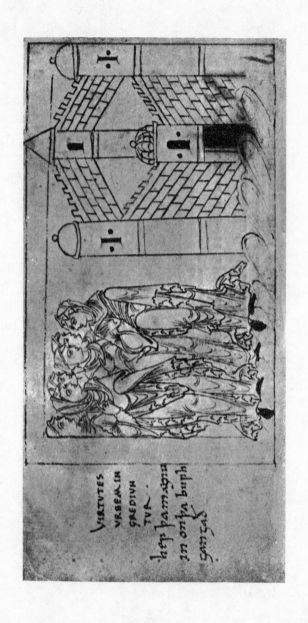

FIG. 2.—ANGLO-SAXON MS. OF PRUDENTIUS.

[*To face p.* 19.

fourteen days after Rogations, and that no market shall be held outside the town.[1] In the laws of Edgar's time not only the borough-moot and the borough-reeve are spoken of, but the *burh-waru* or burgesses.[2] *Burh* is contrasted with wapentake as town with country.[3]

If we wish to multiply proofs that a *burh* was the same thing as a borough, we can turn to the Anglo-Saxon illustrated manuscripts, and we shall find that they give us many pictures of *burhs*, and that in all cases they are fortified towns.[4] Finally, Florence of Worcester, one of the most careful of our early chroniclers, who lived when Anglo-Saxon was still a living language, and who must have known what a *burh* meant, translates it by *urbs* in nineteen cases out of twenty-six.[5] His authority alone is sufficient to settle this question, and we need no longer have any doubt that a *burh* was the same thing which in mediæval Latin is called a *burgus*, that is a fortified town, and that our word *borough* is lawfully descended from it.

It would not have been necessary to spend so much time on the history of the word *burh* if this unfortunate word had not been made the subject of one of the strangest delusions which ever was imposed on the archæological world. We refer of course to the theory of the late Mr G. T. Clark, who contended in his

[1] Schmid, 138. "Butan porte" is the Saxon expression, *port* being another word for town ; see Schmid, 643.

[2] Schmid, Edgar III., 5 ; Ethelred II., 6.   [3] Edgar IV., 2.

[4] The writer was first led to doubt the correctness of the late Mr G. T. Clark's theory of burhs by examining the A.-S. illustrated MSS. in the British Museum. On p. 29 of the MS. of *Prudentius* (Cleopatra, c. viii.), there is an excellent drawing of a four-sided enclosure, with towers at the angles, and battlemented walls of masonry. The title of the picture is "Virtutes urbem ingrediuntur," and *urbem* is rendered in the A.-S. gloss as *burh*. See Fig. 2.

[5] Florence translates *burh* as *urbs* nineteen times, as *arx* four times, as *murum* once, as *munitio* once, as *civitas* once.

Mediæval Military Architecture[1] that the moated mound
of class (*e*), which we have described in our first chapter,
was what the Anglo-Saxons called a *burh*. In other
words, he maintained that the burhs were Saxon
castles. It is one of the most extraordinary and inex-
plicable things in the history of English archæology
that a man who was not in any sense an Anglo-Saxon
scholar was allowed to affix an entirely new meaning
to a very common Anglo-Saxon word, and that this
meaning was at once accepted without question by
historians who had made Anglo-Saxon history their
special study! The present writer makes no pretensions
to be an Anglo-Saxon scholar, but it is easy to pick out
the word *burh* in the *Chronicle* and the Anglo-Saxon
Laws, and to find out how the word is translated in the
Latin chronicles; and this little exercise is sufficient in
itself to prove the futility of Mr Clark's contention.

Sentiment perhaps had something to do with Mr
Clark's remarkable success. There is an almost utter
lack of tangible monuments of our national heroes; and
therefore people who justly esteemed the labours of
Alfred and his house were pleased when they were told
that the mounds at Tamworth, Warwick, and elsewhere
were the work of Ethelfleda, and that other mounds
were the work of Edward the Elder. It did not occur
to them that they were doing a great wrong to the
memory of the children of Alfred in supposing them
capable of building these little earthen and timber castles
for their personal defence and that of their nobles, and
leaving the mass of their people at the mercy of the
Danes. Far other was the thought of Ethelfleda, when

---

[1] Published in 1884, but comprising a number of papers read to various
archæological societies through many previous years, during which Mr
Clark's reputation as an archæologist appears to have been made.

she and her husband built the borough of Worcester.
As they expressed it in their memorable charter, it was
not only for the defence of the bishop and the churches
of Worcester, but "To Shelter all the Folk."[1]   And
we may be sure that the same idea lay at the founding of
all the boroughs which were built by Alfred and by
Edward and Ethelfleda.   They were to be places where
the whole countryside could take refuge during a Danish
raid.   The *Chronicle* tells us in 894 how Alfred divided
his forces into three parts, the duty of one part being
to defend the boroughs ; and from this time forth we
constantly find the men of the boroughs doing good
service against the Danes.[2]   It was by defending and
thus developing the boroughs of England that Alfred
and his descendants saved England from the Danes.

Thus far we have seen that all the fortifications
which we know to have been built by the Anglo-Saxons
were the fortifications of society and not of the individual.
We have heard nothing whatever of the private castle
as an institution in Saxon times ; and although this
evidence is only negative, it appears to us to be entitled
to much more weight than has hitherto been given to it.
Some writers seem to think that the private castle was
a modest little thing which was content to blush unseen.
This is wholly to mistake the position of the private
castle in history.   Such a castle is not merely a social
arrangement, it is a political institution of the highest
importance.   Where such castles exist, we are certain to
hear of some of them, sooner or later, in the pages of
history.

[1] "Eallum thæm folc to gebeorge." Birch's *Cartularium*, ii., 222.

[2] Professor Maitland has claimed that the origin of the boroughs was
largely military, the duty of maintaining the walls of the county borough
being incumbent on the magnates of the shire. *Domesday Book and Beyond*,
189.   See Appendix C.

We can easily test this by comparing Anglo-Saxon history with Norman of the same period, after castles had arisen in Normandy. Who among Saxon nobles was more likely to possess a castle than the powerful Earl Godwin, and his independent sons? Yet when Godwin left the court of Edward the Confessor, because he would not obey the king's order to punish the men of Dover for insulting Count Eustace of Boulogne, we do not hear that he retired to his castle, or that his sons fortified their castles against the king; we only hear that they met together at Beverstone (a place where there was no castle before the 14th century)[1] and "arrayed themselves resolutely."[2] Neither do we hear of any castle belonging to the powerful Earl Siward of Northumbria, or Leofric, Earl of Mercia. And when Godwin returned triumphantly to England in 1052 we do not hear of any castles being restored to him.

Now let us contrast this piece of English history, as told by the *Anglo-Saxon Chronicle*, with the Norman history of about the same period, the history of the rebellion of the Norman nobles against their young duke, William the Bastard. The first thing the nobles do is to put their castles into a state of defence. William has to take refuge in the castle of a faithful vassal, Hubert of Rye, until he can safely reach his own castle of Falaise. After the victory of Val-ès-Dunes, William had to reduce the castles which still held out, and then to order the destruction of all the castles which had been erected against him.[3]

Or let us contrast the *Anglo-Saxon Chronicle* of 1051 with that of 1088, when certain Norman barons

---

[1] Parker's *Domestic Architecture in England from Richard II. to Henry VIII.*, part ii., 256.

[2] *A.-S. C.*, 1048.   [3] *William of Jumièges*, vii.-xvii.

and bishops in England conspired against the new king, William Rufus. The first thing told us is that each of the head conspirators "went to his castle, and manned it and victualled it." Then Bishop Geoffrey makes Bristol Castle the base of a series of plundering raids. Bishop Wulfstan, on the other hand, aids the cause of William by preventing an attempt of the rebels on the castle of Worcester. Roger Bigod throws himself into Norwich Castle, and harries the shire; Bishop Odo brings the plunder of Kent into his castle of Rochester. Finally the king's cause wins the day through the taking of the castles of Tonbridge, Pevensey, Rochester, and Durham.

If we reflect on the contrast which these narratives afford, it surely is difficult to avoid the conclusion that if the chronicler never mentions any Saxon castles it is because there were no Saxon castles to mention. Had Earl Godwin possessed a stronghold in which he could fortify himself, he would certainly have used it in 1051. And as the Norman favourites of Edward the Confessor had already begun to build castles in England, we can imagine no reason why Godwin did not do the same, except that such a step was impossible to a man who desired popularity amongst his countrymen. The Welshmen, we are told (that is the foreigners, the Normans), had erected a castle in Herefordshire among the people of Earl Sweyn, and had wrought all possible harm and disgrace to the king's men thereabout.[1] The language of the *Chronicle* shows the unpopularity, to say the least of it, of this castle-building; and one of the conditions which Godwin, when posing as popular champion, wished to exact from the king, was that the *Frenchmen who were in the castle* should be given up to

[1] *A.-S. C.* (Peterborough), 1048.

him.[1] When Godwin returned from his exile, and the Normans took to flight, the chronicler tells us that some fled west to Pentecost's castle, some north to Robert's castle. Thus we learn that there were several castles in England belonging to the Norman favourites.

It is in connection with these Norman favourites that the word *castel* appears for the first time in the *Anglo-Saxon Chronicle*. This is a fact of considerable importance in itself; and when we weigh it in connection with the expressions of dislike recorded above which become much more explicit and vehement after the Norman Conquest, we cannot but feel that Mr Freeman's conclusion, that the thing as well as the word was new, is highly probable.[2] For the hall of the Anglo-Saxon ealdorman or thane, even when enclosed in an earthwork or stockade, was a very different thing from the castle of a Norman noble. A castle is built by a man who lives among enemies, who distrusts his nearest neighbours as much as any foe from a distance. The Anglo-Saxon noble had no reason to distrust his neighbours, or to fortify himself against them. Later

[1] *A.-S. C.*, 1052 (Worcester). This castle is generally supposed to be Richard's Castle, Herefordshire, built by Richard Scrob; but I see no reason why it should not be Hereford, as the Norman Ralph, King Edward's nephew, was Earl of Hereford. We shall return to these castles later.

[2] Mr Freeman says: "In the eleventh century, the word *castel* was introduced into our language to mark something which was evidently quite distinct from the familiar *burh* of ancient times. . . . Ordericus speaks of the thing and its name as something distinctly French: "munitiones quas Galli castella nuncupant." The castles which were now introduced into England seem to have been new inventions in Normandy itself. William of Jumièges distinctly makes the building of castles to have been one of the main signs and causes of the general disorder of the days of William's minority, and he seems to speak of the practice as something new." *N. C.*, ii., 606. It is surprising that after so clear a statement as this, Mr Freeman should have fallen under the influence of Mr Clark's *burh* theory, and should completely have confused castles and boroughs.

historians, who were familiar with the state of things in
Norman times, tell us frequently of castles in the Saxon
period ; but it can generally be proved that they mis-
understood their authorities. The genuine contemporary
chroniclers of Saxon times never make the slightest
allusion to a Saxon castle.

The word *castellum*, it is true, appears occasionally
in Anglo-Saxon charters, but when it is used it clearly
means a town. Thus Egbert of Kent says in 765 :
"Trado terram intra castelli mœnia supranominati, id
est Hrofescestri, unum viculum cum duobus jugeribus,
etc.," where *castellum* is evidently the city of Rochester.[1]
Offa calls Wermund "episcopus castelli quod nominatur Hroffeceastre."[2] These instances can easily be
multiplied. Mr W. H. Stevenson remarks that "in
Old-English glosses, from the 8th century Corpus
Glossary downwards, *castellum* is glossed by *wic*, that
is town."[3] In this sense no doubt we must interpret
Asser's "castellum quod dicitur Werham."[4] Henry of
Huntingdon probably meant a town when he says that
Edward the Elder built at Hertford "castrum non
immensum sed pulcherrimum." He generally translates
the *burh* of the *Chronicle* by *burgus*, and he shows
that he had a correct idea of Edward's work when he
says that at Buckingham Edward "fecit *vallum*
ex utraque parte aquæ"—where *vallum* is a translation
of *burh*. The difference between a *burh* and a castle
is very clearly expressed by the *Chronicle* in 1092, when
it says concerning the restoration of Carlisle on its
conquest by William Rufus, "He repaired the borough
(burh) and ordered the castle to be built."

---

[1] *Codex Diplomaticus*, i., 138.   [2] *History of Rochester*, 1772, p. 21.
[3] Stevenson's edition of *Asser*, 331.   See Appendix D.
[4] *Asser*, c. xlix.

The following is a table of the thirty boroughs built by Ethelfleda and Edward, arranged chronologically, which will show that we never find a *motte*, that is a moated mound, on the site of one of these boroughs unless a Norman castle-builder has been at work there subsequently. The weak point in Mr Clark's argument was that when he found a motte on a site which had once been Saxon, he did not stop to inquire what any subsequent builders might have done there, but at once assumed that the motte was Saxon. Of course, if we invariably found a motte at *every* place where Edward or Ethelfleda are said to have built a *burh*, it would raise a strong presumption that mottes and burhs were the same thing. But out of the twenty-five burhs which can be identified, in only ten is there a motte on the same site; and in every case where a motte is found, except at Bakewell and Towcester, there is recorded proof of the existence of a Norman castle. In this list, the *burhs* on both sides of the river at Hertford, Buckingham, and Nottingham are counted as two, because the very precise indications given in the *Anglo-Saxon Chronicle* show that each *burh* was a separate construction.

Burhs of Ethelfleda.

Worcester .	.	. 873-899	A motte and a Norman castle.
Chester .	.	. 908	A motte and a Norman castle.
Bremesburh	.	. 911	Unidentified.
Scærgate .	.	. 913	Unidentified.
Bridgenorth	.	. 913	No motte, but a Norman stone keep.
Tamworth .	.	. 914	A motte and a Norman castle.
Stafford, N. of Sowe .		. 914	No motte and no Norman castle.
Eddisbury .	.	. 915	No motte and no Norman castle.
Warwick .	.	. 915	A motte and a Norman castle.
Cyricbyrig (Monk's Kirby)		916	No motte and no Norman castle.
Weardbyrig	.	. 916	Unidentified.
Runcorn .	.	. 916	No motte ; a mediæval castle (?).

Burhs of Edward the Elder.

Hertford, N. of Lea .	. 913	No motte and no Norman castle.
Hertford, S. of Lea .	. 913	A motte and a Norman castle.
Witham . . .	. 914	No motte and no Norman castle.
Buckingham, S. of Ouse	. 915	No motte and no Norman castle.
Buckingham, N. of Ouse	. 915	A motte and a Norman castle.
Bedford, S. of Ouse .	. 916	No motte and no Norman castle.
Maldon . . .	. 917	No motte and no Norman castle.
Towcester . . .	. 918	A motte.
Wigingamere . .	. 918	Unidentified.
Huntingdon . .	. 918	A motte and a Norman castle.
Colchester . . .	. 918	No motte ; an early Norman keep.
Cledemuthan . .	. 918	Unidentified.
Stamford, S. of Welland	. 919	No motte and no Norman castle.
Nottingham, N. of Trent	. 919	A motte and a Norman castle.
Thelwall . . .	. 920	No motte and no Norman castle.
Manchester . .	. 920	No castle on the ancient site.
Nottingham, S. of Trent	. 921	No motte and no Norman castle.
Bakewell (near to) .	. 921	A motte and bailey.

Out of this list of the *burhs* of Ethelfleda and
Edward, thirteen are mentioned as boroughs in
Domesday Book;[1] and as we ought to subtract five
from the list as unidentified, and also to reckon as one
the boroughs built on two sides of the river, the whole
number should be reduced to twenty-two. So that
more than half the boroughs built by the children of
Alfred continued to maintain their existence during the
succeeding centuries, and in fact until the present day.
But the others, for some reason or other, did not take
root. Professor Maitland remarked that many of the
boroughs of Edward's day became rotten boroughs
before they were ripe;[2] and it is a proof of the difficulty
of the task which the royal brethren undertook that,
with the exception of Chester, none of the boroughs
which they built in the north-western districts survived

[1] Worcester, Chester, Tamworth, Stafford, Warwick, Hertford,
Buckingham, Bedford, Maldon, Huntingdon, Colchester, Stamford, and
Nottingham.
[2] *Domesday Book and Beyond,* 216.

till Domesday. In all their boroughs, except Bakewell, the purpose of defending the great Roman roads and the main waterways is very apparent.

Our list is very far from being a complete list of all the Anglo-Saxon boroughs existing in Edward's day. In the document known as the "Burghal Hidage" we have another quite different list of thirty-two boroughs,[1] which, according to Professor Maitland, "sets forth certain arrangements made early in the 10th century for the defence of Wessex against the Danish inroads."[2] Five at least on the list are Roman chesters; twenty are mentioned as boroughs in Domesday Book. There are two among them which are of special interest, because there is reason to believe that the earthen ramparts which still surround them are of Saxon origin : Wallingford and Wareham. Both these fortifications are after the Roman pattern, the earthen banks forming a square with rounded corners.[3] See Fig. 3.

To complete our knowledge of Anglo-Saxon fortification, we ought to examine the places mentioned in Anglo-Saxon charters as royal seats, where possibly defensive works of some kind may have existed. Unfortunately we are unable to learn that there are any such works, except at one place, Bensington in Oxfordshire, where about a hundred years ago "a bank and trench, which seem to have been of a square form," were to be seen.[4]

In the following chapter we shall deal in detail with such archæological remains as still exist of the boroughs

[1] Buckingham is the only place which is included in both lists. See Appendix E.

[2] *Domesday Book and Beyond*, 188. See Appendix E. Southwark, one of the names, which is not called a borough in Domesday, retains its name of *The Borough* to the present day.

[3] No Roman remains have been found in either place.

[4] *Beauties of England and Wales*, Oxfordshire.

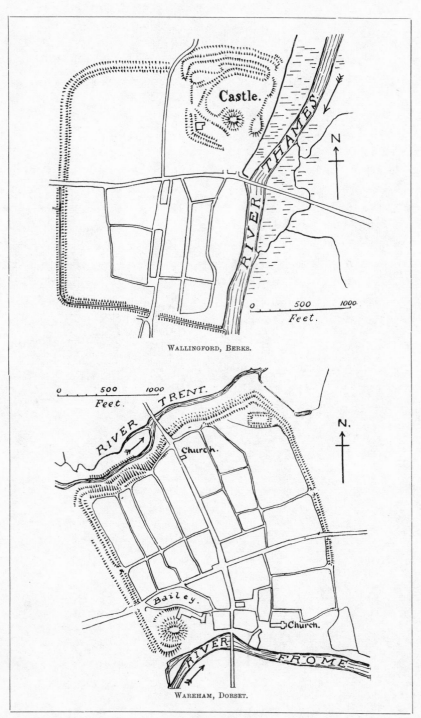

WALLINGFORD, BERKS.

WAREHAM, DORSET.

FIG. 3.

[To face p. 28.

of Edward and Ethelfleda, but here we will briefly
summarise by anticipation the results to which that
chapter will lead. We see that sites defensible by
nature were often seized upon for fortification, as at
Bamborough, Bridgenorth, and Eddisbury ; but that
this was by no means always the case, as a weak site,
such as Witham, for example, was sometimes rendered
defensible by works which appear to have fulfilled their
purpose. In only one case (Witham) do we find an
inner enclosure; and as it is of large size (9½ acres) it
is more probable that the outer enclosure was for cattle,
than that the inner one was designed solely for the
protection of the king and his court. We are not told
of stone walls more than once (at Towcester); ·but the
use of the word *timbrian*, which does not exclusively
mean to build in wood,[1] does not preclude walls of
stone in important places. In the square or oblong
form, with rounded corners, we see the influence which
Roman models exercised on eyes which still beheld
them existing.

We see that the main idea of the borough was the
same as that of the prehistoric or British "camp of
refuge," in that it was intended for the defence of
society and not of the individual. It was intended to
be a place of refuge for the whole countryside. But it
was also something much more than this, something
which belongs to a much more advanced state of
society than the hill-fort.[2] It was a town, a place

[1] See Skeat's *Dictionary*, "Timber."

[2] Excavation has recently shown that many of the great hill-forts were
permanently inhabited, and it is now considered improbable that they were
originally built as camps of refuge. It seems more likely that this use, of
which there are undoubted instances in historic times (see Cæsar, *Bello
Gallico*, vi., 10, and v., 21), belonged to a more advanced stage of development, when population had moved down into the lower and cultivatable
lands, but still used their old forts in cases of emergency.

where people were expected to live permanently and do their daily work. It provided a fostering seat for trade and manufactures, two of the chief factors in the history of civilisation. The men who kept watch and ward on the ramparts, or who sallied forth in their bands to fight the Danes, were the men who were slowly building up the prosperity of the stricken land of England. By studding the great highways of England with fortified towns, Alfred and his children were not only saving the kernel of the British Empire, they were laying the sure foundations of its future progress in the arts and habits of civilised life.

CHAPTER III

ANGLO-SAXON FORTIFICATIONS—*continued*

THE bare list which we have given of the boroughs of Edward and Ethelfleda calls for some explanatory remarks. Let us take first the boroughs of Ethelfleda.

WORCESTER.—We have already noticed the charter of Ethelred and Ethelfleda which tells of the building of the burh at Worcester.[1] There appears to have been a small Roman settlement at Worcester, but there is no evidence that it was a fortified place.[2] This case lends some support to the conjecture of Dr Christison, that the Saxons gave the name of *chester* to towns which they had themselves fortified.[3] The mediæval walls of Worcester were probably more extensive than Ethelfleda's borough, of which no trace remains.

CHESTER is spoken of by the *Anglo-Saxon Chronicle* in 894 as "a waste *chester* in Wirral." It had undoubtedly been a Roman city, and therefore the work of Ethelred and Ethelfleda here was solely one of restoration. Brompton, who wrote at the close of the 13th century "a poor compilation of little authority,"[4] was the first writer to state that the walls of

[1] *Ante*, p. 21.
[2] Haverfield, in V. C. H. Worcester, *Romano-British Worcester*, i.
[3] *Early Fortifications in Scotland*, p. 105.
[4] Gairdner and Mullinger, *Introduction to the Study of English History*, 268.

Chester were enlarged by Ethelfleda so as to take in the castle, which he fancied to be Roman;[1] and this statement, being repeated by Leland, has acquired considerable vogue. It is very unlikely that any extension of the walls was made by the Mercian pair, seeing that the city was deserted at the time when it was occupied by the Danes, only fourteen years before. But it is quite certain that the Norman castle of Chester lay outside the city walls, as the manor of Gloverstone, which was not within the jurisdiction of the city, lay between the city and the castle.[2] A charter of Henry VII. shows that the civic boundary did not extend to the present south wall in his reign. Ethelfleda's borough probably followed the lines of the old Roman castrum.

BREMESBYRIG.—This place has not yet been identified. Bromborough on the Mersey has been suggested, and is not impossible, for the loss of the s sometimes occurs in place-names; thus Melbury, in Wilts, was Melsburie in Domesday. Bremesbyrig was the first place restored after Chester, and as the estuary of the Dee had been secured by the repair of Chester, so an advance on Bromborough would have for its aim to secure the estuary of the Mersey. It was outside the Danish frontier of Watling Street, and could thus be fortified without breach of the peace in 911. There is a large moated work at Bromborough, enclosing an area of 10 acres, in the midst of which stands the courthouse of the manor of Bromborough. But this manor was given by the Earl of Chester to the monks of St

---

[1] The tower called Cæsar's Tower is really a mural tower of the 13th century. E. W. Cox, "Chester Castle," in *Chester Hist. and Archæol. Soc.*, v., 239.

[2] Cox, as above. See also Shrubsole, "The Age of the City Walls of Chester," *Arch. Journ.*, xliv., 1887. The present wall, which includes the castle, is an extension probably not earlier than James I.'s reign.

Werburgh about 1152, and it is possible that the monks
fortified it, as they did their manor of Irby in Wirral,
against the incursions of the Welsh.   One of the
conditions of the Earl's grant was that the manor is
to be maintained in a state of security and convenience
for the holding of the courts appertaining to Chester
Abbey.[1]   Thus the fortification appears to be of
manorial use, though this does not preclude the possibility of an earlier origin.   On the other hand, if
Bromborough is the same as Brunanburh, where
Athelstan's great battle was fought (and there is much
in favour of this), it cannot possibly have been
Bremesbyrig in the days of Edward.   Another site
has been suggested by the Rev. C. S. Taylor, in a
paper on *The Danes in Gloucestershire*, Bromsberrow in
S. Gloucestershire, one of the last spurs of the Malvern
Hills.   Here the top of a small hill has been encircled
with a ditch ; but the ditch is so narrow that it does not
suggest a defensive work, and it is remote from any
Roman road or navigable river.

SCERGEAT has not yet been identified.   Mr Kerslake
argued with some probability that Shrewsbury is the
place ;[2] but the etymological considerations are adverse,
and it is more likely that such an important place as
Shrewsbury was fortified before Edward's time.   Leland
calls it Scorgate, and says it is "about Severn side."[3]
It should probably be sought within the frontier of
Watling Street, which Ethelfleda does not appear to
have yet crossed in 911.

BRIDGENORTH is undoubtedly the Bricge of the
Anglo - Saxon Chronicle, as Florence of Worcester
identifies it with the Bridgenorth which Robert Belesme

---

[1] The charter is given in Ormerod's *History of Cheshire*, ii., 405.
[2] *Journ. of Brit. Arch. Ass.*, 1875, p. 153.   [3] *Itin.*, ii., 2.

fortified against Henry I. in 1101.[1] Bridgenorth is on
a natural fortification of steep rock, which would only
require a stout wall to make it secure against all the
military resources of the 10th century. We may therefore be quite certain that it was here Ethelfleda planted
her borough, and not (as Mr Eyton unfortunately
conjectured) on the mound outside the city, in the
parish of Oldbury.[2] This mound was far more probably the site of the siege castle (no doubt of wood)
which was erected by Henry I. when he besieged the
city.[3]

TAMWORTH was an ancient city of the Mercian kings,
and therefore may have been fortified before its walls
were rebuilt by Ethelfleda.[4] The line of the ancient
town-wall can still be traced in parts, though it is
rapidly disappearing. Dugdale says the town ditch
was 45 feet broad. Tamworth was a borough at the
time of Domesday.

STAFFORD has a motte on which stood a Norman
castle ; but this is not mentioned in the table, because it
stands a mile and a half from the town on the *southern*
side of the river Sowe, while we are expressly told by
Florence that Ethelfleda's borough was on the *northern*
side, as the town is now. Stafford was a Domesday

---

[1] "Arcem quam in occidentali Sabrinæ fluminis plaga, in loco qui
Bricge dicitur lingua Saxonica, Ægelfleda Merciorum domina quondam
construerat, fratre suo Edwardo seniore regnante, Comes Rodbertus
contra regem Henricum, muro lato et alto, summoque restaurare cœpit."
1101.

[2] A good deal has been made of the name Oldbury, as pointing to the
old burh; but Oldbury is the name of the manor, not of the hillock, which
bears the singular name of Pampudding Hill. Tradition says that the
Parliamentary forces used it for their guns in 1646. Eyton's *Shropshire*, i.,
132.

[3] "Bricge cum exercitu pene totius Angliæ obsedit, machinas quoque ibi
construere et castellum firmare præcepit." *Florence*, 1102.

[4] Florence in fact says *urbem restauravit.*

borough ; some parts of the mediæval walls still remain.
The walls are mentioned in Domesday Book.[1]

EDDISBURY, in Cheshire (Fig. 4), is the only case
in which the work of Ethelfleda is preserved in a
practically unaltered form, as no town or village has ever
grown out of it. The *burh* stands at the top of a hill,
commanding the junction of two great Roman roads, the
Watling Street from Chester to Manchester, and the
branch which it sends forth to Kinderton on the east.
As a very misleading plan of this work has been
published in the *Journal of the British Archæological
Association* for 1906, the *burh* has been specially surveyed for this book by Mr D. H. Montgomerie, who
has also furnished the following description :—

" This plan is approximately oval, and is governed by
the shape of the ground ; the work lies at the end of a
spur, running S.E. and terminating in abrupt slopes to
the E. and S. The defences on the N. and W. consist
of a ditch and a high outer bank, the proportions of
these varying according to the slope of the hill. There
are slight remains of a light inner rampart along the
western half of this side. The remains of an original
entrance (shown in Ormerod's *Cheshire*) are visible in
the middle of the N.W. side, beyond which the ditch
and outer bank have been partially levelled by the
encroachments of the farm buildings. The defences of
the S. side seem to have consisted of a long natural
slope, crowned by a steeper scarp, cut back into the
rock, and having traces of a bank along its crest. The
S.E. end of the spur presents several interesting details,
for it has been occupied in mediæval times by a small
fortified enclosure, whose defences are apt to be confused
with those of the older Saxon town. The rock makes a

[1] D. B., i., 246.

triangular projection at this end, containing the foundations of mediæval buildings,[1] and strengthened on the
N.E. by a slight ditch some 7 to 10 feet below the crest;
the rock on the inner side of this ditch has been cut back
to a nearly vertical face, while on the outer bank are
the footings of a masonry wall extending almost to the
point of the spur. There are traces of another wall
defending the crest on the N.E. and S.; but the
base of the triangle, facing the old enclosure, does not
appear to have been strengthened by a cross ditch or
bank.

"It may be noted that this enclosure presents not the
slightest appearance of a motte. It is at a lower level
than the body of the hill, and belongs most certainly to
the Edwardian period of the masonry buildings."

WARWICK Castle has a motte which has been
confidently attributed to Ethelfleda, only because
Dugdale copied the assertion of Thomas Rous, a very
imaginative writer of the 15th century, that she was its
builder. The borough which Ethelfleda fortified probably occupied a smaller area than the mediæval walls
built in Edward I.'s reign; and it is probable that it did
not include the site of the castle, as Domesday states
that only four houses were destroyed when the castle
was built.[2] The borough was doubtless erected to
protect the Roman road from Bath to Lincoln, the Foss
Way, which passes near it. Domesday Book, after
mentioning that the king's barons have 112 houses in
the borough, and the abbot of Coventry 36, goes on to
say that these houses belong to the lands which the

---

[1] These buildings formed part of a hunting lodge built in the reign of
Edward III., called The Chamber in the Forest. See Ormerod's *Cheshire*,
ii., 3. When visiting Eddisbury several years ago, the writer noticed
several Perpendicular buttresses in these ruins.

[2] D. B., i., 238a, 1.

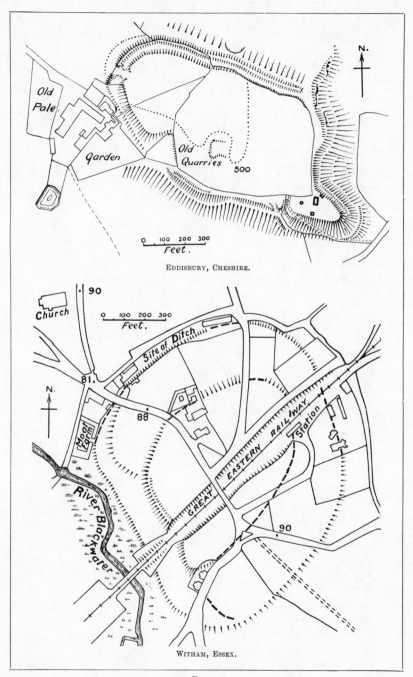

EDDISBURY, CHESHIRE.

WITHAM, ESSEX.

FIG. 4.

[To face p. 36.

barons hold outside the city, and are rated there.[1] This
is one of the passages from which the late Professor
Maitland concluded that the boroughs planted by
Ethelfleda and Edward were organised on a system of
military defence, whereby the magnates in the country
were bound to keep houses in the towns.[2]

CYRICBYRIG.—About this place we adopt the conjecture of Dugdale, who identified it with Monk's Kirby in
Warwickshire, not far from the borders of Leicestershire, and therefore on the edge of Ethelfleda's dominions.
It lies close to the Foss Way, and about three miles from
Watling Street ; like Eddisbury, it is near the junction
of two Roman roads. There are remains of banks and
ditches below the church. Dugdale says "there are
certain apparent tokens that the Romans had some
station here ; for by digging the ground near the church,
there have been discovered foundations of old walls and
Roman bricks."[3] Possibly Ethelfleda restored a Roman
castrum here. At any rate, it seems a much more likely
site than Chirbury in Shropshire, which is commonly
proposed, but which does not lie on any Roman road,
and is not on Ethelfleda's line of advance ; nor are there
any earthworks there.

WEARDBYRIG has not been identified. Wednesbury
was stated by Camden to be the place,[4] and but for the

---

[1] "Abbas de Couentreu habet 36 masuras, et 4 sunt wastæ propter situm
castelli. . . . Hae masurae pertinent ad terras quas ipsi barones tenent
extra burgum, et ibi appreciatae sunt." D. B., i., 238.

[2] *Domesday Book and Beyond*, p. 189. See Appendix D.

[3] Dugdale's *Warwickshire*, 1st edition, pp. 50 and 75. The derivation
of Kirby from Cyricbyrig is not according to etymological rules, but there
can be no doubt about it as a fact ; for in Domesday it is stated that
Chircheberie was held by Geoffrey de Wirche, and that the monks of St
Nicholas [at Angers] had two carucates in the manor. In the charter in
which Geoffrey de Wirche makes this gift Chircheberie is called Kirkeberia
[*M. A.*, vi., 996], but in the subsequent charter of Roger de Mowbray, confirm-
ing the gift, it is called Kirkeby. [4] *Britannia*, ii., 375.

impossibility of the etymology, the situation would suit well enough. Weardbyrig must have been an important place, for it had a mint.[1] Warburton, on the Mersey, has been gravely suggested, but is impossible, as it takes its name from St Werburgh.

RUNCORN has not a vestige to show of Ethelfleda's borough ; but local historians have preserved some rather vague accounts of a promontory fort which once existed at the point where the London and North-Western Railway bridge enters the river. A rocky headland formerly projected here into the Mersey, narrowing its course to 400 yards at high water ; a ditch with a circular curve cut off this headland from the shore. This ditch, from 12 to 16 feet wide, with an inner bank 6 or 7 feet high, could still be traced in the early part of the 19th century. Eighteen feet of the headland were cut off when the Duke of Bridgewater made his canal in 1773, and the ditch was obliterated when the railway bridge was built. From the measurements which have been preserved, the area of this fort must have been very small, not exceeding 3 acres at the outside ;[2] and it is unlikely that it represented Ethelfleda's borough, as the church, which was of pre-Conquest foundation, stood outside its bounds, and we should certainly have expected to find it within. As the Norman earls of Chester established a ferry at Runcorn in the 12th century, and as a castle at Runcorn is spoken of in a mediæval document,[3] it seems not impossible that there may have been a Norman castle on this site, as we

---

[1] *Numismatic Chronicle*, 3rd S., xiii., 220.

[2] Fowler's *History of Runcorn* gives a plan of this fort, and there is another in Hanshall's *History of Cheshire*, p. 418 (1817). A very different one is given in Beaumont's *History of Halton*.

[3] Beaumont's *Records of the Honour of Halton*. In 1368, John Hank received the surrender of a house near to the castle in Runcorn.

constantly find such small fortifications placed to defend a ferry or ford. It is probable that Ethelfleda's borough was destroyed at an early period by the Northmen, for Runcorn was not a borough at Domesday, but was then a mere dependency of the Honour of Halton.

The Burhs of Edward the Elder.

HERTFORD.—Two burhs were built by Edward at Hertford in 913, one on the north and the other on the south side of the river Lea. Therefore if a burh were the same thing as a motte, there ought to be two mottes at Hertford, one on each side of the river ; whereas there is only one, and that forms part of the works of the Norman castle. Mr Clark, with his usual confidence, says that the northern mound has "long been laid low ";[1] but there is not the slightest proof that it ever existed except in his imagination. Hertford was a borough at the time of Domesday. No earthworks remain.

WITHAM (Fig. 4).—There are some remains of a *burh* here which are very remarkable, as they show an inner enclosure within the outer one. They have been carefully surveyed by Mr F. C. J. Spurrell, who has published a plan of them.[2] Each enclosure formed roughly a square with much-rounded corners. The ditch round the outer work was 30 feet wide ; the inner work was not ditched. The area enclosed by the outer bank was $26\frac{1}{4}$ acres, an enclosure much too large for a castle ; the area of the inner enclosure was $9\frac{1}{2}$ acres. As far as is at present known, Witham is the only instance we have of an Anglo-Saxon earthwork which

---

[1] *Mediæval Military Architecture*, ii., 120.
[2] *Essex Naturalist*, January 1887.

has a double enclosure.[1] Witham is not mentioned as
a borough in Domesday Book, but the fact that it had
a mint in the days of Hardicanute shows that it
maintained its borough rights for more than a hundred
years. The name Chipping Hill points to a market
within the borough.

BUCKINGHAM is another case where a *burh* was built
on both sides of the river, and as at Hertford, there
was only one motte, the site of the castle of the Norman
Giffards is now almost obliterated. The river Ouse
here makes a long narrow loop to the south-west,
within which stands the town, and, without doubt,
this would be the site of Edward's borough. No trace
is left of the second borough on the other side of
the river. Buckingham is one of the boroughs of
Domesday.

BEDFORD has had a motte and a Norman castle on
the north side of the Ouse; but this was not the site of
Edward's borough, which the *Chronicle* tells us was placed
on the south side of that river. On the south side an
ancient ditch, 10 or 12 feet broad, with some traces of
an inner rampart, semicircular in plan, but with a square
extension, is still visible, and fills with water at flood
times.[2] This is very likely to be the ditch of Edward's
borough. Both at Bedford and Buckingham the
Chronicle states that Edward spent four weeks in building the *burh*. Mediæval numbers must never be taken
as precise; but the disproportion between four weeks
and eight days, the space often given for the building
of an early Norman castle, corresponds very well to the
difference between the time needed to throw up the bank

---

[1] Danbury Camp, which has also been surveyed by Mr Spurrell (*Essex
Naturalist*, 1890), is precisely similar in plan to Witham, but nothing is
known of its history.

[2] See *Victoria History of Bedfordshire*, i., 281.

and stockade of a town, and that needed for the building
of an earthen and wooden castle.

MALDON.—Only one angle of the earthen bank of
Edward's borough remains now, but Gough states
that it was an oblong camp enclosing about 22 acres.[1]
It had rounded corners and a very wide ditch, with a
bank on both scarp and counterscarp. Maldon was a
borough at Domesday;[2] the king had a hall there, but
there was never any castle, nor is there any trace of a
motte.

TOWCESTER (Fig. 5).—There is a motte at Towcester,
but no direct evidence has yet been found for the
existence of a Norman castle there, though Leland says
that he was told of "certen Ruines or Diches of a
Castelle."[3] There was a mill and an oven to which
the citizens owed soke,[4] and the value of the manor,
which belonged to the king, had risen very greatly since
the Conquest;[5] all facts which render the existence of a
Norman castle extremely likely. But there can be no
question as to the nature of Edward's work at Towcester,
as the *Chronicle* tells us expressly that "he wrought the
burgh at Towcester with a stone wall."[6] Towcester lies
on Watling Street, and is believed to have been the
Roman station of Lactodorum. Baker gives a plan of
the remains existing in his time, which may either be
those of the Roman castrum or of Edward's borough.[7]
The area is stated to be about 35 acres.

WIGINGAMERE.—This place is not yet identified, for

---

[1] Morant's *History of Essex*, i. Three sides of the rampart were visible
in his time.

[2] D. B., ii., 5.   [3] *Itin.*, i., 12.

[4] Baker's *History of Northampton*, ii , 321.   [5] D. B., i., 219b.

[6] *A.-S. C.*, 921. "Wrohte tha burg æt Tofeceastre mid stan wealle."
Florence says 918.

[7] Baker, *History of Northants*, ii., 318. See also Haverfield, *V. C. H.*,
Northants, i., 184.

the identification with Wigmore in Herefordshire, though accepted by many respectable writers, will not stand a moment's examination. Wigmore was entirely out of Edward's beat, and he had far too much on his hands in 918 to attempt a campaign in Herefordshire. As Wigingamere appears to have specially drawn upon itself the wrath of East Anglian and Essex Danes, it must have lain somewhere in their neighbourhood. The *mere* which is included in the name would seem to point to that great inland water which anciently stretched southwards from the Wash into Cambridgeshire. The only approach to East Anglia from the south lay along a strip of open chalk land which lay between the great swamp and the dense forests which grew east of it.[1] Here ran the ancient road called the Icknield way. On a peninsula which now runs out into the great fens of the Cam and the Ouse there is still a village called Wicken, 6 miles west of the Roman road; and possibly, when the land surrounding this peninsula was under water, this bight may have been called Wigingamere. This suggestion of course is merely tentative, but what gives it some probability is that the Danish army which attacked "the borough at Wigingamere" came from East Anglia as well as Mercia.[2]

HUNTINGDON.—The borough of Huntingdon was probably first built by the Danes, as it was only repaired by Edward. In Leland's time there were still some remains of the walls "in places." Huntingdon is one of the *burgi* of Domesday.

COLCHESTER.—This of course was a Roman site, and Edward needed only to restore the walls, as the

---

[1] Atkinson's *Cambridge Described*, p. 1.

[2] There is, however, this difficulty, that Cambridge was still occupied by a Danish force when Wigingamere was built. It submitted to Edward in 918.

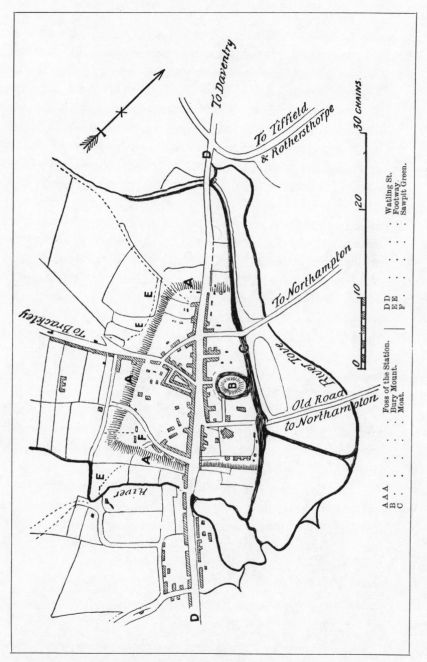

FIG. 5.—PLAN OF TOWCESTER ABOUT 1830.

[To face p. 42.

Chronicle indicates. Colchester was placed so as to defend the river Colne, just as Maldon defended the estuary of the Blackwater. As the repair of Colchester and the successful defence of Wigingamere were followed the same year by the submission of East Anglia, it seems not unlikely that Edward's various forces may have made a simultaneous advance, along the coast, and along the Roman road by the Fen country; but this of course is the merest conjecture, as the *Chronicle* gives us no details of this very important event.

CLEDEMUTHAN.—This place is only mentioned in the Abingdon MS. of the *Chronicle*, but the year 921 is the date given for its building. This date should probably be transposed to 918, the year in which, according to Florence, Edward subjugated East Anglia. It is well known how confused the chronology of the various versions of the *Anglo-Saxon Chronicle* is during the reign of Edward the Elder.[1] Cley, in Norfolk, would be etymologically deducible from Clede (the *d* being frequently dropped, especially in Scandinavian districts), and the *muthan* points to some river estuary. Cley is one of the few havens on the north coast of Norfolk, and its importance in former times was much greater than now, as is shown not only by the spaciousness of its Early English church, but by the fact that the port has jurisdiction for 30 miles along the coast.[2] It would be highly probable that Edward completed the subjugation of East Anglia by planting a borough at some important point. But as the real date of the fortifica-

---

[1] See Mr Plummer's discussion of these variations in his edition of the *Chronicle*, ii., 116.

[2] Lewis, *Topographical Dictionary of England*. Mr Rye remarks:— "The silting up of the harbour has ruined a port which once promised to be of as great importance as Norwich." *History of Norfolk*, p. 228.

tion of Cledemuthan is uncertain, we must be content to leave this matter in abeyance.[1]

STAMFORD is another case where the *borough* is clearly said to have been on the side which is opposite to the one where the Norman castle stands. Edward's borough was on the south side, the motte and other remains of the Norman castle are on the north of the Welland. It is remarkable that the part of Stamford on the south side of the Welland is still a distinct liberty; it is mentioned in Domesday as the sixth ward of the borough. The line of the earthworks can still be traced in parts. The borough on the north side of the Welland was probably first walled in by the Danes, as it was one of the Five Boroughs—Stamford, Leicester, Lincoln, Nottingham, and Derby—which appear to have formed an independent or semi-independent state in middle England.[2] Stamford is a borough in Domesday.

NOTTINGHAM.—The first mention of a fortress in connection with Nottingham seems to suggest that it owed its origin to the Danes. In 868 the Danish host which had taken ·possession of York in the previous year "went into Mercia to Nottingham, and there took up their winter quarters. And Burgræd king of Mercia

---

[1] It is really wonderful that the identification of Cledemuthan with the mouth of the Cleddy in Pembrokeshire could ever have been accepted by any sober historian. That Edward, whose whole time was fully occupied with his conquests from the Danish settlers, could have suddenly transported his forces into one of the remotest corners of Wales, would have been a feat worthy of the coming days of air-ships. William of Worcester has preserved a tradition that Edward repaired Burgh, "quae olim Saxonice dicebatur Burgh-chester," but he confuses it with Norwich. *Itinerarium*, 337. Is it possible that we ought to look for Cledemuthan at Burgh Castle, at the mouth of the Waveney? It would be quite in accordance with Edward's actions elsewhere to restore an old Roman *castrum.*

[2] Leland says: "There were 7 principall Towers or Wards in the waulles of Staunford, to eche of which were certeyne freeholders in the Towne allottid to wache and ward in tyme of neadde." *Itinerarium*, vii., 11.

and his Witan begged of Ethelred, king of the West
Saxons, and of Alfred his brother, that they would help
them, that they might fight against the army. And
then they went with the West Saxon force into Mercia
as far as Nottingham, and there encountered the army
which was in the fortress (geweorc), and besieged them
there ; but there was no great battle fought, and the
Mercians made peace with the army."[1] Nottingham
became another of the Danish Five Boroughs. The
Danish host on this occasion came from York, no doubt
in ships down the Ouse and up the Trent. The site
would exactly suit them, as it occupied a very strong
position on St Mary's Hill, a height equal to that on
which the castle stands, defended on the south front by
precipitous cliffs, below which ran the river Leen, and
only a very short distance from the junction of the Leen
with the Trent, the great waterway of middle England.[2]
Portions of the ancient ditch were uncovered in 1890, and
its outline appears to have been roughly rectangular, like
the Danish camp at Shoebury. The ditch was about
20 feet wide. The area enclosed was about 39 acres.

This borough was captured by Edward the Elder
in 919, when after the death of his sister Ethelfleda he
advanced into Danish Mercia, taking up the work
which she had left unfinished.[3] The *Chronicle* tells us
that he repaired the borough (burh), and garrisoned it
with both English and Danes. Two years later, he
evidently felt the necessity of fortifying the Trent
itself, for he built another borough on the south side of

---

[1] *A.-S. C.*, 868.

[2] Shipman's *Old Town Wall of Nottingham*, pp. 73-75. The evidence
for a Roman origin of the borough is altogether too slight, as, except some
doubtful earthenware bottles, no Roman remains have been found at
Nottingham.

[3] *A.-S. C.*, 921. *Florence of Worcester*, 919.

the river, and connected the two boroughs by a bridge, which must have included a causeway or a wooden stage across the marshes of the Leen. It is not surprising that the frequent floods of the Trent have carried away all trace of this second borough.[1] The important position of Nottingham was maintained in subsequent times, and it was still a borough at Domesday.

THELWALL.—According to Camden, Thelwall explains by its name the kind of work which was set up here, a wall composed of the trunks of trees. This was another attempt to defend the course of the Mersey, which was once tidal as far as Thelwall. No remains of any fortifications can now be seen at Thelwall, which was not one of the boroughs which took root. But the Mersey has changed its course very much at this point, even before the making of the Ship Canal effected a more complete alteration.[2]

MANCHESTER.—The *burh* repaired by Edward the Elder was no doubt the Roman castrum, which was built on the triangle of land between the Irwell and the Medlock. Large portions of the walls were still remaining in Stukeley's time, about 1700, and some fragments have recently been unearthed by the Manchester Classical Association. It was one of the smaller kind of Roman stations, its area being only 5 acres. Manchester is not mentioned as a borough in Domesday, but the old Saxon town was long known as Aldportton, which literally means "the town of the

---

[1] I am indebted for much of the information given here to the local antiquarian knowledge of Mr Harold Sands, F.S.A. He states that the old borough was 1400 yards from the Trent at its nearest point, and that the highest ground on the south side of the Trent is marked by the Trent Bridge cricket ground, the last spot to become flooded. Here, therefore, was the probable site of Edward's second borough.

[2] See Appendix F.

old city." This is its title in mediæval deeds, and it is still preserved in *Alport* Street, a street near the remains of the *castrum*.[1] The later borough of Manchester, which existed at least as early as the 13th century, appears to have grown up round the Norman castle, about a mile from the Roman castrum.[2]

BAKEWELL.—The vagueness of the indication in the *Chronicle*, "nigh to Bakewell," leaves us in some doubt where we are to look for this *burh*, which Florence calls an *urbs*. Just outside the village of Bakewell there are the remains of a motte and bailey castle (a small motte and bailey of 2 acres), which are always assumed to be the *burh* of Edward. But the enclosure is far too small for a borough, and Edward's burh would certainly have enclosed the church; for though the present church contains no Saxon architecture, the ancient cross in the graveyard shows that it stands on a Saxon site. It is more reasonable to suppose that Edward's borough, if it was at Bakewell, has disappeared as completely as those of Runcorn, Buckingham, and Thelwall, and that the motte and bailey belong to one of the many Norman castles whose names never appear in history. There is no conclusive evidence for the existence of a Norman castle at Bakewell, but the names Castle Field, Warden Field, and Court Yard are at least suggestive.[3] Bakewell was the seat of jurisdiction for the High Peak Hundred in mediæval times.[4]

---

[1] Whitaker's *History of Manchester*, i., 43.

[2] *Trans. of Lanc. and Chesh. Hist. and Ant. Soc.*, v., 246.

[3] "Castle" in combination with some other word is often given to works of Roman or British origin, because its original meaning was a fortified enclosure ; but the name Castle Hill is extremely common for mottes.

[4] We may remark here that it is not surprising that there should be a number of motte castles which are never mentioned in history, especially as it is certain that all the "adulterine" castles, which were raised without royal permission in the rebellions of Stephen's and other reigns, were very short-lived.

CHAPTER IV

DANISH FORTIFICATIONS

WE must now inquire into the nature of the fortifications built by the Danes in England, which are frequently mentioned in the *Anglo-Saxon Chronicle*. It has often been asserted, and with great confidence, that the Danes were the authors of the moated mounds of class (*e*); those in Ireland are invariably spoken of by Lewis in his *Topographical Dictionary* as "Danish Raths." This fancy seems to have gone somewhat out of fashion since Mr Clark's *burh* theory occupied the field, though Mr Clark's view is often so loosely expressed as to lead one to think that he supposed all the Northern nations to be makers of mottes; in fact, he frequently includes the Anglo-Saxons under the general title of "Northmen"![1] We must therefore endeavour to find out what the Danish fortifications actually were.

The *Anglo-Saxon Chronicle* mentions twenty-four places where the Danes either threw up fortifications (between 787 and 924) or took up quarters either for the winter, or for such a period of time that we may infer that there was some fortification to protect them. The word used for the fortification is generally *geweorc*,

[1] *Mediæval Military Architecture*, i., 18. See Mr Round's remarks on Mr Clark's vagueness in his "Castles of the Conquest," *Archæologia*, 1902.

a work, or *fæsten* (in two places only), which has also the general vague meaning of a *fastness.* There are ten places where these works or fastnesses are mentioned in the *Chronicle* :—

1. NOTTINGHAM.—We have already seen that the Danish host took up their winter quarters here in 868, and that there is the highest probability that the borough which Edward the Elder restored was first built by them.   We have also seen that it was a camp of roughly rectangular form, and enclosed a very large area, necessary for great numbers.[1]

2. ROCHESTER.—This city was besieged by the Danes in 885, and they fortified a camp outside.   As the artificial mound called Boley Hill is outside the city, most topographers have jumped to the conclusion that this was the Danish camp.   But the character of the Danish fortification is clearly indicated in the *Chronicle* : "they made a work around themselves," that is, it was an enclosure.[2]   They could hardly have escaped by ship, as they did, if their camp had been above the bridge, which is known to have existed in Saxon times. But Boley Hill is above the bridge.

3. MILTON, in Kent (Middeltune).—Hæsten the Dane landed at the mouth of the Thames with 80 ships, and wrought a *geweorc* here in 893.   Two places in the neighbourhood of Milton have been suggested as the site of it, a square earthwork at Bayford Court, near Sittingbourne, and a very small square enclosure called Castle Rough.   Neither of these are large enough to have been of any use to a force which came in 80

---

[1] The *A.-S. C.* speaks of this Danish host as "a great heathen army."   866.

[2] "Worhton other fæsten ymb hie selfe."   The same language is frequently used in the continental accounts of the Danish fortresses : "Munientes se per gyrum avulsæ terræ aggere," *Dudo*, 155 (Duchesne): "Se ex illis (sepibus et parietibus) *circumdando* munierant."   *It.*, p. 81.

ships.[1] Steenstrup has calculated that the average number of men in a Viking ship must have been from 40 to 50 ; Hæsten therefore must have had at least 3200 men with him. It is .therefore probable that the camp at Milton has been swept away.

4. APPLEDORE.—A still larger Danish force, which had been harrying the Carlovingian empire, came in 250 ships, with their horses, in 893, and towed their ships "up the river" (which is now extinct) from Lymne to Appledore, where they wrought a work. There are no earthworks at Appledore now, but at Kenardington, 2 miles off, there are remains of "a roughly defined rectangular work, situated on the north and east of the church, on the slope of the hill towards the marsh, a very likely place for an entrenchment thrown up to defend a fleet of light-draught ships hauled up on the beach."[2] The enclosure was very large, one side which remains being 600 feet long.[3]

5. BENFLEET.—Here Hæsten wrought a work in 894 ; here he was defeated by Alfred's forces, and some of his ships burnt. Mr Spurrell states that there are still some irregular elevations by the stream and about the church, which he believes to be remains of the Danish camp.[4] "As the fleet of ships lay in the Beamfleet,

---

[1] The earthworks at Bayford Court must belong to the mediæval castle which existed there. See *Beauties of England and Wales, Kent*, p. 698. Castle Rough is less than an acre in area.

[2] Mr Harold Sands, *Some Kentish Castles*, p. 10.

[3] See the plan in *Victoria History of Kent*, paper on Earthworks by the late Mr I. C. Gould. Hasted states that there was a small circular mount there as well as an embankment, and that there are other remains in the marsh below, which seem to have been connected with the former by a narrow ridge or causeway, *Kent*, iii., 117. The causeway led to a similar mount in the marsh below, but Mr Gould inclined to think the mounts and causeway later, and possibly part of a dam for "inning" the marsh. *V. C. H.*, p. 397.

[4] " Hæsten's Camps at Shoebury and Benfleet," *Essex Naturalist*, iv., 153.

it is obvious that the camp must have partaken of the character of a fortified *hithe*, with the wall landward and the shore open to the river and the ships." He also learned on the spot that when the railway bridge across the Fleet was being made, the remains of several ancient ships, charred by fire, and surrounded by numerous human skeletons, were found in the mud.[1] Benfleet must have been a very large camp, as not only was the joint army of Danes housed in it, that from Milton and that from Appledore, but they had with them their wives and children and cattle.

6. SHOEBURY (Fig. 6).—After the storming of the camp at Benfleet by the Saxon forces, the joint armies of the Danes built another *geweorc* at Shoebury in Essex. We should therefore expect a large camp here, and Mr Spurrell has shown that the area was formerly about a third of a square mile. About half the camp had been washed away by the sea when Mr Spurrell surveyed it in 1879, but enough was left to give a good idea of the whole. It was a roughly square rampart, with a ditch about 40 feet wide, the ditch having a kind of berm on the inner side. The bank also had a slight platform inside, about 3 feet above the general level.[2] As Hæsten had lost his ships at Benfleet, there would be no fortified hithe connected with it, and if there had been, the sea would have swept it away. The camp was abandoned almost as soon as it was made, and the Danish army started on that remarkable march across England which the *Saxon Chronicle* relates. They were overtaken and besieged by Alfred's forces, in a *fastness* at

7. BUTTINGTON, on the Severn.—It has sometimes

---

[1] The *Chronicle* says that the ships of Hæsten were either broken to pieces, or burnt, or taken to London or Rochester. 894.

[2] *Essex Naturalist*, as above, p. 151. These berms certainly suggest Roman influence.

been contended that this was the Buttington near Chepstow; but as the line of march of the army was "along the Thames till they reached the Severn, then up along the Severn,"[1] it is more probable that it was Buttington in Montgomery, west of Shrewsbury.[2] Here there are remains of a strong bank with a broad deep ditch, which was evidently part of a rectangular earthwork, as it runs at right angles to Offa's Dyke, which forms one side of it. It now encloses both the churchyard and vicarage. Whether the Danes constructed this earthwork, or found it there, we are not told.

8. There appear to be no remains of the *geweorc* on the river Lea, 20 miles above London, made by the Danes in 896. But 20 miles above London, on the Lea, would land us at Amwell, near Ware. In Brayley's *Hertfordshire* it is stated that at Amwell, "on the hill above the church are traces of a very extensive fortification, the rampart of which is very distinguishable on the side overlooking the vale through which the river Lea flows."[3]

9. BRIDGENORTH, or Quatbridge.—The Winchester MS. of the *Chronicle* says the Danes wrought a *geweorc* at Quatbridge, in 896, and passed the winter there. There is no such place as Quatbridge now, only Quatford; and seeing there were so few bridges in those days, we are disposed to accept the statement of the Worcester MS., which must have been the best

[1] *A.-S. C.*, 894.

[2] *Montgomery Collections*, xxxi., 337 ; Dymond, *On the Site of Buttington.* See also Steenstrup, *Normannerne*, ii., 80.

[3] *Beauties of England and Wales*, vii., 246. There is nothing left either at Great or Little Amwell now but fragments of what are supposed to be homestead moats. *Royal Commission on Historical Monuments*, pp. 95, 142, Herts. vol.

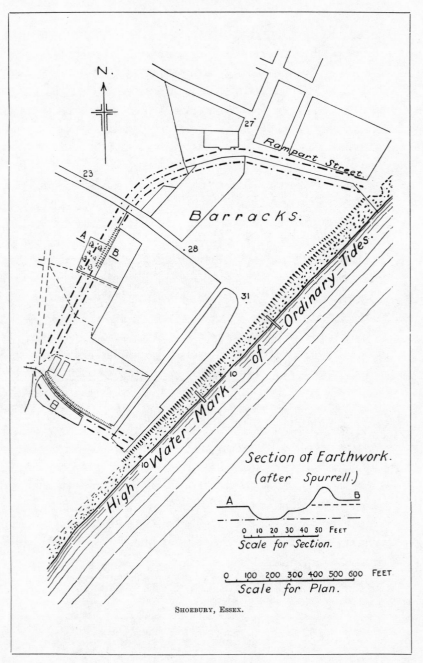

N.

27

Rampart Street.

23

Barracks.

A
B

· 28

31

High Water Mark of Ordinary Tides.

10

10

Section of Earthwork.
(after Spurrell.)

A
B

0 10 20 30 40 50 Feet
Scale for Section.

0 100 200 300 400 500 600 Feet
Scale for Plan.

SHOEBURY, ESSEX.

FIG. 6.

[To face p. 52.

informed about events in the west, that Bridgenorth
was the site of their work, especially as the high rock
at Bridgenorth offers a natural fortification. The only
circumstance that is in favour of Quatford is that it is
mentioned as a *burgus* in Domesday, which shows that
it possessed fortifications of the civic kind ; and we shall
see later on, that such fortifications were often the work
of the Danes. But this burgus may more probably have
been the work of Roger de Montgomeri, who planted
a castle there in the 11th century.

10. TEMPSFORD.—Here the Danes wrought a work
in 918.[1] There is a small oblong enclosure at
Tempsford, still in fair preservation, called Gannock
Castle, which is generally supposed to be this Danish
work. The ramparts are about 11 or 12 feet above the
bottom of the moat, which is about 20 feet wide.
There is a small circular mound, about 5 feet high,
on top of the rampart, which appears to be so placed
as to defend the entrance. This mound is "edged all
round by the root of a small bank, which may have been
the base of a stockaded tower."[2] This curious little
enclosure is different altogether from any of the Danish
works just enumerated, and it is difficult to see what
purpose it could have served. The area enclosed is
only half an acre, which would certainly not have
accommodated the large army "from Huntingdon and
from the East Angles," which built the advanced post at
Tempsford as a base for the forcible recovery of the
districts which they had lost.[3] Such a small enclosure
as this might possibly have been a citadel, but our

[1] Florence's date.
[2] *Victoria History of Bedfordshire*, i., 282, from which this description
is taken.
[3] The *Chronicle* speaks of *Tempsford* as a *burh*, so it must have been a
large enclosure.

knowledge of Danish camps does not tell us of any with citadels, and it is hardly likely that the democratic constitution of these pirate bands would have allowed of a citadel for the chief. It is far more probable that this work belongs to a later time, and that the Danish camp has been swept away by the river.[1]

11. READING.—There is no "work" mentioned by the *Anglo-Saxon Chronicle* at this place, which the Danes made their headquarters in 871, but we add it to the list because Asser not only mentions it, but describes the nature of the fortification. It was a *vallum* drawn between the rivers Thames and Kennet, so as to enclose a peninsula.[2] It had several entrances, as the Danes "rushed out from all the gates" on the Anglo-Saxon attack. Such a fort belongs to the simplest and easiest kind of defence, used at all times by a general who is in a hurry, and it has therefore no significance in determining the general type of Danish works.

Besides these eleven places where *works* are mentioned, there are thirteen places where the Danes are said to have taken up their winter quarters, and where we may be certain that they were protected by some kind of fortifications. These are Thanet, Sheppey, Thetford, York, London, Torkesey, Repton, Cambridge, Exeter, Chippenham, Cirencester, Fulham, and Mersey Island. Four places out of this list—York, London, Exeter, and Cirencester—were Roman *castra*, whose walls were still available for defence. Three—Thanet, Sheppey, and Mersey—were islands, and thus naturally defended, being much more insular than they are

---

[1] Mr Clark actually speaks of a subsequent Norman castle at Tempsford (*M. M. A.*, i., 78), but we have been unable to find any confirmation of this. Faint traces of larger works in the fields below were formerly visible. *V. C. H. Bedfordshire.*

[2] Stephenson's *Asser*, p. 27.

now.[1] Three—Thetford, Torkesey, and Cambridge—appear as burgi in Domesday, showing that they were fortified towns. It is highly probable that the Danes threw up the first fortifications of these boroughs. There are no remains of town banks at Torkesey ; at Cambridge the outline of the town bank can be traced in places ;[2] and at Thetford there was formerly an earthwork on the Suffolk side of the river, which appears to have formed three sides of a square, abutting on the river, and enclosing the most ancient part of the town.[3] Chippenham and Repton were ancient seats of the Anglo-Saxon kings, and may have had fortifications, but nothing remains now. Chippenham is a borough by prescription, therefore of ancient date. At Fulham, on the Thames, there is a quadrangular moat and bank round the Bishop of London's palace, which is sometimes supposed to be the camp made by the Danes in 879 ; but it may equally well be mediæval. There was formerly a harbour at Fulham.[4]

It must be confessed that this list of Danish fortresses furnishes us with a very slender basis for generalisation as to the nature of Danish fortifications, judging from the actual remains. All we can say is that in six cases out of twenty-four (not including Tempsford or Fulham) the work appears to have been rectangular. In the case of Shoebury, about which we have the best

[1] There are no remains of earthworks in Thanet or Sheppey, except a place called Cheeseman's Camp, near Minster in Thanet, which the late Mr Gould regarded as of the "homestead-moat type." *V. C. H. Kent*, i., 433. Nor are there any earthworks on Mersey Island mentioned by Mr Gould in his paper on Essex earthworks in the *V. C. H.*

[2] Stukeley, who saw this earthwork when it was in a much more perfect state, says that it contained 30 acres. See Mr Hope's paper in *Camb. Antiq. Soc.*, vol. xi.

[3] Blomefield's *Norfolk*, ii., pp. 7, 8, 27. His description is very confused.

[4] See Erlingssen's *Ruins of the Saga Time*, Viking Club, p. 337.

evidence, the imitation of Roman models seems to be clear. If we turn from remaining facts to *à priori* likelihoods, we call to mind that the Danes were a much-travelled people, had been in Gaul as well as in England, and had had opportunities of observing Roman fortifications, as well as much practice both in the assault and defence of fortified places. It may not be without significance that it is not until after the return of "the army" from France that we hear of their building camps at all, except in the case of Reading.

As far as our information goes, their camps were without citadels. What evidence we have from the other side of the channel supports the same conclusion. Richer gives us an account of the storming of a fortress of the Northmen at Eu, by King Raoul, in 925, from which it is clear that as soon as the king's soldiers had got over the vallum, they were masters of the place ; there was no citadel to attack.[1] Dudo speaks of the Vikings "fortifying themselves, after the manner of a *castrum*, by heaped up earth-banks drawn round themselves," and it is clear from the rest of his description that the camp had no citadel.[2]

In no case do we find anything to justify the theory that mottes were an accompaniment of Danish camps. In five cases out of the twenty-four there are or were mottes at the places mentioned, but in all cases they belonged to Norman castles. The magnificent motte called the Castle Hill at Thetford was on the opposite side of the river to the borough, which we have seen reason to think was the site of the Danish winter quarters. Torkesey in Leland's time had by the river

---

[1] Richerii, *Historiarum Libri Quatuor*, edition Guadet, p. 67.

[2] "In modo castri, munientes se per girum avulsæ terræ aggere." *Dudo*, 155 (edition Duchesne).

side "a Hille of Yerth cast up," which he judged to be the donjon of some old castle, probably rightly, though we have been unable as yet to find any mention of a Norman castle at Torkesey ; a brick castle of much more recent date is still standing near the river, and probably the motte to which Leland alludes was destroyed when this was built. The motte at Cambridge is placed inside the original bounds of the borough, and was part of the Norman castle.[1] We have already dealt with the Boley Hill at Rochester, and shall have more to say about it hereafter. The rock motte at Nottingham was probably not cut off by a ditch from the rest of the headland until the Norman castle was built.

It seems highly probable that besides providing accommodation in their camps for very large numbers of people, the Danes sometimes fortified the hithes where they drew up their ships on shore, or even constructed fortified harbours.[2] We have already quoted Mr Spurrell's remark on the hithe[3] at Benfleet (p. 51), and there is at least one place in England which seems to prove the existence of fortified harbours. This is Willington, on the river Ouse, in Bedfordshire, which has been carefully described by Mr A. R. Goddard.[4] This "camp" consists of two wards, and a wide outer enclosure (Fig. 7). "But one of the most interesting features is the presence of two harbours, contained within the defences and communicating with the

---

[1] "The castle end of Cambridge was called the Borough within the memory of persons now living." Atkinson's *Cambridge Described* (1897), p. 9.
[2] Steenstrup says that the Northmen built themselves shipyards all round Europe, especially on the islands where they had their winter settlements. *Normannerne*, i., 354.
[3] A.-S., *hyth*, a shore, a landing-place.
[4] *Victoria County History of Beds.*, i., 282.

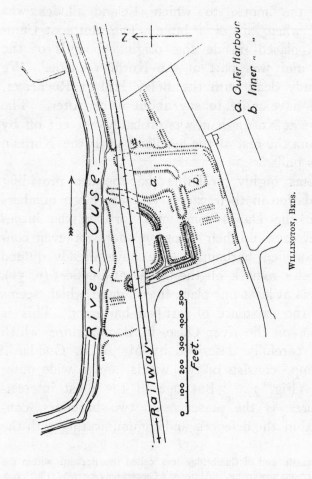

River Ouse.

Railway.

a. Outer Harbour.
b. Inner   "   "

0 100 200 300 400 500
Feet.

WILLINGTON, BEDS.

FIG. 7.

river." Mr Goddard points out that the dimensions of the smaller one are almost the same as those of the "nausts" (ship-sheds or small docks) of the Vikings in Iceland. He also cites from the *Jomsvikinga Saga* the description of a harbour made by the Viking Palnatoki at Jomsborg. "There he had a large and strong sea *burg* made. He also had a harbour made within the *burg* in which 300 long ships could lie at the same time, all being locked within the burg." The harbours at Willington are large enough to accommodate between twenty-five and thirty-five ships of the Danish type. Unfortunately there is no historical proof that the Willington works were Danish, though their construction makes it very likely. Nor have any works of a similar character been as yet observed in England, as far as we are aware.

But if archæology and topography give a somewhat scanty answer to our question about the nature of Danish fortifications, there are other fields of research, opened up of late years, from which we can glean important facts, bearing directly on the subject which we are treating. Herr Steenstrup's exhaustive inquiry into the Danish settlement in England has shown that the way in which the Danes maintained their hold on the northern and eastern shires was by planting fortified towns on which the soldiers and peasants dwelling around were dependent.[1] The *Anglo-Saxon Chronicle* gives us a glimpse of these arrangements when it speaks of the Danes who owed obedience to Bedford, Derby, Leicester, Northampton, and Cambridge.[2] It also tells us of the Five Boroughs, which, as we have already said, appear to have been a confederation

[1] Steenstrup's *Normannerne*, vol. iv. ; *Danelag*, p. 40.
[2] *A.-S. C.*, 914-921.

of boroughs forming an independent Danish state between the Danish kingdoms of East Anglia and Northumbria.

The same system was followed by the Danes who colonised Ireland. "The colony had a centre in a fortified town, or it consisted almost exclusively of dwellers in one. But round this town was a district, in which the Irish inhabitants had to pay taxes to the lords of the town."[1] The Irish chronicle called *The Wars of the Gaedhil and the Gaill* says, further, that Norse soldiers were quartered in the country round these towns in the houses of the native Irish, and it even says that there was hardly a house without a Norseman.[2] Herr Steenstrup does not go so far as to assert that this system of quartering obtained in England also; but he shows that it is probable, and we may add that such a system would help to explain the speedy absorption of the Danes into the Anglo-Saxon population, which took place in the Danelaw districts.[3]

The large numbers of the Danish forces, and the fact that in the second period of their invasions they brought their wives and children with them, would render camps of large area necessary. These numbers alone make it ridiculous to attribute to the Danes the small motte castles of class (*e*), whose average area is not more than 3 acres.

Finally, the Danish host was not a feudal host. Steenstrup asserts that the principle of the composition of the host was the voluntary association of equally

---

[1] Steenstrup, *Danelag*, p. 41.   [2] *Ibid.*, pp. 22, 23.

[3] Such quartering must have been confined to the unmarried Danes, but there must have been plenty of unmarried men in the piratical host, even at the period when it became customary to bring wives and children with the army.

powerful leaders, of whom one was chosen as head, and was implicitedly obeyed, but had only a temporary authority.[1] We should not, therefore, expect to find the Danish camps provided with the citadels by which the feudal baron defended his personal safety. When Rollo and his host were coming up the Seine, the Frankish king Raoul sent messengers to ask them who they were, and what was the name of their chief. "Danes," was the reply, "and we have no chief, for we are all equal."[2] That such an answer would be given by men who were following a leader so distinguished as Rollo shows the spirit of independence which pervaded the Danish hosts, and how little a separate fortification for the chief would comport with their methods of warfare.[3]

We may conclude, then, with every appearance of certainty that the Danish camps were enclosures of large area which very much resembled the larger Roman *castra*, and that, like these, they frequently grew into towns. Placed as they generally were on good havens, or on navigable rivers, they were most suitable places for trade ; and it turned out that the Danes, who were a people of great natural aptitudes, had a special aptitude for commerce.[4] Dr Cunningham remarks that they were the leading merchants of the country, and he attributes to them a large share in the development of town life in England.[5] The organisation of their armies was purely military, but at the same time

---

[1] *Normannerne*, i., 282.   [2] *Dudo*, 76 (Duchesne).

[3] Herr Steenstrup shows that so far from the settlement of the Danes in Normandy being on feudal lines, they only reluctantly accepted the feudal yoke, and not till the next century. *Normannerne*, i., 305, 310. It is not till the 11th century that feudal castles become general in Normandy.

[4] The Danes in Normandy soon made Rouen a great centre of trade. *Normannerne*, i., 190.

[5] Cunningham's *Growth of English Industry*, i., 92.

democratic ; and when it was applied to a settled life in
the new country, the organisation of the town was the
form which it took. The Lagmen of Lincoln, Stamford,
Cambridge, Chester, and York are a peculiarly Scandinavian institution, which we find still existing at the
time of the Domesday Survey.[1]

Thus we see that the fortifications of the Danes,
like those of the Anglo-Saxons, were the fortifications
of the community. And we shall see in the next
chapter that this was the general type of the fortifications which were being raised in Western Europe in
the 9th century.

[1] See Vinogradoff, *English Society in the 11th Century*, pp. 5, 11, 478.

CHAPTER V

THE ORIGIN OF PRIVATE CASTLES

WE have now seen that history furnishes no instance of the existence of private castles among the Anglo-Saxons or the Danes (previous to the arrival of Edward the Confessor's Norman friends), and we have endeavoured to show that this negative evidence is of great significance. If, assuming that we are right in accepting it as conclusive, we ask why the Anglo-Saxons did not build private castles, the answer is ready to hand in the researches of the late Dr Stubbs, the late Professor Maitland, Dr J. H. Round, and Professor Vinogradoff, which have thrown so much fresh light on the constitutional history of England. These writers have made it clear that whatever tendencies towards feudalism there were in England before the Conquest, the system of military tenure, which is the backbone of feudalism, was introduced into England by William the Conqueror.[1] "Feudalism, in both tenure and government was, so far as it existed in England, brought full-grown from France," says Dr Stubbs; and this statement is not merely supported, but strengthened, by the work of the

---

[1] See Stubbs, *Constitutional History*, i., 251 ; Maitland's *Domesday Book and Beyond*, p. 157 ; Round's *Feudal England*, p. 261 ; Vinogradoff's *English Society in the* 11th *Century*, p. 41.

later writers named.[1] The institutions of the Anglo-Saxons, when they settled in England, were tribal; and though these institutions were in a state of decay in the 11th century, they were not completely superseded by feudal institutions till after the Norman Conquest.

We should naturally expect, then, that the fortifications erected by the Anglo-Saxons would be those adapted to their originally tribal state, that is, in the words which we have so often used already, they would be those of the community and not of the individual. And as far as we can discover the character of these fortifications, we find that this was actually the case. As we have seen, we find one of the earliest kings, Ida, building for the defence of himself and his followers what Bede calls a city; and we find Alfred and his children also building and repairing cities, at the time of the Danish invasions.

The same kind of thing was going on at about the same time in Germany and in France. Henry the Fowler (919-936), that great restorer of the Austrasian kingdom, planted on the frontiers which were exposed to the attacks of the Danes and Huns a number of walled strongholds, not only for the purpose of resisting invasion, but to afford a place of refuge to all the inhabitants of the country. He ordained that every ninth man of the peasants in the district must build

[1] Professor Maitland wrote: "The definitely feudal idea that military service is the tenant's return for the gift of land did not exist [before the Norman Conquest], though a state of things had been evolved which for many practical purposes was indistinguishable from the system of knight's fees." *Domesday Book and Beyond*, p. 157. Dr Round holds that "the military service of the Anglo-Norman tenant-in-chief was in no way derived or developed from that of the Anglo-Saxons, but was arbitrarily fixed by the king, from whom he received his fief." *Feudal England*, p. 261. Similarly, Professor Vinogradoff states that "the law of military fees is in substance French law brought over to England by the [Norman] conquerors." *English Society in the 11th Century*, p. 41.

for himself and his nine companions a dwelling in the " Burg," and provide barns and storehouses, and that the third part of all crops must be delivered and housed in these towns.[1] In this way, says the historian Giesebrecht, he sought to accustom the Saxons, who had hitherto dwelt in isolated farms, or open villages, to life in towns. He ordered that all assemblies of the people should be held in towns. Giesebrecht also remarks that it is not improbable that Henry the Fowler had the example of Edward the Elder of England before his eyes when he established these rows of frontier towns.[2]

The same causes led, on Neustrian soil, to the fortification of a number of cities, the walls of which had fallen into decay during the period of peace before the invasions of the Danes. Thus Charles the Bald commanded Le Mans and Tours to be fortified " as a defence *for the people* against the Northmen."[3] The bishops were particularly active in thus defending the people of their dioceses. Archbishop Fulk rebuilt the walls of Rheims, between 884 and 900 ;[4] his successor, Hervey, fortified the town of Coucy[5] (about 900) ; the Bishop of

[1] Giesebrecht, *Geschichte der Kaiserzeit*, i., 224. The word *Burg*, which Giesebrecht uses for these strongholds, means a castle in modern German ; but its ancient meaning was a town (see Hilprecht's *German Dictionary*), and it corresponded exactly to the Anglo-Saxon *burh*. It was used in this sense at least as late as the end of the 12th century ; see, *e.g.*, Lamprecht's *Alexanderlied*, passim. It is clear by the context that Giesebrecht employs it in its ancient sense.

[2] *Ibid.*, 222. Henry's son Otto married a daughter of Edward the Elder. Henry received the nickname of Townfounder (Städtegründer).

[3] " Carolus civitates Transsequanas ab incolis firmari rogavit, Cinomannis scilicet et Turonis, ut præsidio contra Nortmannos *populis* esse possent." *Annales Bertinianorum*, Migne, Pat., 125, 53.

[4] Flodoard, *Hist. Ecc. Remensis*, iv., viii.

[5] Modern historians generally say that he built the *castle* of Coucy ; but from Flodoard's account it seems very doubtful whether anything but the town is meant. *Annales*, iv., xiii. His words are : " Munitionem quoque apud Codiciacum tuto loco constituit atque firmavit." *Munitio* properly means a bulwark or wall.

Cambray built new walls to his city in 887-911 ;[1] and Bishop Erluin fortified Peronne in 1001, "as a defence against marauders, and a refuge for the husbandmen of the country."[2] But permission had probably to be asked in all these cases, as it certainly had in the last. The Carlovingian sovereigns represented a well-ordered state, modelled on the pattern of the Roman Empire ; they were jealous of any attempts at self-defence which did not proceed from the State, and thus as long as they had the power they strove to put down all associations or buildings of a military character which did not emanate from their imperial authority.

The history of the 9th and 10th centuries is the history of the gradual break-up of the Carlovingian Empire, and the rise of feudalism on its ruins. In 877, the year of his death, Charles the Bald signed a decree making the counts of the provinces, who until then had been imperial officers, hereditary. He thus, as Sismondi says, annihilated the remains of royal authority in the provinces.[3] The removable officers now became local sovereigns. Gradually, as the Carlovingian Empire fell to pieces, the artificial organisation of the feudal system arose to take its place. By the end of the 10th century the victory of feudalism was complete ; and the victory of feudalism was the victory of the private castle.

"The very word castle," says Guizot, "brings with it the idea of feudal society ; we see it rising before us. It was feudalism that built these castles which once covered our soil, and whose ruins are still scattered upon it. They were the declaration of its triumph. Nothing like them had existed on Gallo-Roman soil. Before the

---

[1] *Gesta Episcop. Cameracensium*, Pertz, vii., 424.
[2] *Chron. Camarense et Atrebatorum*, Bouquet, x., 196.
[3] Sismondi, *Histoire des Français*, ii., 172.

Germanic invasion, the great landed proprietors dwelt either in the cities, or in beautiful houses agreeably situated near the cities." [1] These Gallo-Roman villas had no fortifications; [2] nor were the Roman villas in England fortified. [3] It was the business of the State to defend the community; this was the theory so long sustained by imperial Rome, and which broke down so completely under the later Carlovingians.

In the time of Charlemagne and Louis le Debonnaire, even the royal palaces do not appear to have been fortified. They were always spoken of as *palatia*, never as *castella*. The Danes, when they took possession of the palace of Nimeguen in 880, fortified it with ditches and banks. [4] Charles the Bald appears to have been the first to fortify the palace of Compiègne. [5]

Although there can be no doubt that private castles had become extremely common on the mainland of Western Europe before the end of the 10th century, it is more difficult than is generally supposed to trace their first appearance. Historians, even those of great repute, have been somewhat careless in translating the words *castrum* or *castellum* as *castle* or *château*, and taking them in the sense of the feudal or private castle. [6] We

---

[1] Guizot, *Histoire de la Civilisation en France*, iii., 311.

[2] Enlart, *Manuel d'Archæologie Française*, ii., 494.

[3] See Dr Haverfield's articles in the *Victoria County Histories*, passim. The late J. H. Burton justly wrote: " We have nothing from the Romans answering to the feudal stronghold or castle, no vestige of a place where a great man lived apart with his family and his servants, ruling over dependants and fortifying himself against enemies." *History of Scotland*, i., 385.

[4] *Annals of Fulda*, 394, Pertz, i.   [5] *Cap. Regum Francor.*, ii., 360.

[6] Thus De Caumont unfortunately spoke of the fortress built by Nicetus, Bishop of Treves, in the 6th century, as a *château* (*Abécédaire*, ii., 382); but Venantius Fortunatus, in his descriptive poem, tells us that it was a vast enclosure with no less than thirty towers, built by the good pastor for the protection of his flock. It even contained fields and vineyards, and altogether was as different from a private castle as anything can well be.

have already pointed out that these words in our Anglo-Saxon charters mean a town or village.[1] The fact is that from Roman times until toward the end of the 9th century the words *castrum* and *castellum* are used indifferently for a fortified city or town, or a temporary camp. The expression *civitates et castella* is not uncommon, and might lead one to think that a distinction was drawn between large and small towns, or forts. But it is far more likely that it is a mere pleonasm, a bit of that redundancy which was always dear to the mediæval scribe who was trying to write well. For as the instances cited in the Appendix will prove, we constantly find the words *castrum* and *castellum* used for the same town, sometimes even in the same paragraph. Later, from the last quarter of the 9th century to the middle of the 12th century, these same words are used indifferently for a town or a castle, and it is impossible to tell, except by the context, whether a town or a castle is meant ; and often even the context throws no light upon it.

This makes it extremely difficult to say with any exactness when the private castle first arose. We seem indeed to have a fixed date in the Capitulary of Pistes, issued by Charles the Bald in 864,[2] in which he

---

Similarly the *castrum* of Merliac, spoken of by Enlart (*Architecture Militaire*, p. 492) as a " veritable château," is described as containing cultivated lands and sheets of water ! (Cited from Gregory of Tours, *Hist. Francorum*, liii., 13.) De Caumont himself says : "Les grandes exploitations rurales que possédaient les rois de France et les principaux du royaume du Vième au Xième siècle ne furent pas des forteresses et ne doivent point être confondues avec les chateaux." *Abécédaire*, ii., 62.

[1] See Appendix D.

[2] " Volumus et expresse mandamus, ut quicunque istis temporibus castella et firmitates et haias sine nostro verbo fecerint, Kalendis Augusti omnes tales firmitates disfactas habeant ; quia vicini et circummanentes exinde multas depredationes et impedimenta sustinent." *Capitularia Regum Francorum*, Boretius, ii., 328.

straightly ordered that all who had made castles, forts, or hedge-works without his permission should forthwith be compelled to destroy them, because through them the whole neighbourhood suffered depredation and annoyance. This edict shows, we might argue, that private castles were sufficiently numerous by the year 864 to have become a public nuisance, calling for special legislation. But the chronicles of the second half of the 9th century do not reveal any extensive prevalence of private castles. Indeed, after studying all the most important chronicles of Neustria and Austrasia during this period, the present writer has only been able to find four instances of fortifications which have any claim at all to be considered private castles; and even this claim is doubtful.[1]

When we come to the chroniclers of the middle of the 10th century we find a marked difference. It is true that the words *castrum, castellum, municipium, oppidum, munitio*, are still used quite indifferently by Flodoard and other writers for one and the same thing, and that in a great many cases they obviously mean a fortified town. But there are other cases where they evidently mean a castle. And if we compare these writers with the earlier ones in the same way as we have already compared the pre-Conquest portion of the *Anglo-Saxon Chronicle* with the chroniclers of the 11th and

---

[1] These instances are as follows:—868, A certain Acfrid shut himself up in a *casa firmissima* in the *villa* of Bellus Pauliacus on the Loire, and it was burnt over his head (*Annales Bertinianorum*, pp. Migne, 125, 1237); 878, The sons of Goisfrid attack the *castellum* and lands of the son of Odo (*ibid.*, p. 1286); 879, Louis the Germanic besieges some men of Hugh, son of Lothaire, *in quodam castello juxta Viridunum:* he takes and destroys the castellum (*Annals of Fulda*, Pertz, i., 393); 906, Gerard and Matfrid fortify themselves in a certain *castrum*, in a private war (*Regino*, Pertz, i., 611). Sismondi states that the great nobles wrested from Louis-le-Bègue (877-879) the right of building private castles. So far, we have been unable to find any original authority for this statement.

12th centuries, we find the same contrast between them. In the pages of . Flodoard or Ademar the action constantly turns on the building, besieging, and burning of castles, which by whatever name they are called, have every appearance of being private castles. In fact before we get to the end of the century, the private castle is as much the leading feature of the drama as it is in the 11th or 12th centuries.

Why, then, had the chroniclers no fresh word for a thing which was in its essential nature so novel? The obvious and only answer is that the private castle in its earlier stages was nothing more than an embankment with a wooden stockade thrown round some *villa* or farm belonging to a private owner, and was therefore indistinguishable in appearance, though radically different in idea, from the fortifications which had hitherto been thrown up for the protection of the community.[1] How easily we may be mistaken in the meaning of the word *castellum*, if we interpret it according to modern ideas, may be seen by comparing the account of the bridge built by Charlemagne over the Elbe, in the *Annales Laurissenses*, with Eginhard's narrative of the same affair. The former states that Charlemagne built a *castellum* of wood and earth at each end of the bridge, while the latter tells us that it was a *vallum* to protect a garrison which he placed there. This, however, was a work of public utility, and not a private castle. But scanty as the evidence is, it all leads us to infer that the first private castles were fortifications of this simple nature.[2] Mazières-on-the-Meuse, which was besieged

---

[1] See Guizot, *Histoire de la Civilisation*, iii., 309. "On voit les *villæ* s'entourer peu à peu de fossés, de remparts de terre, de quelques apparences de fortifications."

[2] We hear of monasteries being fortified in this way; in 869 Charles the Bald drew a bank of wood and stone round the monastery of St Denis;

for four weeks by Archbishop Hervey, took its name from the *macerias* or banks which Count Erlebald had constructed around it. It is impossible to say whether this enclosure should be called a castle or a town, but in idea it was certainly a castle, since it was an enclosure formed for private, not for public interests.

Whether these first private castles were provided with towers we have no evidence either to prove or to disprove. No instance occurs from which we can conclude that they possessed any kind of citadel, before the middle of the 10th century.[1] But before the century is far advanced, we hear of towers in connection with the great towns, which, whether they were originally mural towers or not, are evidently private strongholds, and may justly be called keeps. The earliest instance known to the writer is in 924, when the tower of the *presidium* where Herbert Count of Vermandois had imprisoned Charles the Simple was burnt accidentally.[2] This tower must have been restored, as nine years later it withstood a six weeks' siege from King Raoul. A possibly earlier instance is that of Nantes, where Bishop Fulcher had made a castle in 889 ; for when this castle was restored by Count Alan Barbetorte (937-943), we are

"castellum in gyro ipsius monasterii ex ligno et lapide conficere cœpit." *Ann. Bertinian*, Migne, pp. 125, 1244. In 889 the Bishop of Nantes made a *castrum* of his church by enclosing it with a wall, and this wall appears to have had a tower. *Chron. Namnetense*, p. 45, in *Lobineau's Bretagne*, vol. ii. In 924 Archbishop Hervey made a *castellum* of the monastery of St Remi by enclosing it with a wall. *Flodoard*, p. 294 (Migne). But the fortification of monasteries was a very different thing from the fortification of private castles.

[1] In 951 Duke Conrad, being angry with certain men of Lorraine, threw down the *towers* of some of them ; these may have been the keeps of private castles. Flodoard, *Annales*, p. 477.

[2] *Presidium* is one of those vague words which chroniclers love to use ; it means a defence of any kind, and may be a town, a castle, or a garrison. The town in which this turris stood appears by the context to have been Chateau Thierry. *Cf.* Flodoard, *Annales*, pp. 924, with 933.

told that he *restored* the principal tower and made it into his own house.[1]   Count Herbert built a keep in Laon before 931 ; and this appears to have been a different tower to the one attached to the royal house which Louis d'Outremer had built at the gate of the city.[2]   We hear also of towers at Amiens (950), Coucy (958), Chalons (963), and Rheims (988).   All these towers, it will be observed, are connected with towns.[3] The first stone keep in the country for whose date we have positive evidence, is that of Langeais, built by Fulk Nerra, Count of Anjou, about the year 994 ; its ruins still exist.

But we are concerned more particularly here with the origin of the motte-and-bailey castle.   The exact place or time of its first appearance is still a matter of conjecture.   Certainly there is not a word in the chronicles which is descriptive of this kind of castle before the beginning of the 11th century.[4]   The first historical mention of a castle which is clearly of the motte-and-bailey kind is in the Chronicle of St Florent

---

[1] "Castrum muro factum circa eam [ecclesiam]." *Chron. Namnetense*, p. 45.   "Precepit [Alanus] eis terrarium magnum in circuitu Ecclesiæ facere, sicut murus prioris castri steterat, quo facto turrem principalem *reficiens*, in ea domum suam constitit." *Ibid.*

[2] Flodoard, *Annales*, pp. 931 and 949.   This tower was heightened by Charles, the last of the Carlovingians, and furnished with a ditch and bank, in 988.

[3] It is often supposed that these towers were derived from the *Pretoria*, or general's quarters in the Roman *castra*.   It is far more probable that they were derived from mural towers.   The Pretorium was not originally fortified, and it was placed in the centre of the Roman camp.   But one great object of the feudal keep was to have communication with the open country.   The keep of Laon was certainly on the line of the walls, as Bishop Ascelin escaped from it down a rope in 989, and got away on a horse which was waiting for him.   Palgrave, *England and Normandy*, ii., 880.

[4] The word *motte* or *mota* does not occur in any contemporary chronicle, as far as is known to the writer, before the 12th century ; nor is the word *dangio* to be found in any writer earlier than Ordericus.   But the *thing* certainly existed earlier.

le Vieil, where, at a date which the modern biographer of Fulk Nerra fixes at 1010, we learn that this same Count of Anjou built a castle on the western side of the hill Mont-Glonne, at St Florent le Vieil, on the Loire, and threw up an *agger* on which he built a wooden tower.[1] In this case the word *agger* evidently means a motte. But Fulk began to reign in 987 ; he was a great builder of castles, and was famed for his skill in military affairs.[2] One of his first castles, built between 991 and 994, was at Montbazon, not far from Tours. About 500 metres from the later castle of Montbazon is a motte and outworks, which De Salies not unreasonably supposes to be the original castle of Fulk.[3] Montrichard, Chateaufort, Chérament, Montboyau, and Baugé are all castles built by Fulk, and all have or had mottes. Montboyau is the clearest case of all, as it was demolished by Fulk a few years after he built it, and has never been restored, so that the immense motte and outworks which are still to be seen remain very much in their original state, except that a modern tower has been placed on the motte, which is now called Bellevue.[4]

---

[1] [Fulk and his son Geoffrey] in occidentali parte montis castellum determinaverunt. . . . Aggerem quoque in prospectu monasterii cum turre lignea erexerunt." *Chron. St Florentii*, in Lobineau's *Bretagne*, ii., 87. Some remains of this motte are still visible. De Salies, *Foulques Nerra*, p. 263.

[2] " Elegantissimus in rebus bellicis" is the quaint language of the Angevin chronicler, 176.

[3] See De Salies, *Histoire de Foulques Nerra*, which indirectly throws considerable light on the archæological question.

[4] Salies, *Histoire de Foulques Nerra*, p. 170. M. Enlart, in his *Manuel d'Archæologie Française*, ii., 495, has been misled about this castle by the *Chronicon Andegavense*, which says : "Odo. . . . Fulconem expugnare speravit, et totis nisibus adorsus est. Annoque presenti (1025) Montis Budelli castellum, quod circiter annos decem retro abhinc contra civitatem Turonicam firmaverat Fulco, obsedit, et turrim ligneam miræ altitudinis super domgionem ipsius castri erexit." Bouquet, x., 176. M. Enlart takes this to be the first recorded instance of a motte. But the passage is evidently corrupt, as the other accounts of this affair show that Count Odo's wooden

It was a tempting theory at one time to the writer to see in Fulk Nerra the inventor of the motte type of castle, for independently of his fame in military architecture, he is the first mediæval chieftain who is known to have employed mercenary troops.[1] Now as we have already suggested in Chapter I., the plan of the motte-and-bailey castle strongly suggests that there may be a connection between its adoption and the use of mercenaries. For the plan of this kind of castle seems to hint that the owner does not only mistrust his enemies, he also does not completely trust his garrison. The keep in which he and his family live is placed on the top of the motte, which is ditched round so as to separate it from the bailey ; the provisions on which all are dependent are stored in the cellar of the keep, so that they are under his own hand ; and the keys of the outer ward are brought to him every night, and placed under his pillow.[2]

But unfortunately for this theory, there is some evidence of the raising of mottes at an earlier period in the 10th century than the accession of Fulk Nerra. Thibault-le-Tricheur, who was Count of Blois and Chartres from 932 to 962, was also a great builder, and it is recorded of him that he built the keeps of Chartres,

tower was a siege engine, employed to attack Fulk's castle, and afterwards burnt by the besieged. See the *Gesta Ambasiens. Dom.*, *ibid.*, p. 257, and the *Chron. St Florentii.* Probably we should read *contra* domgionem instead of *super*. The *Chronicon Andegavense* was written in the reign of Henry II.

[1] When Fulk invaded Bretagne in or about 992, he collected an army "tam de suis quam conductitiis." *Richerius*, edition Guadet. The editor remarks that this is perhaps the first example of the use of mercenaries since the time of the Romans (ii., 266). Spannagel, citing Peter Damian, says that mercenaries were already common at the end of the 10th century. *Zur Geschichte des Deutschen Heerwesens*, pp. 72, 73.

[2] This was always the custom in mediæval castles. See Cohausen, *Befestigungen der Vorzeit*, p. 282.

Chateaudun,[1] Blois, and Chinon,[2] and the castle of
Saumur ; these must have been finished before 962.
Now there was anciently a motte at Blois, for in the
12th century, Fulk V. of Anjou burnt the whole fortress,
"*except the house on the motte.*"[3]   There was also a
motte at Saumur ;[4] and the plan of the castle of Chinon
is not inconsistent with the existence of a former motte.[5]
These instances seem to put back the existence of the
motte castle to the middle of the 10th century.

We know of no earlier claim than this, unless we
were to accept the statement of Lambert of Ardres that
Sigfrid the Dane, who occupied the county of Guisnes
about the year 928, fortified the town, and enclosed his
own *dunio* with a double ditch.[6]   If this were true, we
have a clear instance of a motte built in the first half of
the 10th century.   But Lambert's work was written at
the end of the 12th century, with the object of glorifying

---

[1] " Qui vivens turres altas construxit et ædes, Unam Carnotum, sed apud
Dunense reatum." *Chron. St Florentii.*

[2] *Chron. Namnetense,* Lobineau, ii., 47.

[3] *Gesta Ambasiensium Dominorum,* in *Spicilegium,* p. 273.

[4] *Guide Joanne,* p. 234.

[5] The furthest point of the headland on which the castle is placed is a
small circular court, with a fosse on all sides but the precipices.   From
personal visitation.

[6] *Dunio* is subsequently explained by Lambert as *motte :* " Motam altis-
simam sive dunionem eminentem in munitionis signum firmavit." *Lamberti
Ardensis,* p. 613.   It is the same word as the Saxon *dun,* a hill (preserved
in our South Downs), and has no connection with the Irish and Gaelic *dun,*
which is cognate with the German *zaun,* a hedge, A.-S. *tun,* and means a
hedged or fortified place.   The form *dange* appears in Northern France,
and this seems to be the origin of the word *domgio* or *dangio* which we find
in the chroniclers, the modern form of which is *donjon.*   If we accept this
etymology, we must believe that the word *dunio* or *domgio* was originally
applied to the hill, and not to the tower on the hill, to which it was afterwards transferred.   It is against this view that Ordericus, writing some fifty
years before Lambert, uses the form *dangio* in the sense of a tower.   Professor Skeat and the *New English Dictionary* derive the word *donjon* or
dungeon from Low Lat. *domnionem,* acc. of *domnio,* thus connecting it
with *dominus,* as the seignorial residence.

the counts of Guisnes, and its editor regards the early part of it as fabulous. That Sigfrid fortified the *town* of Guisnes we can easily believe, as we know the Danes commonly did the like (see Chapter IV.) ; but that he built himself a personal castle is unlikely.[1]

It is the more unlikely, because the Danes in Normandy do not appear to have built personal castles until the feudal system was introduced there by Richard Sans Peur. The settlement in Normandy was not on feudal lines. "Rollo divided out the lands among his powerful comrades, and there is scarcely any doubt that they received these lands as inheritable property, without any other pledge than to help Rollo in the defence of the country."[2] "The Norman constitution at Rollo's death can be described thus, that the duke ruled the country as an independent prince in relation to the Franks ; but for its internal government he had a council at his side, whose individual members felt themselves almost as powerful as the duke himself."[3] Sir Francis Palgrave asserts that feudalism was introduced into Normandy by the Duke Richard Sans Peur, the grandson of Rollo, towards the middle of the 10th century. He "enforced a most extensive conversion of allodial lands into feudal tenure," and exacted from his baronage the same feudal submission which he himself had rendered to Hugh Capet.[4]

It is quite in accordance with this that in the narrative of Dudo, who is our only authority for the history of Normandy in the 10th century, there is no mention of a private castle anywhere. We are told

---

[1] Ducange conjectured that the motte-castle took its origin in Flanders, but it was probably the passage cited above from Lambert which led him to this conclusion. See art. "Mota" in Ducange's *Glossarium*.

[2] Steenstrup, *Normannerne*, i., 297.   [3] *Ibid.*, i., 301.

[4] *England and Normandy*, ii., 535.

that Rollo restored the walls and towers of the *cities* of
Normandy,[1] and it is clear from the context that the
castra of Rouen, Fécamp, and Evreux, which are mentioned, are fortified cities, not castles. Even the ducal
residence at Rouen is spoken of as a *palatium* or an
aula, not as a castle; and it does not appear to have
possessed a keep until (as we are told by a later writer)
the same Duke Richard who introduced the feudal
system into Normandy built one for his own residence.[2]
It is possible that when the feudal oath was exacted
from the more important barons, permission was given
to them to build castles for themselves; thus we hear
from Ordericus of the castle of Aquila, built in the days
of Duke Richard; the castle of the lords of Grantmesnil
at Norrei; the castle of Belesme; all of which appear
to have been private castles.[3] But there seems to have
been no general building of castles until the time of
William the Conqueror's minority, when his rebellious
subjects raised castles against him on all sides. "Plura
per loca aggeres erexerunt, et tutissimas sibi munitiones
construxerunt."[4] It is generally, and doubtless cor-
rectly, supposed that *aggeres* in this passage means
mottes, and taking this statement along with the great
number of mottes which are still to be found in
Normandy, it has been further assumed (and the present
writer was disposed to share the idea) that this was the
time of the first invention of mottes. But the facts

[1] "Muros et propugnacula civitatum refecit et augmentavit." *Dudo*, p.
85 (Duchesne's edition).
[2] Henricus rex circa turrem Rothomagi, *quam ædificavit primus
Richardus dux Normannorum in palatium sibi*, murum altum et latum cum
propugnaculis ædificat." *Robert of Toringy*, R.S., p. 106.
[3] *Ordericus*, ii., 15, 17, 46 (edition Prévost).
[4] *William of Jumièges*, anno 1035. Mr Freeman remarks that the
language of William would lead us to suppose that the practice of castle-
building was new.

which have been now adduced, tracing back the first known mottes to the time of Thibault-le-Tricheur, and the county of Blois, show that the Norman claim to the invention of this mode of fortification must be given up. If the Normans were late in adopting feudalism, they were probably equally late in adopting private castles, and the fortifications of William I.'s time were most likely copied from castles outside the Norman frontier.[1]

It might be thought that the general expectation of the end of the world in the year 1000, which prevailed towards the end of the 10th century, had something to do with the spread of these wooden castles, as it might have seemed scarcely worth while to build costly structures of stone. But it is not necessary to resort to this hypothesis, because there is quite sufficient evidence to show that long before this forecast of doom was accepted, wood was a very common, if not the commonest, material used in fortification. The reader has only to open his Cæsar to see how familiar wooden towers and wooden palisades were to the Romans; and he has only to study carefully the chronicles of the 9th, 10th, 11th, and 12th centuries to see how all-prevalent this mode of fortification continued to be. The general adoption of the feudal system must have brought about a demand for cheap castles, which was excellently met by the motte with its wooden keep and its stockaded bailey. M. Enlart has pointed out that

[1] There are some facts which render it probable that the earliest castles built in Normandy were without mottes, and were simple enclosures like those we have described already. Thus the castle of the great family of Montgomeri is an enclosure of this simple kind. Domfront, built by William Talvas in Duke Robert's time, has no motte. On the other hand, Ivry, built by the Countess Albereda in Duke Richard I.'s days, "on the top of a hill overlooking the town" (William of Jumièges), may possibly have been a motte; and there is a motte at Norrei, which we have just mentioned as an early Norman castle.

wooden defences have one important advantage over stone ones, their greater cohesion, which enabled them to resist the blows of the battering-ram better than rubble masonry.[1] Their great disadvantage was their liability to fire; but this was obviated, as in the time of the Romans, by spreading wet hides over the outsides. Stone castles were still built, where money and means were available, as we see from Fulk Nerra's keep at Langeais; but the devastations of the Northmen had decimated the population of Gaul; labour must have been dear, and skilled masons hard to find. In these social and economic reasons we have sufficient cause for the rapid spread of wooden castles in France.

The sum of the evidence which we have been reviewing is this : the earliest mottes which we know of were *probably* built by Thibault-le-Tricheur about the middle of the 10th century. But in the present state of our knowledge we must leave the question of the time and place of their first origin open. The only thing about which we can be certain is that they were the product of feudalism, and cannot have arisen till it had taken root; that is to say, not earlier than the 10th century.

[1] *Manuel d'Archæologie Française*, p. 457.

CHAPTER VI

DISTRIBUTION AND CHARACTERISTICS OF MOTTE-CASTLES

THE motte-and-bailey type of castle is to be found throughout feudal Europe, but is probably more prevalent in France and the British Isles than anywhere else. We say *probably*, because there are as yet no statistics prepared on which to base a comparison.[1] How recent the inquiry into this subject is may be learned from the fact that Krieg von Hochfelden, writing in 1859, denied the existence of mottes in Germany;[2] and even Cohausen in 1898 threw doubt

[1] This want will be supplied, as regards England, by the completion of the *Victoria County Histories*, and as regards France, by the *Societé Préhistorique*, which is now undertaking a catalogue of all the earthworks of France. The late M. Mortillet, in an article in the *Revue Mensuelle de l'École d'Anthropologie*, viii., 1895, published two lists, one of actual mottes in France, the other of place-names in which the word motte is incorporated. Unfortunately the first list is extremely defective, and the second, as it only relates to the name, is not a safe guide to the proportional numbers of the thing. All that the lists prove is that mottes are to be found in all parts of France, and that place-names into which the word *motte* enters seem to be more abundant in Central France than anywhere else. It is possible that a careful examination of local chroniclers may lead to the discovery of some earlier motte-builder than Thibault-le-Tricheur. We should probably know more about Thibault's castles were it not that the Pays Chartrain, as Palgrave says, is almost destitute of chroniclers.

[2] Cited at length by De Caumont, *Bulletin Monumental*, ix., 246. Von Hochfelden considered that the origin of feudal fortresses in Germany hardly goes back to the 10th century; only great dukes and counts then thought of fortifying their manors; those of the small nobility date at earliest from the end of the 12th century.

upon them,[1] although General Köhler in 1887 had already declared that "the researches of recent years have shown that the motte was spread over the whole of Germany, and was in use even in the 13th and 14th centuries."[2] The greater number of the castles described by Piper in his work on Austrian castles are on the motte-and-bailey plan, though the motte in those mountainous provinces is generally of natural rock, isolated either by nature or art. Mottes were not uncommon in Italy, according to Muratori,[3] and are especially frequent in Calabria, where we may strongly suspect that they were introduced by the Norman conqueror, Robert Guiscard.[4] It is not improbable that the Franks of the first crusade planted in Palestine the type of castle to which they were accustomed at home, for several of the excellent plans in Rey's *Architecture des Croisés* show clearly enough the motte-and-bailey plan.[5] In most of these cases the motte was a natural rock.

On the other hand, we are told by Köhler that motte-castles are not found among the Slavonic nations, because they never adopted the feudal system.[6] Nor are there any in Norway or Sweden.[7] Denmark has

---

[1] *Die Befestigungen der Vorzeit*, p. 28.

[2] *Entwickelung des Kriegswesens*, iii., 370.

[3] *Antiquitates Italicæ*, ii., 504. He says they are many times mentioned both in charters and chronicles in Italy.

[4] We hear of Robert Guiscard building a wooden castle on a hill at Rocca di St Martino in 1047. Amari, *Storia dei Musulmani di Sicilia*, i., 43. Several place-names in Italy and Sicily are compounded with *motta*, as the Motta Sant' Anastasia in Sicily. See Amari, *ibid.*, p. 220.

[5] Especially Montfort and Blanchegarde. But there is a wide field for further research both in Palestine and Sicily.

[6] "Bei den Sclaven haben die Chateaux-à-motte keinen Eingang gefunden, weil ihnen das Lehnswesen fremd geblieben ist." iii., 338.

[7] Professor Montelius informed the writer that they are quite unknown in Norway or Sweden ; and Dr Christison obtained an assurance to the same effect from Herr Hildebrand.

some, which are attributed by Dr Sophus Müller to the
mediæval period.[1]

Of course whenever a motte was thrown up, the first
castle upon it must have been a wooden one. A stone
keep could not be placed on loose soil.[2] The motte,
therefore, must always represent the oldest castle. But
there is no reason to think that the motte and its
wooden keep were merely temporary expedients, intended
always to be replaced as soon as possible by stone
buildings. Even after stone castles had been fully
developed, wood continued to hold its ground as a solid
building material until a very late period.[3] And mottes
were used not only throughout the 11th and 12th
centuries, but even as late as the 13th. King John
built many castles of this type in Ireland; and as late
as 1242 Henry III. ordered a motte and wooden castle
to be built in the island of Rhé.[4] Muratori gives a
much later instance: in 1320 Can Grande caused a
great motte to be built near Pavia, and surrounded with
a ditch and hedge, in order to build a castle on it.[5]

[1] "These are small well-defended places, the stronghold of the individual,
built for a great man and his followers, and answering to mediæval
conditions, to a more or less developed feudal system." *Vor Oldtid*, p. 642.

[2] I am informed by a skilled engineer that even in the wet climate of
England it would take about ten years for the soil to settle sufficiently to
bear a stone building.

[3] Köhler says: "By far the greater part of the castles of the Teutonic
knights in Prussia, until the middle of the fourteenth century, were of wood
and earth." *Die Entwickelung des Kriegswesen*, iii., 376.

[4] *Cal. of Patent Rolls*, 1232-1247, p. 340. Mandate to provost of Oléron to
let Frank De Brene have tools to make a new motte in the isle of Rhé.
Later the masters and crews of the king's galleys are ordered to help in
building the motte and the wooden castle. P. 343.

[5] *Antiquitates Italicæ*, ii., 504. Can Grande's motte at Padua. Anno
1320. "Dominus Alternerius [podesta of Padua] . . . cum maxima quantitate
peditum et balistariorum Civitatis Paduæ, iverunt die predicto summo mane
per viam Pontis Corvi versus quamdam motam magnam, quam faciebat
facere Dominus Canis, cum multis fossis et tajatis ad claudendum
Paduanos, ne exirent per illam partem, et volendo ibidem super illam

And as will be seen in the next chapter, there is considerable evidence that many mottes in England which were set up in the reign of William I., retained their wooden towers or stockades even till as late as the reign of Edward I. The motte at Drogheda held out some time against Cromwell, and is spoken of by him as a very strong place, having a good graft (ditch) and strongly palisaded.[1] Tickhill Castle in Yorkshire had a palisade on the counterscarp of the ditch when it was taken by Cromwell.[2]

The position of these motte-castles is wholly different from that of prehistoric fortresses. They are almost invariably placed in the arable country, and as a rule not in isolated situations, but in the immediate neighbourhood of towns or villages. It is rare indeed to find a motte-castle in a wild, mountainous situation in England. The only instance which occurs to the writer is that of the motte on the top of the Hereford Beacon; but there is great probability that this was a post fortified by the Bishop of Hereford in the 13th century to protect his game from the Earl of Gloucester. Nothing pointing to a prehistoric origin was found in this motte when it was excavated by Mr Hilton Price,[3] though the camp in which it is placed is supposed to be prehistoric.

The great majority of mottes in England are planted

---

motam ædificare castrum. Tunc prædictus Potestas cum aliis nominatis splanare incœperunt, et difecerunt dictam motam cum tajatis et fossa magna."

We may remark here that as early as the 17th century the learned Muratori protested against the equation of *mota* and *fossatum*, and laughed at Spelman for making this translation of *mota* in his *Glossary*. *Antiquitates Italicæ*, ii., 504.

[1] Cited by Westropp, *Journal of R.S.A., Ireland*, 1904.
[2] Vicars' *Parliamentary Chronicle*, cited by Hunter, *South Yorks*, ii., 235. [3] "Camps on the Malvern Hills," *Journ. Anthrop. Inst.*, x., 319.

either on or near Roman or other ancient roads, or on navigable rivers.[1] It was essential to the Norman settlers that they should be near some road which would help them to visit their other estates, which William had been so careful to scatter, and would also enable them to revisit from time to time their estates in Normandy.[2] The rivers of England were much fuller of water in mediæval times than they are now, and were much more extensively used for traffic; they were real waterways. When we find a motte perched on a river which is not navigable, the purpose probably was to defend some ford, or to exact tolls from passengers. Thus the Ferry Hill (corrupted into Fairy Hill) at Whitwood stands at the spot where the direct road from Pontefract to Leeds would cross the Calder. It was probably not usual for the motte to be dependent on a stream or a spring for its supply of water, and this is another point in which the mediæval castle differs markedly from the prehistoric camp; wells have been found in a number of mottes which have been excavated, and it is probable that this was the general plan, though we have not sufficient statistics on this subject as yet.[3]

Occasionally, but very rarely, we find two mottes in the same castle. The only instances in England known to the writer are at Lewes and Lincoln.[4] It is not

[1] M. de Salies has traced in detail the connection between Fulk Nerra's castles and the Roman roads of Anjou and Touraine.

[2] See some excellent remarks on this subject in Mr W. St John Hope's paper on "English Fortresses" in *Arch. Journ.*, lx., 72-90.

[3] Only a very small number of mottes have as yet been excavated. Wells were found at Almondbury, Berkeley, Berkhampstead, Carisbrook, Conisborough, Kenilworth, Northallerton, Norwich, Pontefract, Oxford, Tunbridge, Worcester, and York. At Caus, there is a well in the ditch between the motte and the bailey. Frequently there is a second well in the bailey.

[4] The writer at one time thought that the ruins at the east end of the castle of Pontefract concealed a second motte, but wishes now to recant this opinion. *Eng. Hist. Review*, xix., 419.

unfrequent to find a motte very near a stone castle. In
this case it is either the abandoned site of the original
wooden castle, or it is a siege castle raised to blockade
the other one. We constantly hear of these siege
castles being built in the Middle Ages; their purpose
was not for actual attack, but to watch the besieged fort
and prevent supplies from being carried in.[1] Hillocks
were also thrown up for the purpose of placing *balistæ*
and other siege engines upon them; but these would be
much smaller than mottes, and would be placed much
nearer the walls than blockade castles.

The mottes of France are in all probability much
more decidedly military than those of England.
France was a land of private war, after the dissolution
of the empire of Charlemagne; and no doubt one of the
reasons for the rapid spread of the motte-castle, after its
invention, was due to the facilities which it offered for
this terrible game. In England the reasons for the
erection of mottes seem to have been manorial rather
than military; that is, the Norman landholder desired a
safe residence for himself amidst a hostile peasantry,
rather than a strong military position which could hold
out against skilful and well-armed foes.

Attached to the castle, both in England and abroad,
we frequently find an additional enclosure, much larger
than the comparatively small area of the bailey proper.
This was the *burgus* or borough, which inevitably
sprang up round every castle which had a lengthened
existence. Our older antiquaries, finding that the word
burgenses was commonly used in Domesday in connection

---

[1] Thus Henry I. erected a siege castle to watch Bridgenorth (probably
Pampudding Hill), and then went off to besiege another castle. Mr Orpen
kindly informs me that the camp from which Philip Augustus besieged
Château Gaillard contains a motte. Outside Pickering, Corfe, and Exeter
there are earthworks which have probably been siege castles.

with a site where a castle existed, formed the mistaken idea that a *burgus* necessarily implied a castle. But a *burgus* was the same thing as a *burh*, that is, a *borough* or fortified town. It may have existed long before the castle, or it may have been created after the castle was built. The latter case was very common, for the noble who built a castle would find it to his advantage to build a *burgus* near it.[1] In exchange for the protection offered by the borough wall or bank, he could demand *gablum* or rent from the burghers; he could compel them to grind their corn at his mill, and bake their bread at his oven; he could exact tolls on all commodities entering the borough; and if there was a market he would receive a certain percentage on all sales. The borough was therefore an important source of revenue to the baron. Domesday Book mentions the *new borough* at Rhuddlan, evidently built as soon as the castle had been planted on the deserted banks of the Clwydd. In some cases a "new borough" is clearly a new suburb, doubtless having its own fortifications, built specially for the protection of the Norman settlers in England, as at Norwich and Nottingham.[2]

That even in the 12th century a motte was considered an essential feature of a castle is shown by Neckham's treatise " De Utensilibus," where he gives directions as to how a castle should be built; the motte should be placed on a site well defended by nature; it should have a stockade of squared logs round the top; the keep on the motte should be furnished with turrets and battlements, and crates of stones for missiles should be

---

[1] Henry II. built a castle and very fine borough (burgum pergrande) at Beauvoir in Maine. *Robert of Torigny*, R.S., p. 243. Minute regulations concerning the founding of the borough of Overton are given in *Close Rolls*, Edward I. (1288-1296), p. 285.

[2] See Round, *Studies in Domesday*, pp. 125, 126.

always provided, as well as a perpetual spring of water, and secret passages and posterns, by which help might reach the besieged.[1]

What the outward appearance of these motte-castles was we learn from the Bayeux Tapestry, which gives us several instructive pictures of motte-castles existing in the 11th century at Dol, Rennes, Dinan, and Bayeux.[2] There is considerable variety in these pictures, and something no doubt must be ascribed to fancy; but all show the main features of a stockade round the top of the motte, enclosing a wooden tower, a ditch round the foot of the motte, with a bank on the counterscarp, and a stepped wooden bridge, up which horses were evidently trained to climb, leading across the moat to the stockade of the motte. In no case is the bailey distinctly depicted, but we may assume that it has been already taken, and that the horsemen are riding over it to the gate-house which (in the picture of Dinan) stands at the foot of the bridge. The towers appear to be square, but in the case of Rennes and Bayeux, are surmounted by a cupola roof. Decoration does not appear to be have been neglected, and the general appearance of the buildings, far from being of a make-shift character, must have been very picturesque.

The picture of the building of the motte at Hastings shows only a stockade on top of the motte ; this may be because the artist intended to represent the work as incomplete. What is remarkable about this picture is that the motte appears to be formed in layers of different materials. We might ascribe this to the fancy

[1] Neckham, " De Utensilibus," in Wright's *Volume of Vocabularies*, pp. 103, 104. Unfortunately this work of Neckham's was not written to explain the construction of motte castles, but to furnish his pupils with the Latin names of familiar things ; a good deal of it is very obscure now.

[2] See frontispiece.

of the embroiderer, were it not that layers of this kind
have occasionally been found in mottes which have been
excavated or destroyed.　Thus the motte at Carisbrook,
which was opened in 1903, was found to be composed of
alternate layers of large and small chalk rubble.　In
some cases, layers of stones have been found ; in others
(as at York and Burton) a motte formed of loose
material has been cased in a sort of pie-crust of heavy
clay.　In the Castle Hill at Hallaton in Leicestershire
layers of peat and hazel branches, as well as of clay
and stone boulders, were found.　But our information on
this subject is too scanty to justify any generalisations
as to the general construction of mottes.

The pictures shown in the Bayeux Tapestry agree
very well with the description given by a 12th-century
writer of the castle of Merchem, near Dixmüde, in the
life of John, Bishop of Terouenne, who died in 1130.
" Bishop John used to stay frequently at Merchem when
he was going round his diocese.　Near the churchyard
was an exceedingly high fortification, which might be
called a castle or *municipium*, built according to the
fashion of that country by the lord of the manor many
years before.　For it is the custom of the nobles of that
region, who spend their time for the most part in private
war, in order to defend themselves from their enemies
to make a hill of earth, as high as they can, and encircle
it with a ditch as broad and deep as possible.　They
surround the upper edge of this hill with a very strong
wall of hewn logs, placing towers on the circuit, according to their means.　Inside this wall they plant their
house, or keep (arcem), which overlooks the whole thing.
The entrance to this fortress is only by a bridge, which
rises from the counterscarp of the ditch, supported on
double or even triple columns, till it reaches the upper

edge of the motte (agger)." [1] The chronicler goes on to relate how this wooden bridge broke down under the crowd of people who were following the bishop, and all fell 35 feet into the ditch, where the water was up to their knees. There is no mention of a bailey in this account, but a bailey was so absolutely necessary to a residential castle, in order to find room for the stables, lodgings, barns, smithies and other workshops, which were necessary dependencies of a feudal household, that it can seldom have been omitted, and the comparatively rare instances which we find of mottes which appear never to have had baileys were probably outposts dependent on some more important castle.

Lambert of Ardres, the panegyrist of the counts of Guisnes,[2] writing about 1194, gives us a minute and most interesting description of the wooden castle of Ardres, built about the year 1117. "Arnold, lord of Ardres, built on the motte of Ardres a wooden house, excelling all the houses of Flanders of that period both in material and in carpenter's work. The first storey was on the surface of the ground, where were cellars and granaries, and great boxes, tuns, casks, and other domestic utensils. In the storey above were the dwelling and common living rooms of the residents, in which were the larders, the rooms of the bakers and butlers, and the great chamber in which the lord and his wife slept. Adjoining this was a private room, the dormitory of the waiting maids and children. In the inner part of the great chamber was a certain private room, where at

---

[1] *Acta Sanctorum*, 27th January, Bolland, iii., 414. This biography was written only nine months after Bishop John's death, by an intimate friend, John de Collemedio.

[2] Guisnes is now in Picardy, but in the 12th century it was in Flanders, which was a fief of the Empire.

early dawn or in the evening or during sickness or at time of blood-letting, or for warming the maids and weaned children, they used to have a fire. . . . In the upper storey of the house were garret rooms, in which on the one side the sons (when they wished it) on the other side the daughters (because they were obliged) of the lord of the house used to sleep. In this storey also the watchmen and the servants appointed to keep the house took their sleep at some time or other. High up on the east side of the house, in a convenient place, was the chapel, which was made like unto the tabernacle of Solomon in its ceiling and painting. There were stairs and passages from storey to storey, from the house into the kitchen, from room to room, and again from the house into the *loggia* (logium), where they used to sit in conversation for recreation, and again from the loggia into the oratory." [1]

This description proves that these wooden castles were no mere rude sheds for temporary occupation, but that they were carefully built dwellings designed for permanent residence. The description is useful for the light it throws on the stone keeps whose ruins remain to us. They probably had very similar arrangements, and though only their outside walls are now existing, they must have been divided into different rooms by wooden partitions which have now perished. [2]

In this account of Lambert's it is further mentioned that the kitchen was joined to the house or keep, and was a building of two floors, the lower one being occupied by live stock, while the upper one was the actual kitchen. We must remember that this account

[1] This description is from the *Historia Ardensium* of Walter de Clusa, which is interpolated in the work of Lambert, Bouquet, pp. 13, 624.

[2] Yet in some of the later keeps, such as Conisburgh, where we find only one window to a storey, the room must have been undivided.

was written at the end of the 12th century. In the earlier and simpler manners of the 11th century it is probable that the cooking was more generally carried on in the open air, as it was among the Anglo-Saxons.[1] The danger of fire would prevent the development of chimneys in wooden castles ; we have seen that there was only one in this wonderful castle of Ardres. But even after stone castles became common, we have evidence that the kitchen was often an isolated building in the courtyard. One such kitchen still exists in the monastic ruins of Glastonbury.

The word *mota*, which was used in the 12th century for the artificial hills on which the wooden keeps of these castles were placed, comes from an old French word *motte*, meaning a clod of earth, which is still used in France for a small earthen hillock.[2] The keep itself appears to have been called a *bretasche*, though this word seems to have meant a wooden tower of any kind, and was used both for mural towers and for the movable wooden towers employed for sieges.[3] At a much later period it was given to the wooden balconies by which walls were defended, but the writer has found no instance of this use of the word before the 14th century. On the contrary, these wooden galleries for the purpose of defending the foot of the walls by throwing missiles down are called *hurdicia* or hourdes in the documents, a

---

[1] See Wright, *History of Domestic Manners*, p. 26.

[2] According to Littré, the original derivation of the word *motte* is unknown. I have not found any instance of the word *mota* in chronicles earlier than the 12th century, but the reason appears to be that *mota* or motte was a folk's word, and appeared undignified to an ambitious writer. Thus the author of the *Gesta Consulum Andegavensium* says that Geoffrey Martel, Count of Anjou, gave to a certain Fulcoius the fortified house which is still called by the vulgar Mota Fulcoii. D'Achery, *Spicilegium*, p. 257.

[3] See Appendix G.

word of cognate origin to our word *hoarding*.[1] The word *bretasche* is also of Teutonic origin, akin to the German *brett*, a board.

The court at the base of the hillock is always called the *ballium*, *bayle*, or *bailey*, a word for which Skeat suggests the Latin *baculus*, a stick, as a possible though very doubtful ancestor. The wooden wall which surrounded this court was the *palum*, *pelum*, or *palitium* of the documents, a word which Mr Neilson has proved to be the origin of the *peels* so common in Lowland Scotland, though it has been mistakenly applied to the towers enclosed by these peels.[2] The *palitium* was the stockade on the inner bank of the ditch which enclosed the bailey; but the outer or counterscarp bank had also its special defence, called the *hericio*, from its bristling nature (French *hérisson*, a hedgehog). There can be little doubt that it was sometimes an actual hedge of brambles, at other times of stakes intertwined with osiers or thorns.[3]

Thus the words most commonly used in connection with these wooden castles are chiefly French in form, but a French that is tinctured with Teutonic blood. This is just what we might expect, since the first castles of feudalism arose on Gallic soil (France or Flanders), but on soil which was ruled by men of Teutonic descent. We may regard it as fairly certain that it was in the region anciently known as Neustria that the motte-castle first appeared; and as we have previously shown, there is some reason to think that the centre of that region

---

[1] See Appendix H.

[2] *Peel, its Meaning and Derivation*, by George Neilson.

[3] See Appendix I. Cohausen has some useful remarks on the use of hedges in fortification. *Befestigungen der Vorzeit*, pp. 8-13. A quickset hedge had the advantage of resisting fire. The word *sepes*, which properly means a hedge, is often applied to the palitium.

was the place where it originated.   But this must for
the present remain doubtful.   What we regard as certain
is that it was from France, and from Normandy in
particular, that it was introduced into the British Isles ;
and to those islands we must now turn.

CHAPTER VII

THE CASTLES OF THE NORMANS IN ENGLAND

IN this chapter we propose to give a list, in alphabetical order for convenience of reference, of the castles which are known to have existed in England in the 11th century, because they are mentioned either in Domesday Book, or in charters of the period, or in some contemporary chronicle.[1] We do not for a moment suppose that this catalogue of eighty-four castles is a complete list of those which were built in England in the reigns of William I. and William II. We have little doubt that all the castles in the county towns, such as Leicester, Northampton, and Guildford, and those which we hear of first as the seats of important nobles in the reign of Henry II., such as Marlborough, Groby, Bungay, Ongar, were castles built shortly after the Conquest, nearly all of them being places which have (or had) mottes. Domesday Book only mentions fifty castles in England, and Wales,[2] but

---

[1] This list or *catalogue raisonné* was originally published in the *English Historical Review* for 1904 (vol. xix.). It is now reproduced with such corrections as were necessary, and with the addition of five more castles, as well as of details about thirty-four castles for which there was not space in the *Review*. The Welsh castles are omitted from this list, as they will be given in a separate chapter.

[2] The list is brought up to fifty by interpreting the *regis domus* of Winchester to be Winchester castle ; the reasons for this will be given later. The number would be increased to fifty-two if we counted Ferle and Bourne in Sussex as castles, as Mr Freeman does in his *Norman Conquest,* v., 808.

it is well known that the Survey is as capricious in its mention of castles as in its mention of churches.   It is possible that further research in charters which the writer has been unable to examine may furnish additional castles, but the list now given may be regarded as complete as far as materials generally accessible will allow.[1]   One of the castles mentioned (Richard's Castle) and probably two others (Hereford and Ewias) existed before the Conquest; they were the work of those Norman friends of Edward the Confessor whom he endowed with lands in England.

Out of this list of eighty-four castles we shall find that no less than seventy-one have or had mottes.   The exceptions are the Tower of London, Colchester, Pevensey, and Chepstow, where a stone keep was part of the original design, and a motte was therefore unnecessary : Bamborough, Peak, and Tynemouth, where the site was sufficiently defended by precipices : Carlisle and Richmond, whose original design is unknown to us : Belvoir, Dover, Exeter, and Monmouth, which might on many grounds be counted as motte-castles, but as the evidence is not conclusive, we do not mark them as such ; but even if we leave them out, with the other exceptions, we shall find that nearly 86 per cent. of our list of castles of the 11th century are of the motte-and-bailey type.

About forty-three of these castles are attached to

But the language of Domesday seems only to mean that the lands of these manors were held of Hastings castle by the service of castle-guard. See D. B., i., pp. 21 and 206.

[1] The total number would be eighty-six if Burton and Aldreth were included. Burton castle is mentioned in Domesday, but there is no further trace of its existence. The castle of Alrehede or Aldreth in the island of Ely is stated by the *Liber Eliensis* to have been built by the Conqueror, but no remains of any kind appear to exist now. Both these castles are therefore omitted from the list.

towns. Of these, less than a third are placed inside the Roman walls or the Saxon or Danish earthworks of the towns, while at least two-thirds are wholly or partly outside these enclosures.[1] This circumstance is important, because the position outside the town indicates the mistrust of an invader, not the confidence of a native prince. In the only two cases where we know anything of the position of the residence of the Saxon kings we find it in the middle of the city.[2] Even when the castle is inside the town walls it is almost invariably close to the walls, so that an escape into the country might always be possible.[3]

Of the towns or manors in which these castles were situated, Domesday Book gives us the value in King Edward's and King William's time in sixty-two instances. In forty-five cases the value has risen; in twelve it has fallen; in five it is stationary. Evidently something has caused a great increase of prosperity in these cases, and it can hardly be anything else than the impetus given to trade through the security afforded by a Norman castle.

Our list shows that Mr Clark's confident statement, that the moated mounds were the centres of large and important estates in Saxon times, was a dream. Out of forty-one mottes in country districts, thirty-six are found in places which were quite insignificant in King Edward's day, and only five can be said to occupy the centres of important Saxon manors.[4]

[1] Exact numbers cannot be given, because in some cases the bounds of the ancient borough are doubtful, as at Quatford.

[2] At Winchester and Exeter. For Winchester, see Milner, *History of Winchester*, ii., 194 ; for Exeter, Shorrt's *Sylva Antiqua Iscana*, p. 7.

[3] Colchester is the only exception to this rule, as the castle there is in the middle of the town ; but even this is only an apparent exception, as the second bailey extended to the town wall on the north, and had been royal demesne land even before the Conquest. See Round's *Colchester Castle*, ch. vii.

[4] These five are Berkeley, Berkhampstead, Bourn, Pontefract, Rayleigh.

In the table in the Appendix, the area occupied by
the original baileys of the castles in this list has
been measured accurately by a planimeter, from the
25-in. Ordnance maps, in all cases in which that was
possible.[1] This table proves that the early Norman
castles were very small in area, suitable only for the
personal defence of a chieftain who had only a small
force at his disposal, and absolutely unsuited for a
people in the tribal state of development, like the
ancient Britons, or for the scheme of national defence
inaugurated by Alfred and Edward. We may remark
here that in not a single case is any masonry which
is certainly early Norman to be found on one of these
mottes; where the date can be ascertained, the stone-
work is invariably later than the 11th century.

ABERGAVENNY (Fig. 8). — This castle, being in
Monmouthshire, must be included in our list. The
earliest notice of it is a document stating that Hamelin
de Ballon gave the church and chapel of the castle of
Abergavenny, and the land for making a *bourg*, and an
oven of their own, to the Abbey of St Vincent at
Le Mans.[2]

The castle occupies a pointed spur at the S. end
of the town, whose walls converge so as to include the
castle as part of the defence. The motte has been
much altered during recent years, and is crowned by
a modern building; but a plan in *Coxe's Tour in
Monmouthshire*, 1800, shows it in its original round
form. The bailey is roughly of a pentagonal shape,
covering 1 acre, and is defended by a curtain wall with
mural towers and a gatehouse. The ditch on the W.

[1] I am indebted for these measurements to Mr D. H. Montgomerie.
[2] Notification in Round's *Calendar of Documents preserved in France*,
p. 367. Mr Round dates the Notification 1087-1100.

and N. is much filled in and obscured by the encroachment of the town. On the E. the ground descends in a steep scarp, which merges into those of the headland on which the motte is placed.[1]

ARUNDEL (Fig. 8).—"The castrum of Arundel," says Domesday Book, "paid 40s. in King Edward's time from a certain mill, and 20s. from three boardlands (or feorm-lands), and 2s. from one pasture. Now, between the town feorm and the water-gate and the ships' dues, it pays 12l."[2] *Castrum* in Domesday nearly always means a castle; yet the description here given is certainly that of a town and not of a castle. We must therefore regard it as an instance of the fluctuating meaning which both *castrum* and *castellum* had in the 11th century.[3] Arundel is one of the towns mentioned in the "Burghal Hidage."[4] But even accepting that the description in Domesday refers to the town, we can have very little doubt that the original earthen castle was reared by Roger de Montgomeri, to whom William I. gave the Rapes of Arundel and Chichester, and whom he afterwards made Earl of Shrewsbury.[5]

---

[1] Description furnished by Mr D. H. Montgomerie, F.S.A.

[2] "Castrum Harundel T. R. E. reddebat de quodam molino 40 solidos, et de 3 conviviis 20 solidos, et de uno pasticio 20 solidos. Modo inter burgum et portum aquæ et consuetudinem navium reddit 12 libras, et tamen valet 13. De his habet S. Nicolaus 24 solidos. Ibi una piscaria de 5 solidos et unum molinum reddens 10 modia frumenti, et 10 modia grossæ annonæ. Insuper 4 modia. Hoc appreciatum est 12 libras. Robertus filius Tetbaldi habet 2 hagas de 2 solidis, et de hominibus extraniis habet suum theloneum." Several other *hagæ* and *burgenses* are then enumerated. (D. B., i., 23a, 1.)

[3] See Mr Round's remarks on the words in his *Geoffrey de Mandeville*, Appendix O. The above was written before the appearance of Mr Round's paper on "The Castles of the Conquest" (*Archæologia*, lviii.), in which he rejects the idea that *castrum Harundel* means the castle.

[4] See *ante*, p. 28.

[5] Florence of Worcester mentions the castle of Arundel as belonging to Roger de Montgomeri in 1088.

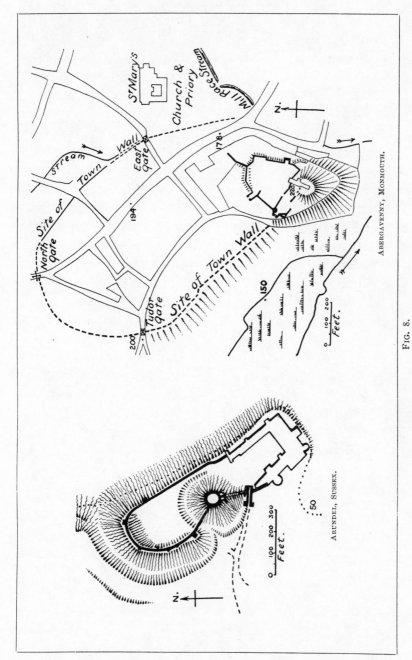

ABERGAVENNY, MONMOUTH.

ARUNDEL, SUSSEX.

Fig. 8.

[To face p. 98.

Roger had contributed sixty ships to William's fleet, and both he and his sons were highly favoured and trusted by William, until the sons forfeited that confidence. We shall see afterwards that their names are connected with several important castles of the early Norman settlement. We shall see also that the Rapes into which Sussex was divided—Chichester, Arundel, Bramber, Lewes, Pevensey, and Hastings—were all furnished with Norman castles, each with the characteristic motte, except Pevensey, which had a stone keep. Each of these castles, at the time of the Survey, defended a port by which direct access could be had to Normandy. It was to protect his base that William fortified these important estuaries, and committed them to the keeping of some of the most prominent of the Norman leaders.

The castle stands on the end of a high and narrow ridge of the South Downs, above the town of Arundel. It consists of an oblong ward, covering $4\frac{1}{2}$ acres, in the middle of which, but on the line of the west wall, is a large motte, about 70 feet high, surrounded by its own ditch. The lower and perhaps original bailey is only 2 acres in extent. Round the top of the motte is a slightly oval wall, of the kind called by Mr Clark a shell keep. We have elsewhere expressed our doubts of the correctness of this term.[1] In all the more important castles we find that the keep on top of the motte has a small ward attached to it, and Arundel is no exception to this rule; it has the remains of a tower, as well as the wall round the motte. The tower is a small one, but it is large enough for the king's chamber in times which were not extravagant in domestic architecture. It is probable that this tower, and the stone wall round

[1] See Appendix R.

the motte are the work of Henry II., as he spent nearly 340*l.* on this castle between the years 1170 and 1187. His work consisted chiefly of a wall, a king's chamber, a chapel, and a tower.[1] The wall of the motte corresponds in style to the work of the middle of his reign ; it is built of flints, but cased with Caen stone brought from Normandy, and has Norman buttresses. The original Norman doorway on the south side (now walled up) has the chevron moulding, which shows that it is not earlier than the 12th century. The tower, which we may assume to be the tower of Henry II.'s records, has a round arched entrance, and contains a chapel and a chamber (now ruined) besides a well chamber.

There is earlier Norman work still remaining in the bailey, namely, the fine gateway, which though of plain and severe Norman, is larger and loftier than the early work of that style, and of superior masonry.[2] The one Pipe Roll of Henry I. which we possess shows that he spent 78*l.* 6*s.* 2*d.* on the castle in 1130, and possibly this refers to this gatehouse.[3] We know that Henry was a great builder, but so was the former owner of this castle, Robert Belesme, son of Roger de Montgomeri.

The value of the town of Arundel had greatly increased since the Conquest, at the time of the Domesday Survey.[4]

BAMBOROUGH, Northumberland.—We first hear of

---

[1] The expenses entered in the *Pipe Rolls* (1170-1187) are for the works of the castle, the chamber and wall of the castle, the *houses* of the castle (an expression which generally refers to the keep), and for flooring the tower (turris) and making a garden. *Turris* is the usual word for a keep, and is never applied to a mere mural tower.

[2] This gateway is masked by a work of the 13th century, which serves as a sort of barbican.

[3] In operibus castelli de Arundel 22*l.* 7*s.* 8*d.* Et debet 55*l.* 18*s.* 6*d.* *Pipe Roll*, 31, Henry I., p. 42.

[4] D. B., i., 23a, 1.

this castle in the reign of Rufus, when it was defended against the king by Robert Mowbray, the rebel Earl of Northumberland; but there can be little doubt that the earliest castle on this natural bastion was built in the Conqueror's reign. In the 13th century certain lands were held by the tenure of supplying wood to the castle of Bamborough, and it was declared that this obligation had existed ever since the time of William I.[1] William certainly found no castle there, for Bamborough had fallen into utter ruin and desolation by the middle of the 11th century.[2] William's hold on Northumberland was too precarious to give opportunity for so long and costly a work as the building of a stone keep. It is more probable that a strong wooden castle was the fortress of the governors of Northumberland under the first Norman kings, and that the present stone keep was built in Henry II.'s reign.[3] There is no motte at Bamborough, nor was one needed on a site which is itself a natural motte, more precipitous and defensible than any artificial hill.[4] As the Domesday Survey does not extend to Northumberland, we have no statement of the value of Bamborough. The area of the castle is 4¾ acres.

[1] *Testa de Nevill*, i., iii., 236, cited by C. Bates, in a very valuable paper on Bamborough Castle, in *Archæologia Æliana*, vol. xiv., "Border Holds." Mr Bates gives other evidence to the same effect. The early existence of the castle is also proved by the fact that Gospatric, whom William had made Earl of Northumberland, after his raid on Cumberland in 1070, brought his booty to the *firmissimam munitionem* of Bamborough. Symeon of Durham, 1070.

[2] *Vita S. Oswaldi*, ch. xlviii., in Rolls edition of Symeon.

[3] This was the opinion of the late Mr Cadwalader Bates, who thought that the smallness of the sums entered for Bamborough in Henry II.'s reign might be accounted for by the labour and materials having been furnished by the crown tenants. *Border Strongholds*, p. 236.

[4] Bamborough rock has every appearance of having been once an island. As late as 1547 the tide came right up to the rock on the east side; the sea is now separated from the castle by extensive sandhills.

BARNSTAPLE, Devon (Fig. 9).—This castle is not
mentioned in Domesday, but the town belonged to
Judhael, one of the followers of the Conqueror, whose
name suggests a Breton origin. William gave him
large estates in Devon and Cornwall. A charter of
Judhael's to the priory which he founded at Barnstaple
makes mention of the castle.[1] Barnstaple, at the head
of the estuary of the Taw, was a borough at Domesday,
and the castle was placed inside the town walls.[2] The
motte remains in good condition; the winding walks
which now lead to the top are certainly no part of the
original plan, but are generally found in cases where the
motte has been incorporated in a garden. There was
formerly a stone keep, of which no vestige remains.[3]
The castle seems to have formed the apex of a town
of roughly triangular shape. The bailey can just be
traced, and must have covered $1\frac{1}{3}$ acres.

The former value of Barnstaple is not given in the
Survey, so we cannot tell whether it had risen or not.

BELVOIR, Leicester.—This castle was founded by
the Norman Robert de Todeni, who died in 1088.[4] It
stands on a natural hill, so steep and isolated that it
might be called a natural motte. The first castle was
destroyed by King John, and the modernising of the
site has entirely destroyed any earthworks which
may have existed on the hill. There appears to have

---

[1] *M. A.*, v., 197.

[2] *Domesday* mentions the destruction of twenty-three houses at Barnstaple, which may have been due partly or wholly to the building of the
castle. I., 100.

[3] From a lecture by Mr J. R. Chanter.

[4] The *Fundatio* of Belvoir priory says that Robert founded the church of
St Mary, *juxta castellum suum*, *M. A.*, iii., 288. As Robert's coffin was
actually found in the Priory in 1726, with an inscription calling him Robert
de Todnei *le Fundeur*, the statement is probably more trustworthy than
documents of this class generally are.

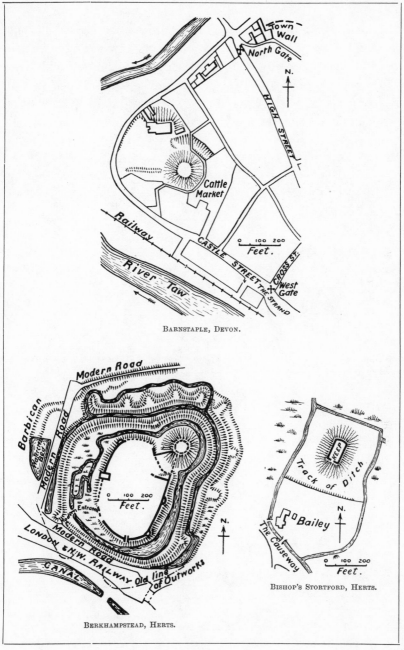

BARNSTAPLE, DEVON.

BERKHAMPSTEAD, HERTS.

BISHOP'S STORTFORD, HERTS.

FIG. 9.

[To face p. 102.

been a shell wall, from the descriptions given by Nicholls and Leland.[1] It was situated in the manor of Bottesdene, a manor of no great importance, but which had risen in value at the date of the Survey.[2]

BERKELEY, or NESS.—The identity of Berkeley Castle with the Ness castle of Domesday may be regarded as certain. All that the Survey says about it is : " In Ness there are five hides belonging to Berkeley, which Earl William put out to make a little castle."[3] Earl William is William FitzOsbern, the trusty friend and counsellor of the Conqueror, who had made him Earl of Herefordshire. He had also authority over the north and west of England during William's first absence in Normandy, and part of the commission he received from William was to build castles where they were needed.[4] Berkeley was a royal manor with a large number of berewicks, and the probable meaning of the passage in Domesday is that Earl William removed the *geldability* of the five hides occupying the peninsula or *ness* which stretches from Berkeley to the Severn, bounded on the south by the Little Avon, and appropriated these lands to the upkeep of a small castle. This castle can hardly have been placed anywhere but at Berkeley, for there is no trace of any other castle in the district.[5] Earl Godwin had sometimes resided at Berkeley, but prob-ably his residence there was the monastery which by

[1] Nicholls, *History of Leicester*, i., 110.

[2] D. B., i., 233b.

[3] " In Ness sunt 5 hidæ pertinentes ad Berchelai, quas comes Willielmus misit extra ad faciendum unum castellulum." D. B., i., 163a, 2.

[4] "Castella per loca firmari præcepit." *Flor. Wig.*, 1067. See Freeman, *N. C.*, iv., 72. Domesday tells us that FitzOsbern built Ness, Clifford, Chepstow, and Wigmore, and rebuilt Ewias.

[5] Robert Fitzhardinge, in his charter to St Austin's Abbey at Bristol, says that King Henry [II.] gave him the manor of Berchall, and all Bercheleiernesse. *Mon. Ang.*, vi., 365.

evil means had come into his hands;[1] for we never hear
of any castle in connection with Godwin. But a
Norman motte exists at Berkeley, though buried in the
stone shell built by Henry II. Mr Clark remarks : " If
the masonry of Berkeley Castle were removed, its
remains would show a mound of earth, and attached to
three sides of it a platform, the whole encircled with a
ditch or scarp."[2] The motte raised by Earl William
has, in fact, been revetted with a stone shell of the 12th
century, whose bold chevron ornament over the entrance
gives evidence of its epoch. What is still more remarkable is that documentary evidence exists to fix the date
of this transformation. A charter of Henry II. is
preserved at Berkeley Castle, in which he grants the
manor to Robert Fitzhardinge, pledging himself at the
same time to fortify a castle there, according to Robert's
wish.[3] Robert's wish probably was to possess a stone
keep, like those which had been rising in so many
places during the 12th century. But there had been a
Norman lord at Berkeley before Fitzhardinge, Roger
de Berkeley, whose representatives only lost the manor
through having taken sides with Stephen in the civil
war.[4] This Roger no doubt occupied the wooden castle
on the motte built by William FitzOsbern. Henry II.'s
shell was probably the first masonry connected with

---

[1] It is not necessary to discuss the authenticity of the story preserved by
Walter Map; it is enough that Gytha, the wife of Godwin, held in horror
the means by which her husband got possession of Berkeley Nunnery.
D. B., i., 164.

[2] *Mediæval Military Architecture*, i., 236.

[3] The gift of the manor was made before Henry became king, and was
confirmed by charter on the death of Stephen in 1154. Fitzhardinge
was an Englishman, son of an alderman of Bristol, who had greatly
helped Henry in his wars against Stephen. See Fosbroke's *History of
Gloucester*.

[4] He held Berkeley under the crown at the time of the Survey.
D. B., i., 163a.

the castle. This remarkable keep is nearly circular, and has three round turrets and one oblong. As the latter, Thorpe's Tower, was rebuilt in Edward III.'s reign, it probably took the place of a round tower. The keep is built of rubble, and its Norman buttresses (it has several later ones) project about a foot. The cross loopholes in the walls are undoubtedly insertions of the time of Edward III. The buildings in the bailey are chiefly of the time of Edward III., but the bailey walls have some Norman buttresses, and are probably of the same date as the keep.[1] This bailey is nearly square, and the motte, which is in one corner, encroaches upon about a quarter of it. The small size of the area which it encloses, not much more than half an acre, corresponds to the statement of Domesday Book that it was "a little castle." There is no trace of the usual ditch surrounding the motte, and the smallness of the bailey makes it unlikely that there ever was one. A second bailey has been added to the first,[2] and the whole is surrounded on three sides by a moat, the fourth side having formerly had a steep descent into swamps, which formed sufficient protection.[3]

There is no statement in the Survey of the value of Ness, but the whole manor of Berkeley had risen since the Conquest.[4]

BERKHAMPSTEAD, Herts (Fig. 9). — Mr D. H. Montgomerie rightly calls this a magnificent example of

---

[1] From information received from Mr Duncan Montgomerie.

[2] Fosbroke's *History of Gloucester* attributes this bailey to Maurice, son of Robert Fitzhardinge. One of the most interesting features in this highly interesting castle is the wooden pentice leading from the main stairway of the keep to the chamber called Edward II.'s. Though a late addition, it is a good instance of the way in which masonry was eked out by timber in mediæval times.

[3] Clark, *M. M. A.*, i., 229.   [4] D. B., i., 163.

an earthwork fortress.[1] It is first mentioned in a charter of Richard I., which recapitulates the original charter of William, son of Robert, Count of Mortain, in which he gives the chapel of this castle to the Abbey of Grestein in Normandy.[2] We may, therefore, with all probability look upon this as one of the castles built by the Conqueror's half-brother. And this will account for the exceptional strength of the work, which comprises a motte 40 feet high, ditched round (formerly), and a bailey of $2\frac{2}{3}$ acres, surrounded not only with the usual ditch and banks, but with a second ditch outside the counterscarp bank, which encircles both motte and bailey. At two important points in its line, this counterscarp bank is enlarged into mounds which have evidently once carried wooden towers;[3] if this arrangement belonged to the original plan, as it most probably did, it confirms a remark which we have made elsewhere as to the early use of wooden mural towers. Works in masonry were added to the motte and the bailey banks in the 12th, 13th, and 14th centuries. There are traces of a semicircular earthwork outside the second ditch on the west, which appears to have formed a barbican. But the most exceptional thing about this castle is the series of earthen platforms on the north and east, connected by a bank, and closely investing the external ditch, which were formerly supposed to form part of the castle works. Mr W. St John Hope has suggested the far more plausible theory that they were the siege platforms erected by Louis, the Dauphin of France, in 1216. We are

[1] *Victoria County History of Herts*, from which the description of these earthworks is entirely taken.

[2] *Mon. Ang.*, vii., 1090.

[3] They were excavated by Mr Montgomerie in 1905, and no trace of masonry was found.

told that his engines kept up a most destructive fire of stones.[1]

The value of the manor of Berkhampstead had considerably decreased, even since the Count of Mortain received it.[2]

BISHOP'S STORTFORD, Herts (Fig. 9).—Waytemore Castle is the name given to the large oval motte at this place, which is evidently the site of the castle of "Estorteford," given by William the Conqueror to Maurice, Bishop of London.[3] The manor of Stortford had been bought from King William by Maurice's predecessor, William, who had been one of the Norman favourites of Edward the Confessor.[4] He may have built this castle, but he cannot have built it till after the Conquest, as the land did not belong to his see till then.

"The castle consists of a large oval motte, 250 × 200 feet at its base, rising 40 feet above the marshes of the river Stort, and crowned by a keep with walls of flint rubble, 12 feet thick. On the S. of the motte there are traces of a pentagonal bailey, covering 2½ acres. It is enclosed on four sides by the narrow streams which intersect the marshes. The dry ditch on the fifth side, facing the motte, is discernible. The castle abuts on the road called The Causeway, which crosses the valley; it is in a good position to command both road and river."[5] The value of the manor had gone down at Domesday.[6]

BOURN, Lincolnshire (Fig. 10).—The manor of Bourn

---

[1] Roger of Wendover, 1216.   [2] D. B., i., 163.

[3] The charter, which is in both Anglo-Saxon and Latin, is given in Dugdale's *History of St Paul's*, 304.

[4] See *Freeman*, ii., 356; and D. B., i., 134a.

[5] From report by Mr D. H. Montgomerie.

[6] *Waytemore* has sometimes been identified with the puzzling Wiggingamere, but in defiance of phonology.

or Brune appears to have been much split up amongst various owners at the time of Domesday. A Breton named Oger held the demesne.[1] A charter of Picot, the Sheriff of Cambridgeshire, a person often mentioned in Domesday Book, gives the church of Brune and the chapel of the castle to the priory which he had founded near the castle of Cambridge—afterwards removed to Barnwell.[2] Bourn was the centre of a large soke in Anglo-Saxon times. Leland mentions the "Grete Diches, and the Dungeon Hill of the ancient Castel,"[3] but very little of the remains is now visible, and the motte has been almost removed.

"The castle lies in flat ground, well watered by springs and streams. The motte was placed at the southern apex of a roughly oval bailey, from which it was separated by its own wet ditch, access being obtained through a gatehouse which stood on the narrow neck by which this innermost enclosure, at its N.W. end, joined the principal bailey, which, in its turn, was embraced on all sides but the S. by a second and concentric bailey, also defended by a wet ditch, which broadens out at the S.W. corner into St Peter's Pool. There is another enclosure beyond this which may be of later date. The inner bailey covers 3 acres. Very little is now left of the motte, but a plan made in 1861 showed it to be fairly perfect,[4] and some slight remains of the gatehouse were excavated in that year. The castle is on the line of the Roman road from Peterborough to Sleaford, and close to the Roman Car-Dyke."[5]

The value of Bourn had risen at Domesday.

[1] D. B., i., 351b.   [2] M. A., vi., 86.   [3] Itin., i., 27.
[4] Associated Archæological Societies, VI., ix.
[5] Report by Mr D. H. Montgomerie.

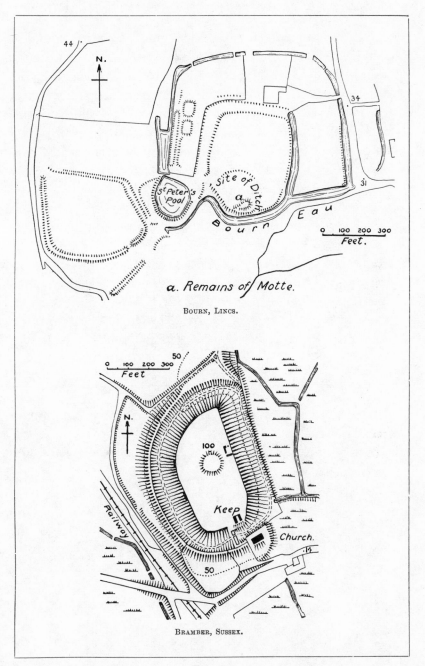

a. Remains of Motte.

BOURN, LINCS.

BRAMBER, SUSSEX.

FIG. 10.

[To face p. 108.

BRAMBER, Sussex (Fig. 10). — Of the manor of
Washington, in which Bramber is situated, the
Survey says that it formerly paid geld for fifty-nine
hides; and in one of these hides sits the castle of
Bramber.[1] It must not be imagined that the castle
occupied a whole hide, which according to the latest
computations would average about 120 acres. It is
evident that there had been some special arrangement
between the King and William de Braose, the Norman
tenant-in-chief, by which the whole geld of the manor
had been remitted. The Domesday scribe waxes almost
pathetic over the loss to the fisc of this valuable prey.
"It used to be ad firmam for 100*l*," he says. The
manor of Washington belonged to Gurth, the brother of
Harold, before the Conquest, but it is clear that
Bramber was not the *caput* of the manor in Saxon times;
nor was Washington the centre of a large soke.
Bramber Castle was constructed to defend the estuary
of the river, now known as the Adur, one of the waterways to Normandy already alluded to.

The castle occupies a natural hill which forms on the
top a pear-shaped area of 3 acres. Towards the middle
rises an artificial motte about 30 feet high; there is no
sign of a special ditch around it, except that the ground
sinks slightly at its base. The bailey is surrounded by
a very neatly built wall of pebbles and flints, laid
herring-bone-wise in places, which does not stand on
an earthen bank. The absence of this bank makes it
likely, though of course not certain, that this wall was
the original work of De Braose; the stones of which it
is composed would be almost as easily obtained as the

---

[1] Ipse Willielmus tenet Wasingetune. Guerd Comes tenuit T. R. E.
Tunc se defendebat pro 59 hidis. Modo non dat geldum. In una ex his
hidis sedet castellum Brembre. D. B., i., 28a, 1.

earth for a bank.   On the line of the wall, just east of
the entrance, stands a tall fragment of an early Norman
tower.   The workmanship of this tower, which is also of
flints laid herring-bone-wise, with quoins of ashlar, so
strongly resembles that of the neighbouring church that
it seems obvious that both were built at about the same
time.[1]   The church is dedicated to St Nicholas, who was
worshipped in Normandy as early as 1067;[2] it was
probably the Normans who introduced his worship into
England.   Both church and tower are undoubtedly early
Norman.   The motte shows no sign of masonry.

The value of the manor of Washington had slightly
risen since the Conquest.

BRISTOL.—Robert, Earl of Gloucester, the Empress
Matilda's half-brother and great champion, is always
credited with the building of Bristol Castle; but this is
one of the many instances in which the man who first
rebuilds a castle in stone receives the credit of being the
original founder.[3]   For it is certain that there was a
castle at Bristol long before the days of Earl Robert, as
the *Anglo-Saxon Chronicle* mentions it in 1088, when it
was held by Geoffrey, Bishop of Coutances, and Robert
Curthose against William II.; and Symeon of Durham,
in the same year, speaks of it as a "castrum fortissimum."   Bishop Geoffrey held Bristol at the date of

---

[1] We often find that the architecture of the nearest church throws light
on the date of the castle.   A Norman seldom built or restored his castle
without doing something for the church at the same time.

[2] See Ordericus, ii., 178.

[3] The *Chronica de Fundatoribus of Tewkesbury Abbey* seems to be the
origin of the tradition that Earl Robert was the builder of Bristol Castle.
There can be no doubt that his work was in stone, as the same authority
states that he gave every tenth stone to the Chapel of Our Lady in St James'
Priory.   *M. A.*, ii., 120.   According to Leland, the keep was built of Caen
stone.   *Itin.*, vii., 90.   Robert of Gloucester calls it the flower of all the
towers in England.

the Domesday Survey, and he probably built the castle by William's orders.[1] It was completely destroyed in 1655 (only a few 13th century arches in a private house now remain), and no trustworthy plan has been preserved, but there is clear evidence that it was a motte-and-bailey castle of the usual Norman type.[2] In Stephen's reign it was described as standing on a very great *agger*.[3] An *agger* does not necessarily mean a motte, but it is often used for one, and there is other evidence which shows that this is its meaning here. A Perambulation of the bounds of Bristol in 1373 shows that the south-western part of the castle ditch, which enclosed the site of the keep, was called *le Mot-dich;* which should certainly be translated the ditch of the motte, and not, as Seyer translates it, the moat ditch.[4] Finally, the description of the castle in 1642 by Major Wood, says : " The castle stood upon a lofty steep mount, that was not minable, as Lieutenant Clifton informed me, for he said the mount whereon the castle stood was of an earthy substance for a certain depth, but below that a firm strong rock,. and that he had searched purposely with an auger and found it so in all parts."[5] He goes on to describe the wall of the bailey as resting on an earthen rampart, testifying to the wooden stockade of the first castle. The great tower of Earl Robert appears to have been placed on the motte, which must have been of considerable size, as it held not only

---

[1] We have no historical account of the Norman conquest of Bristol, and the city is only mentioned in the most cursory manner in D. B.

[2] Seyer (*Memoirs of Bristol*, i.) was convinced that the plan published by Barrett, and attributed to the monk Rowlie, was a forgery ; his own plan, as he candidly admits, was largely drawn from imagination.

[3] Castellum plurimo aggere exaltatum. *Gesta Stephani*, 37.

[4] Seyer, i., 391, and ii., 82.

[5] Quoted by Seyer, ii., 301, from *Prynne's Catal.*, p. 11.

the keep, but a courtyard, a chapel, and the constable's house, besides several towers on its walls. The whole area of the castle was very nearly 4 acres.[1]

Bristol Castle was no doubt originally a royal castle, though Earl Robert of Gloucester held it in right of his wife, who had inherited it from her father, Robert Fitz Hamon; but the crown did not abdicate its claim upon it, and after the troubles of 1174, Henry II. caused 'the son of Earl Robert to surrender the keep into his hands.[2]

Seyer very pertinently remarks that Bristol Castle "was erected with a design hostile to the town; for it occupies the peninsula between two rivers, along which was the direct and original communication between the town and the main part of Gloucestershire."[3] It was outside the city, and was not under its jurisdiction till James I. granted this authority by charter.[4] The value T. R. E. is not given in Domesday Book.

BUCKINGHAM.—The only mention of this castle as existing in the 11th century is in the *Gesta Herewardi*,[5] an undated work which is certainly in great part a romance, but as it is written by some one who evidently had local knowledge, we may probably trust him for the existence of Buckingham Castle at that date; especially as Buckingham was a county town, and one of the boroughs of the Burghal Hidage, the very place which we should expect to find occupied by a Norman castle. This writer speaks of the castle as belonging to Ivo de

---

[1] Calculated from the measurements given by William of Worcester. *Itin.*, p. 260. William probably alludes to the motte when he speaks of the "mayng round" of the castle.

[2] *Benedict of Peterborough*, i., 92.

[3] *Hist. of Bristol*, i., 373.   [4] *Ibid.*, vol. ii.

[5] *De Gestis Herewardi Saxonis*, Wright's edition. See Freeman, N. C., iv., 804.

Taillebois; this is not inconsistent with the fact shown by Domesday Book, that the borough belonged to the king. That it was a motte-and-bailey castle is indicated by Speed's map of Buckingham in 1611; he speaks of the "high hill," though he only indicates it slightly in his plan, with a shield-shaped bailey. Brayley states that the present church is "proudly exalted on the summit of an artificial mount, anciently occupied by a castle."[1]

The castle hill occupies a strong position on the neck of land made by a bend of the river; it extends nearly half-way across it, and commands both town and river. The original earthworks of the castle were destroyed and levelled for the erection of a church in 1777, but the large oval hill remains, having a flat summit about 2 acres in extent, and about 30 feet above the town below. Its sides descend in steep scarps behind the houses on all sides but the north-east. There can be no doubt that the motte has been lowered, and thus enlarged, in order to build the church. The foundations of a stone castle were found in digging a cellar on the slope of the motte.[2]

The value of Buckingham had considerably risen at the date of Domesday.[3]

CAERLEON, Monmouthshire (Fig. 11). — Domesday Book speaks of the *castellaria* of Caerleon.[4] A *castellaria* appears to have meant a district in which the land

---

[1] *Beauties of England and Wales*, Buckingham, p. 282.
[2] Camden's *Britannia*, i., 315.   [3] D. B., i., 143.
[4] "Willielmus de Scohies tenet 8 carucatas terræ in castellaria de Carliun, et Turstinus tenet de eo. Ibi habet in dominio unam carucam, et tres Walenses lege Walensi viventes, cum 3 carucis, et 2 bordarios cum dimidio carucæ, et reddunt 4 sextares mellis. Ibi 2 servi et una ancilla. Hæc terra wasta erat T. R. E., et quando Willelmus recepit. Modo valet 40 solidos." D. B., i., 185b, 1.

was held by the service of castle-guard in a neighbouring castle.   The Survey goes on to say that this
land was waste in the time of King Edward, and when
William de Scohies, the Domesday tenant, received it;
now it is worth 40s.   *Wasta*, Mr Round has remarked,
is one of the pitfalls of the Survey.   Perhaps we shall
not be far wrong if we say that in a general way it
means that there was nobody there to pay geld.   When
this occurs in a town it may point to the devastations
committed at the Conquest; but when it occurs in the
country, and when it is accompanied by so clear a statement that the land which was *wasta* in King Edward's
time and at the Conquest is now producing revenue, the
inference would seem to be clear that the castle of
Caerleon was built on uninhabited land.   Caerleon, however, had been a great city in Roman times, and had
kept up its importance at least till the days of Edgar,
when it is twice mentioned in Welsh history.[1]   It must
therefore have gone downhill very rapidly.   Giraldus
mentions among the ruins of Roman greatness which
were to be seen in his day, a gigantic tower, and this is
commonly supposed to have belonged to the castle.[2]   It
certainly did not, for Giraldus is clearly speaking of a
Roman tower, and the motte of the Norman castle not
only has no signs of masonry, but has been thrown up
over the ruins of a Roman villa which had been burnt.[3]
The motte and other remains of the castle are outside
the Roman *castrum*, between it and the river.   The

---

[1] The *Gwentian Chronicle*, Cambrian Archæological Association, A.D.
962, 967. It is not absolutely impossible that these passages refer to
Chester. Caerleon appears to have been seized by the Welsh very soon
after the death of William I.

[2] *Itin. Camb.*, p. 55.

[3] Loftus Brock, in *Journ. Brit. Arch. Ass.*, xlix. J. E. Lee, in *Arch.
Camb.*, iv., 73.

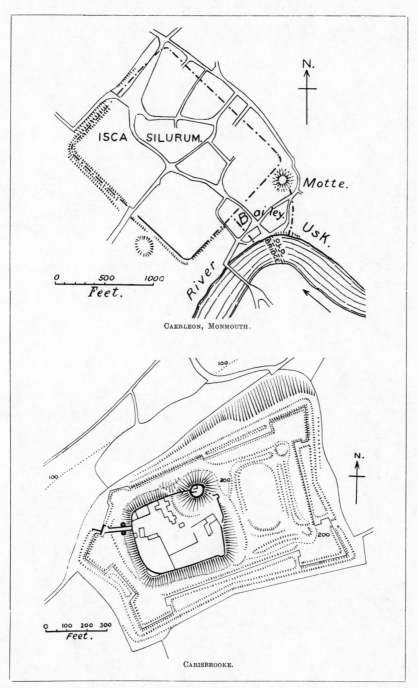

CAERLEON, MONMOUTH.

CARISBROOKE.

FIG. 11.

[To face p. 114.

bailey is roughly pentagonal, and covers 4¾ acres.
The manor of Caerleon was waste T. R. E. and had
risen to 40s. T. R. W.[1]

CAMBRIDGE.—Ordericus tells us that William built
this castle on his return from his first visit to Yorkshire
in 1068,[2] and Domesday Book states that twenty-seven
houses were destroyed to make room for the castle.[3]
There can hardly be a clearer statement that the castle
was entirely new. We have already seen that there is
some probability that Cambridge was first fortified by
the Danes ; for though it has been assumed to be a
Roman castrum, no Roman remains have ever been
found there, and the names which suggest Roman
occupation, Chesterton and Grantchester, are at some
distance from Cambridge. The castle, according to Mr
St John Hope's plan,[4] was placed inside this enclosure,
and the destruction of the houses to make room for it is
thus explained. The motte and a portion of the bank of
the bailey are all that now remain of the castle, but the
valuable ancient maps republished by Mr Hope show
that the motte had its own ditch, and that the bailey was
rectangular. There was formerly a round tower on the
motte, which, if it had the cross-loop-holes and machicolations represented in the print published in 1575, was
certainly not of Norman date. The area of the bailey
was 4¼ acres.[5] The castle was a royal one, and like

---

[1] D. B., i., 185b.
[2] [Rex] "in reversione sua Lincolniæ, Huntendonæ et Grontebrugæ
castra locavit." *Ord. Vit.*, p. 189.
[3] D. B., i., 189.
[4] A similar plan was made independently by the late Professor Babington.
Some traces of the original earthwork of the city are still to be seen. See
Mr Hope's paper on *The Norman Origin of Cambridge Castle*, Cambridge
Antiquarian Soc., vol. xi. ; and Babington's *Ancient Cambridgeshire*, in the
same society's *Octavo Publications*, No. iii., 1853.
[5] W. H. St John Hope, as above, p. 342.

many royal castles, went early to ruin.   Henry IV. gave the materials of the hall to the master and wardens of King's Hall for building their chapel.

The value of Cambridge T. R. W. is not given in Domesday Book.

CANTERBURY.—Domesday Book only mentions this castle incidentally in connection with an exchange of land : "The archbishop has seven houses and the abbot of St Augustine fourteen for the exchange of the castle."[1]   It has been too hastily assumed that it was a pre-Conquest castle which was thus exchanged for twenty - one houses ; but anyone who knows the kind of relations which existed chronically between the archbishop of Canterbury and the abbot of St Augustine's will perceive that it was an impossibility that these two potentates should have held a castle in common.   It was the land for the castle, not the castle itself, which the king got from these ecclesiastics.   This is rendered clear by a passage in the Chartulary of St Augustine's, which tells us that the king, who was mesne lord of the city of Canterbury, had lost the rent of thirty-two houses through the exchange of the castle : seven having gone to the archbishop, fourteen to the abbot, and eleven having been destroyed in making the ditch of the castle.[2]   There can scarcely be any doubt that the hillock now known by the ridiculous name of Dane John is the motte of this original castle of the Conqueror.   Its proper name, the Dungeon Hill, which it bore till the 16th and

---

[1] "Archiepiscopus habet ex eis [burgensibus] 7 et abbas S. Augustini 14 pro excambio castelli." D. B., i. a, 2.

[2] "Et undecim sunt perditi infra fossatum castelli"; cited by Larking, *Domesday of Kent*, App. xxiv. Domesday says, "sunt vastatæ xi. in fossa *civitatis*." There can be no doubt that the Chartulary gives the correct account.

even the 18th century,[1] shows what its origin was ; it was
the hill on which stood the dungeon or donjon of a
Norman castle.[2] The name Dane John is not so much a
corruption as a deliberate perversion introduced by the
antiquary Somner about 1640, under the idea that the
Danes threw up the hill— an idea for which there is not
the slightest historical evidence.[3] We have seen that
there is no reason to think that the Danes ever
constructed fortifications of this kind, and their connection with this earthwork is due to one of those guesses,
too common in English archæology, which have no
scientific basis whatever.

Somner makes the important statement that this
earthwork was originally outside the city walls. His
words are :—

"I am persuaded (and so may easily, I think, anyone be that well
observes the place) that the works both within and without the present wall
of the city were not counterworks one against the other, as the vulgar
opinion goes, but were sometimes all one entire plot containing about 3
acres of ground, of a triangular form (the outwork) with a mount or hill
entrenched round within it ; and that when first made or cast up it lay
wholly without the city wall ; and hath been (the hill or mount, and most
part also of the outwork), for the city's more security, taken in and walled
since ; that side of the trench encompassing the mound now lying without
and under the wall fitly meeting with the rest of the city ditch, after either
side of the earthwork was cut through to make way for it, at the time of the
city's inditching."[4]

It is not often we are so fortunate as to have so clear
a description of an earthwork which has almost entirely
disappeared ; but the description is confirmed by
Stukeley and Hasted, and down to the making of the
Chatham and Dover railway in 1860 the earthworks of

[1] The hill is called the Dungan, Dangon, or Dungeon Hill in many old
local deeds. See "Canterbury in Olden Times," *Arch. Journ.*, 1856.
Stukeley and Grose both call it the Dungeon Hill.
[2] See Appendix N.
[3] Somner's *Antiquities of Canterbury*, p. 144. Published in 1640.
[4] *Antiquities of Canterbury*, p. 75.

the part of the bailey which was left outside the city wall were still to be seen, and were noticed by Mr G. T. Clark.[1]   It is clear that Somner's description corresponds exactly, even in the detail of size, to the type of a motte-and-bailey castle.

There are certain facts, which have not been put together before, which enable us to make a very probable guess as to the date at which this ancient castle was cut through by the newer city bank.   The walls of Canterbury have never yet received so careful an examination as those of Rochester have had from the Rev. Greville Livett;[2] but the researches of Mr Pilbrow about thirty years ago showed that the original Roman walls included a very small area, which would leave both the motte and the Plantagenet castle outside.[3]   Certain entries in the *Close Rolls* show that the fortification of the town of

[1] Mr Clark thought there was another motte in the earthworks outside the walls, though he expresses himself doubtfully : " I rather think they [the mounds outside the city ditch] or one of them, looked rather like a moated mound, but I could not feel sure of it. *Arch. Cantiana*, xv., 344. Gostling (*A Walk about Canterbury*, 1825) says there were *two*, which is perhaps explained by a passage in Brayley's *Kent* (1808), in which he describes the external fortification as " a lesser mount, now divided into two parts, with a ditch and embankment." P. 893. Stukeley's description (circa 1700) is as follows : " Within the walls is a very high mount, called Dungeon Hill ; a ditch and high bank enclose the area before it ; it seems to have been part of the old castle.   Opposite to it without the walls is a hill, seeming to have been raised by the Danes when they besieged the city.   The top of the Dungeon Hill is equal to the top of the castle." *Itin. Curiosum*, i., 122.   It is of course not impossible that there may have been two mottes to this castle, as at Lewes and Lincoln, but such instances are rare, and it seems more likely that a portion of the bailey bank which happened to be in better preservation and consequently higher was mistaken for another mount.   Mr Clark committed this very error at Tadcaster, and the other writers we have quoted were quite untrained as observers of earthen castles.   At any rate there can be no doubt that the Dane John is the original chief citadel of this castle, as the statements of Somner, Stukeley, and we may add, Leland, are explicit.   The most ancient maps of Canterbury, Hoefnagel's (1570), Smith's (*Description of England*, 1588), and Grose's (1785), all show the Dungeon Hill within the walls, but take no notice of the outwork outside.

[2] *Archæologia Cantiana*, xxxiii., 152.   [3] *Ibid.*, xxi.

Canterbury was going on in the years 1215-1225.[1]   But it is too often forgotten that where a wall stands on an earthen bank it is a clear proof that before the wall was built there was a wooden stockade in its place.   Now the portion of the city wall which encloses the Dane John stands on an earthen bank ; so, indeed, does the whole wall from the Northgate to the castle.   It is clear that this piece of bank cannot have been made till the first Norman castle, represented by the earthwork, was abandoned ; and fortunately we have some evidence which suggests a date for the change.   In the *Pipe Rolls* of Henry II.'s reign there are yearly entries, beginning in 1168, of 5s. paid to Adeliza Fitzsimon " for the exchange of her land which is in the castle of Canterbury."   There can be little doubt that this land was purchased to build the great Plantagenet castle whose splendid keep was once one of the finest in England.[2]   The portion of the castle wall which can still be seen does not stand on an earthen bank, an indication (though not a proof) that the castle was on a new site.   Henry II. was a great builder of stone keeps, but he seldom placed them on artificial mottes.   It is no uncommon thing to find an old motte-and-bailey castle abandoned for a better or larger site close at hand.[3]

The bailey of the second castle, according to Hasted, extended almost to the Dane John, which is about 800 feet from the present keep.   The part of the older castle which lay outside the new city bank was possessed by a family of the name of Chiche from the time of Henry II. to that of Edward IV., while the

---

[1] *Close Rolls*, i., 234b, ii., 7b, 89.

[2] Now, to the disgrace of the city of Canterbury, converted into gasworks.

[3] For instance, at Middleham, Rochester, Rhuddlan, and Morpeth.

Dungeon Hill itself remained royal property.[1] That the new bank was Henry II.'s work we may conjecture from the passages in the *Pipe Rolls*, which show that between the years 1166 and 1173 he spent about £30 in enclosing the city of Canterbury and making a gate. We are therefore not without grounds for concluding that Henry II. was the first to enlarge the city by taking in the Dane John, cutting through the ancient bailey, and at the same time enclosing a piece of land for a new stone castle.[2]   The very small sum paid for the city gate (11s., equal to about £11 of our money) suggests that the gate put up by Henry II. was a wooden gateway in the new stockaded bank. The stone walls and towers which were afterwards placed on the bank are of much later date than his reign.[3]

[1] *Beauties of England and Wales, Kent*, p. 893.
[2] The passages from the *Pipe Roll* bearing on this subject (which have not been noticed by any previous historian of Canterbury) are as follows :—

			£	s	d
1166-7.	In operatione civitatis Cantuar. claudendæ	. . .	5	19	6
„	Ad claudendam civitatem Cantuar. . . .	.	20	0	0
1167-8.	Pro claudenda civitate Cantuar.	.	5	1	1
1168-9.	In terris datis Adelizæ filie Simonis 15 solidos de tribus annis				
	pro escambio terræ suæ quæ est in Castello de Cantuar.	.	0	15	0
1172-3.	In operatione turris ejusdem civitatis . . .	.	10	0	0
„	In operatione predicte turris	.	53	6	8
„	Summa denariorum quos vicecomes misit in operatione turris	.	73	1	4
1173-4.	In operatione turris et Castelli Chant. . . .	.	24	6	0
„	In operatione turris Cantuar.	.	5	11	7
1174-5.	Et in warnisione ejusdem turris	.	5	8	0

The latter extract, which refers to the provisioning of the keep, seems to show that it was then finished.   The sums put down to the castle, amounting to about £4000 of our money, are not sufficient to defray the cost of so fine a keep.   But the entries in the *Pipe Rolls* relate only to the Sheriff's accounts, and it is probable that the cost of the keep was largely paid out of the revenues of the archbishopric, which Henry seized into his own hands during the Becket quarrel.
[3] The portion of the wall of Canterbury, which rests on an earthen bank, extends from Northgate to the Castle, and is roughly semicircular in plan. In the middle of it was St George's Gate, which was anciently called *Newingate* (Gostling, p. 53) and may possibly have been Henry II.'s new

The Dungeon Hill appears to have been used for the last time as a fortification in 1643, when ordnance was placed upon it, and it was ordered to be guarded by the householders.[1] In 1790 it was converted into a pleasure-ground for the city; the wide and deep ditch which had surrounded it was filled up, and serpentine walks cut to lead up to the summit. Brayley says that "the ancient and venerable character of this eminence was wholly destroyed by incongruous additions." Still, enough remains to show that it was once a very fine motte, such as we might expect the Conqueror to raise to hold in check one of the most important cities of his new realm.

The value of Canterbury had increased from 51*l*. to 54*l*. since the days of King Edward.[2]

CARISBROOKE, Isle of Wight (Fig. 11).—There can be no doubt that this is the castle spoken of in Domesday Book under the manor of Alwinestone. Carisbrooke is in the immediate neighbourhood of Alvington. The language in which the Survey speaks of this manor is worthy of note. " The king holds Alwinestone: Donnus held it. It then paid geld as two and a half hides: now as two hides, because the castle sits in one virgate."[3] Certain entries similar to this in other places seem to indicate that there was some remission of geld granted on the building of a castle;[4] but as here the king was himself the owner, the remission must have been granted to his tenants.

---

gate. The part enclosing the Dungeon Hill is angular, and appeared to Mr Clark, as well as to Somner and Hasted, to have been brought out at this angle in order to enclose the hill.

[1] *Arch. Journ.*, 1856.   [2] D. B., i., 2a, 1.
[3] "Isdem rex tenet Alwinestone. Donnus tenuit. Tunc pro duabus hidis et dimidia. Modo pro duabus hidis, quia castellum sedet in una virgata." D. B., i., 2a, 1.   [4] See below, under Windsor.

The original castle of Carisbrooke consists of a high motte, ditched round, placed at the corner of a parallelogram with rounded corners. This bailey, covering 2¾ acres, is surrounded by high banks, which testify to the former presence of a wooden stockade. There is another bailey on the eastern side, called the Tilt-yard. The excellent little local guide - book compiled by Mr Stone calls this a British camp, but there is no reason to believe that it was anything else than what it appears to be—a second bailey added as the castle grew in importance. On the motte is a shell of polygonal form, of rubble masonry, but having quoins of well-dressed ashlar. It is believed to be of the time of Henry I., since the author of the *Gesta Stephani* states that Baldwin de Redvers, son of Richard de Redvers, to whom Henry granted the lordship of the Isle of Wight, had a castle there splendidly built of stone, defended by a strong fortification.[1] This would indicate that, besides the stone keep, stone walls were added to the earthworks of the Domesday castle. The keep is of peculiar interest, as it still retains the remains of the old arrangements in keeps of this style, though of much later date. The motte was opened in 1893, and was found to be composed of alternate layers of large and small chalk rubble.[2] Little attention has hitherto been paid to the construction of these Norman mottes, but other instances have been noted which show that they were often built with great care. The whole castle, including the Tilt-yard, was surrounded with an elaborate polygonal fortification in Elizabeth's reign, when the Spanish invasion was expected.

[1] "In hac [insula] castellum habebat ornatissimum lapidum ædificio constructum, validissimo munimine firmatum." *Gesta Stephani*, R. S., p. 28.
[2] Stone's *Official Guide to the Castle of Carisbrooke*, p. 39.

The value of the manor of Alvington had increased at the time of the Survey, though the number of ploughs employed had actually decreased. This increase must have been owing to the erection of the castle, which provided security for trade and agriculture. Alvington was not the centre of a large soke in the Confessor's time, so it is unlikely that there was any fortification there in Saxon days.[1]

CARLISLE, Cumberland (Fig. 12).—This castle was built by William Rufus in 1092, when for the first time Cumberland was brought under Norman sway. The *Anglo-Saxon Chronicle* says, " he repaired the *burh*, and reared the castle," a passage which is sufficient of itself to show that *burh* and castle were two quite different things. Carlisle of course was a Roman fortress, and needed only the repairing of its walls. The castle was a new thing, and was placed outside the city. Its plan, which is roughly a triangle, with the apex formed into a small court by a ditch which (formerly) separated it from the bailey, looks very suggestive of a previous motte and bailey, such as we might expect the Norman king to have thrown up. The keep is known to have been built by David, king of Scotland, in Stephen's reign,[2] and it is possible that he may have removed the motte. The castle appears to have had a wooden *pelum* or *palicium* on its outer banks as late as 1319.[3] The whole area covers 4 acres.

---

[1] Mr W. H. Stevenson, in his edition of *Asser*, pp. 173, 174, shows that the name Carisbrooke cannot possibly be derived from Wihtgares-burh, as has been sometimes supposed, as the older forms prove it to have come from *brook*, not *burh*. The lines of the present castle banks, if produced, would not correspond with those of the Tilt-yard, which is proof that the Norman castle was not formed by cutting an older fortification in two.

[2] Bower's *Scotochronicon*, v., xlii. Cited by Mr Neilson, *Notes and Queries*, viii., 321. See also Palgrave, *Documents and Records*, i., 103.

[3] *Cal. of Close Rolls*, Edward II., iii., 161.

CASTLE ACRE, Norfolk (Fig. 12).—There can be no doubt that this castle existed in the 11th century, as William de Warenne mentions it in the charter of foundation of Lewes Priory, one of the most interesting and human of monastic charters.[1] The earthworks still remaining of this castle are perhaps the finest castle earthworks in England; the banks enclosing the bailey are vast. The large and high motte carries a wall of flint rubble, built outside and thus revetting the earthen bank which formed its first defence. In the small court thus enclosed (about 100 feet in diameter) the foundations of an oblong keep can be discerned. A very wide ditch surrounds the motte, and below it is a horse-shoe bailey, about 2 acres in extent, stretching down to the former swamps of the river Nar. On the east side of the motte is a small half-moon annexe, with its own ditch; this curious addition is to be found in several other motte castles,[2] and is believed to have been a work intended to defend the approach, of the nature of a barbican. On the west side of the motte is the village of Castle Acre, enclosed in an oblong earthwork with an area of 10 acres. This work now goes by the name of the Barbican, but probably this name has been extended to it from a barbican covering the castle entrance (of which entrance the ruins still remain). It is most likely that this enclosure was a *burgus* attached to the castle. Mr Harrod, who excavated the banks, found quantities of Roman pottery, which led him to think that the work was Roman; but as the pottery was all broken, it is more likely that the banks were thrown up on the site of some Roman villa.[3] This earthwork has a northern

---

[1] *Mon. Ang.*, v., 12. "Castelli nostri de Acra."

[2] As at Burton, Mexborough, Lilbourne, and Castle Colwyn.

[3] Harrod's *Gleanings among the Castles and Convents of Norfolk*. See also *Arch. Journ.*, xlvi., 441.

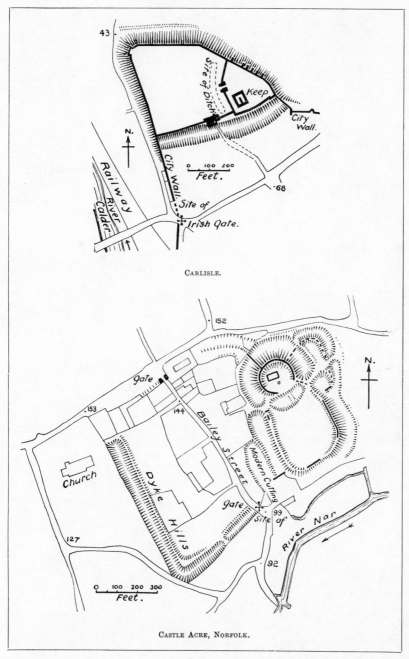

CARLISLE.

CASTLE ACRE, NORFOLK.

FIG. 12.

[To face p. 124.

entrance in masonry, evidently of 13th century date; and as the scanty masonry remaining of the castle is similar in character, it is probably all of the same date. The area covered by the motte and the two original baileys is 3½ acres; that of the whole series of earthworks, 15 acres.

Acre was only a small manor in Saxon times; its value at the time of the Survey had risen from 5*l.* to 9*l.*[1]

CHEPSTOW (Estrighoel or Strigul), Monmouthshire.— Notwithstanding the fact that there is another castle of the name of Strigul about 9 miles from Chepstow (known also as Troggy Castle), it is clear that Chepstow is the castle meant by Domesday, as the entry speaks of ships going up the river, a thing impossible at Strigul.[2] The castle occupies a narrow ridge, well defended by the river on one side, and on the other by a valley which separates it from the town. There are four wards, and the last and smallest of all seemed to the writer, when visiting the castle, to mark the site of a lowered motte. This opinion, however, is not shared by two competent observers, Mr Harold Sands and Mr Duncan Montgomerie, who had much ampler opportunities for studying the remains. This ward is now a barbican, and the masonry upon it belongs clearly to the 13th century; it occupies the highest ground in the castle, and is separated from the other wards, and from the ridge beyond it, by two ditches cut across the headland. The adjoining court must have belonged to the earliest

[1] D. B., ii., 160b.

[2] "Castellum de Estrighoiel fecit Willelmus comes, et ejus tempore reddebat 40 solidos, tantum de navibus in silvam euntibus." D. B., i., 162. Tanner has shown that while Chepstow was an alien priory of Cormeille, in Normandy, it is never spoken of by that name in the charters of Cormeille, but is always called Strigulia. *Notitia Monastica*, Monmouthshire. See also Marsh's *Annals of Chepstow Castle*.

part of the castle, as it contains a very remarkable early Norman building (splendidly restored in the 13th century) which is regarded by most authorities as the original hall of William FitzOsbern.   It must, however, have combined both hall and keep, otherwise the castle was not provided with any citadel, if there was no motte.[1] What is now the second ward has a Norman postern in the south wall, and may have been the bailey to the keep. All the other masonry is of the late Early English or the Perpendicular period, and the entrance ward is probably an addition of the 13th century.   The shape of all the baileys is roughly quadrangular, except that of the fourth, which would be semicircular but for the towers which make corners to it.   The whole area of the castle is $1\frac{2}{3}$ acres.

We are not told what the value of the manor was before William FitzOsbern built his castle there, but from the absence of this mention we may infer that the site was waste.   It paid 40s. in his time from ships' dues, 16l. in his son Earl Roger's time, and at the date of the Survey it paid the king 12l.[2]   Chepstow was not the centre of a large soke, and it appears to have owed all its importance to the creation of William Fitz-Osbern's castle.

CHESTER. — The statement of Ordericus, that William I. founded this castle on his return from his third visit to York, is sufficiently clear.[3]   The very valuable paper of Mr E. W. Cox on Chester Castle[4]

[1] I must confess that in spite of very strong opposing opinions, I see no reason why this building should not be classed as a keep. It is of course a gross error to call Martin's Tower the keep ; it is only a mural tower.

[2] D. B., 162, 1a.

[3] "Cestriæ munitionem condidit." P. 199 (Prévost's edition).

[4] *Chester Historical and Archæological Society*, v., 239.

answers most of the questions which pertain to our present inquiry. The original castle of Chester consisted of the motte, which still remains, though much built over, and the small ward on the edge of which it stands, a polygonal enclosure scarcely an acre in extent. On the motte the vaulted basement of a tower still remains, but the style is so obscured by whitewash and modern accretions that it is impossible to say whether the vaulting is not modern. The first buildings were certainly of wood, but Mr Cox regarded some of the existing masonry on the motte as belonging to the 12th century; and this would correspond with the entry in the *Pipe Rolls* of 102*l*. 7*s*. 0*d*. spent on the castle by Henry II. in 1159.[1] The tower, nicknamed Cæsar's Tower, and frequently mistaken for the keep, is shown in Mr Cox's paper to be only a mural tower of the 13th century, probably built when the first ward was surrounded with walls and towers in masonry.[2] The large outer bailey was first added in the reign of Henry III.[3] It is further proved by Mr Cox that Chester Castle stood outside the walls of the Roman city. The manor of Gloverstone lay between it and the city, and was not under the jurisdiction of the city until quite recent times.[4] This disposes of the ball set rolling by Brompton at the end of the 13th century, and sent on by most Chester topographers ever since, that Ethelfleda, when she restored the Roman walls of Chester,

[1] *Pipe Rolls*, ii., 7. Ranulph, Earl of Chester, died in 1153, and the castle would then escheat into the king's hands.

[2] This work seems to have been completed in the reign of Edward II., who spent £253 on the houses, towers, walls, and gates. *Cal. of Close Rolls*, Edward II., ii., 294.

[3] *Close Rolls*, 35, Henry III., cited by Ormerod, *History of Cheshire*, i., 358.

[4] See Mr Cox's paper, as above, and Shrubsole, *Chester Hist. and Arch. Soc.*, v., 175, and iii., New Series, p. 71.

enlarged their circuit so as to take in the castle. We have already referred to this in Chapter III.

Chester, as we have seen, was originally a royal castle. And though it was naturally committed to the keeping of the Norman earls of Chester, and under weak kings may have been regarded by the earls as their own property, no such claim was allowed under a strong ruler. After the insurrection of the younger Henry, Hugh, Earl of Chester, forfeited his lands; Henry II. restored them to him in 1177, but was careful to keep the castle in his own hands.[1]

The city of Chester, Domesday Book tells us, had greatly gone down in value when the earl received it, probably in 1070; twenty-five houses had been destroyed. But it had already recovered its prosperity at the date of the Survey; there were as many houses as before, and the ferm of the city was now let by the earl at a sum greatly exceeding the ferm paid in King Edward's time.[2] This prosperity must have been due to the security provided for the trade of Chester by the Norman castle and Norman rule.

CLIFFORD, Herefordshire (Fig. 13). — It is clearly stated by Domesday Book that William FitzOsbern built this castle on waste land.[3] At the date of the Survey it was held by Ralph de Todeni, who had sublet it to the sheriff. In the many castles attributed to William FitzOsbern, who built them as the king's vicegerent, we may see an indication that the building of castles, even on the marches of Wales, was not undertaken without royal license. In the reign of Henry I. Clifford Castle had already passed into the

---

[1] *Benedict of Peterborough*, i., 135, R. S.   [2] D. B., i., 262b.
[3] "Willelmus comes fecit illud [castellum] in wasta terra quam tenebat Bruning T. R. E." D. B., i., 183a, 2.

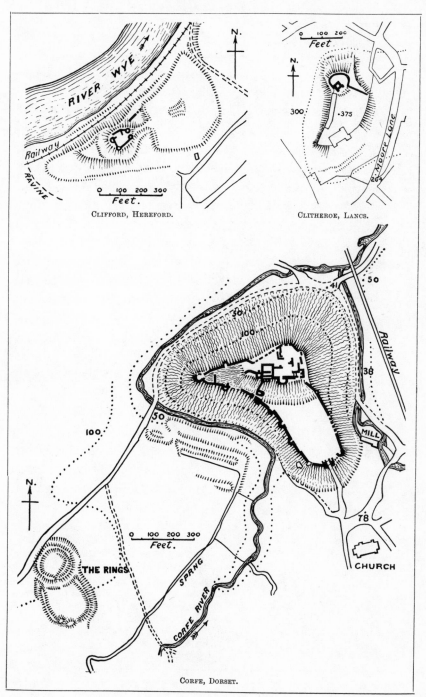

CLIFFORD, HEREFORD.

CLITHEROE, LANCS.

CORFE, DORSET.

FIG. 13.

[To face p. 128.

hands of Richard Fitz Pons, the ancestor of the celebrated house of Clifford, and one of the *barons* of Bernard de Neufmarché, the Norman conqueror of Brecon.[1]

The castle has a large motte, roughly square in shape, which must be in part artificial.[2] Attached to it on the south-west is a curious triangular ward, included in the ditch which surrounds the motte. The masonry on the motte is entirely of the "Edwardian" style, when keepless castles were built; it consists of the remains of a hall, and a mural tower which is too small to be called a keep. There is also a small court, with a wall which stands on a low bank. Below the motte is an irregular bailey of about 2⅓ acres, with earthen banks which do not appear to have ever carried any masonry, though in the middle of the court there is a small mound which evidently covers the remains of buildings. The whole area of the castle, including the motte and the two baileys, is about 3½ acres.

The value of the manor had apparently risen from nothing to 8*l.* 5*s.* Clifford was not the centre of a large soke.

CLITHEROE, Lancashire (Fig. 13). — There is no express mention of this castle in Domesday Book, but of two places in Yorkshire, Barnoldswick and Calton, it is said that they are in the *castellate* of Roger the Poitevin.[3] A castellate implies a castle, and as there is

---

[1] "Ancient Charters," *Pipe Roll Society*, vol. x., charter xiii., and Mr Round's note, p. 25.

[2] It is extraordinary that Mr Clark, in his description of this castle, does not mention the motte, except by saying that the outer ward is 60 or 70 feet lower than the inner. *M. M. A.*, i., 395.

[3] This passage occurs in a sort of appendix to Domesday Book, which is said to be in a later hand, of the 12th century. (Skaife, *Yorks. Arch. Journ.*, Part lv., p. 299.) It cannot, however, be very late in the 12th century, as it speaks of Roger's holdings in Craven in the present tense.

no other castle in the Craven district (to which the words of the Survey relate) except Skipton, which did not form part of Roger's property, there is no reason to doubt that this castle was Clitheroe, which for centuries was the centre of the Honour of that name. The whole land between the Ribble and the Mersey had been given by William I. to this Roger, the third son of his trusted supporter, Earl Roger of Shrewsbury. One can understand why William gave important frontier posts to the energetic and unscrupulous young men of the house of Montgomeri, one of whom was the adviser and architect of William Rufus, another a notable warrior in North Wales, another the conqueror of Pembrokeshire. As it appears from the Survey that Roger's possessions stretched far beyond the Ribble into Yorkshire and Cumberland, it seems quite possible—though here we are in the region of conjecture—that just as his father and brothers had a free hand to conquer as they listed from the North and South Welsh, so Roger had a similar commission for the hilly districts still unconquered in the north-west of England. But fortune did not favour the Montgomeri family for long. They were exiled from England in 1102 for siding with Robert Curthose, and in the same year we find the castle of Clitheroe in the hands of Robert de Lacy, lord of the great Yorkshire fief of Pontefract.[1]

The castle of Clitheroe stands on a lofty motte of natural rock.[2] There are no earthworks on the summit,

---

[1] See Farrer's *Lancashire Pipe Rolls*, p. 385. The castle is not actually mentioned, but "le Baille" (the bailey) is spoken of. Mr Farrer also prints an abstract of a charter of Henry I. (1102): "per quam concessit eidem Roberto [de Laci] Boelandam [Bowland] quam tenuit de Rogero Comite Pictavensi, ut extunc eam de eodem rege teneat." P. 382.

[2] In an inquisition of Henry de Laci (+1311) it is said that "castelli mote et fossæ valent nihil." (Whitaker's *History of Whalley*, p. 280.) This is probably an instance of the word *motte* being applied to a natural rock

but a stout wall of limestone rubble without buttresses encloses a small court, on whose south-west side stands the keep. It is just possible that the outer wall may be the original work of Roger, as limestone rubble would be easier to get than earth on this rocky hill. The keep is small, rudely built of rubble, and has neither fireplace nor garde-robe, nor the slightest ornamental detail—not even a string course. But in spite of the entire absence of ornament, a decorative effect has been sought and obtained by making the quoins, voussoirs, and lintels of a dressed yellow sandstone. The care with which this has been done is inconsistent with the haste with which Roger must inevitably have constructed his first fortification, if we suppose, as is probable, that he received the first grant of his northern lands on William's return in 1070 from his third visit to the north, when he made that remarkable march through Lancashire to Chester which is described by Ordericus. It seems more likely that even if the outer wall or shell were the work of Roger, he had only wooden buildings inside its circuit. Dugdale attributes the building of the keep to the second Robert de Lacy, between 1187 and 1194, and it is probable that this date is correct.[1] The bailey of Clitheroe lay considerably below the keep, and is now overbuilt with a modern house, offices, and garden. It covers one acre. A Roman road up the valley of the Ribble passes near the foot of the rock.[2]

which served that purpose. See another instance under Nottingham, *post*, p. 176.

[1] Dugdale's *Baronage*, i., p. 99. Dugdale's authority appears to have been the "Historia Laceiorum," a very untrustworthy document, but which may have preserved a genuine tradition in this instance. The loopholes in the basement of the keep, with the large recesses, appear to have been intended for crossbows, and the crossbow was not reintroduced into England till the reign of Richard I.

[2] *Victoria History of Lancashire*, ii., 523.

As the very name of Clitheroe is not mentioned in Domesday Book, it clearly was not an important centre in Saxon times. The value of Blackburn Hundred, in which Clitheroe is situated, had fallen between the Confessor's time and the time when Roger received it. It is quite possible that he never lived at Clitheroe, as he sub-infeoffed the manor and Hundred of Blackburn to Roger de Busli and Albert Greslet before 1086.[1]

COLCHESTER, Essex.—The remarkable keep of this castle has been the subject of antiquarian legend for many centuries, and Mr Clark has the merit of having proved its early Norman origin, by its plan and architecture. A charter of Henry I. is preserved in the cartulary of St John's Abbey at Colchester, which grants to Eudes the Dapifer "the city of Colchester, and the tower and the castle, and all the fortifications of the castle, just as my father had them and my brother and myself."[2] This proves that the keep and castle were in existence in the Conqueror's time; the Norman character of the architecture proves that the keep was not in existence earlier. We see, then, that the reason there is no motte at Colchester is that there was a stone keep built when first the castle was founded. As far as we are aware, Colchester, the Tower of London, and the recently discovered keep of Pevensey are the only certain instances of stone keeps of the 11th century in England.

That one of the most important of the Conqueror's castles, second only to the Tower of London, and actually exceeding it in the area it covers, should be found in Colchester, is not surprising, because the Eastern counties at the time of the Conquest were not

---

[1] See Farrer, *Lancashire Pipe Rolls*, i., 260.
[2] Printed by Mr Round in *Essex Arch. Society's Transactions*, vii., Part ii. The charter is dated 1101.

only the wealthiest part of the kingdom (as Domesday Book clearly shows[1]), but they also needed special protection from the attacks of Scandinavian enemies. Mr Round has conjectured that the castle was built at the time of the invasion of St Cnut, between 1080 and 1085.[2]

The castle is built of Roman stones used over again, with rows of tiles introduced between the courses with much decorative effect.[3] The original doorway was on the first floor, as in most Norman keeps; but at some after time, probably in the reign of Henry I.,[4] the present doorway was inserted; and most likely the handsome stairway which now leads up from this basement entrance was added, as it shows clear marks of insertion. Henry II. was working on the walls of the castle in 1282, and it may be strongly suspected that the repairs in ashlar, and the casing of the buttresses with ashlar, were his work.[5] One item in the accounts of Henry II. is £50 "for making the bailey round the castle."[6] There were two baileys to the castle of Colchester—the inner one, which scarcely covered 2 acres, and the outer one, which contained about 11. The inner bailey was enclosed at first with an earthwork and stockade, the earthwork being thrown up over the remains of some

[1] See Maitland, *Domesday Book and Beyond*, p. 22.

[2] *History of Colchester Castle*, p. 141.

[3] It has been much debated whether these tiles are Roman or Norman ; the conclusion seems to be that they are mixed. See Round's *History of Colchester*, p. 78.

[4] The single *Pipe Roll* of Henry I. shows that he spent £33, 15s. on repairs of the castle and borough in 1130.

[5] In operatione unius Rogi (a kiln), £13, 18s. In reparatione muri castelli, £16, 3s. 2d. The projection of the buttresses (averaging 1 ft. 3 ins.) is about the same as that found in castles of Henry I. or Henry II.'s time.

[6] Ad faciendum Ballium circa castellum, £50. *Pipe Rolls*, xix., 13. This is followed by another entry of £18, 13s. 7d. " in operatione castelli," which may refer to the same work.

Roman walls, whose line it does not follow. Afterwards a stone wall was built on the earthwork, the foundations of which can still be traced in the west rampart.[1] The outer bailey, which lay to the north, extended on two sides to the Roman walls of the town; on the west side it had a rampart and stockade. If the £50 spent by Henry II. represents the cost of a stone wall round the inner bailey, then the *palicium* blown down by the wind in 1219 must have been the wooden stockade on the west side of the outer bailey.[2] The question is difficult to decide, but at any rate the entry proves that as late as Henry III.'s reign, some part of the outer defences of Colchester Castle was still of timber.

The position of Colchester Castle is exceptional in one respect, that the castle is almost in the middle of the town. But this very unusual position is explained by Mr Round's statement that the land forming the castle baileys, as well as that afterwards given to the Grey Friars on the east, was crown demesne before the Conquest, and consequently had been cultivated land, so that we do not hear of any houses in Colchester being destroyed for the site of the castle.[3] But by keeping this land as the inalienable appendage of the royal castle William secured that communication between the castle and the outside country which was so essential to the invaders.

The value of the city of Colchester had risen enormously at the date of the Survey.[4]

[1] Round's *History of Colchester*.

[2] *Close Rolls*, i., 389. Mandamus to the bishop of London to choose two lawful and discreet men of Colchester, "et per visum eorum erigi faceatis palicium castri nostri Colecestrie, quod nuper prostratum fuit per tempestatem."

[3] Round's *History of Colchester*, pp. 135, 136.

[4] Tota civitas ex omnibus debitis reddebat T. R. E., £15, 5s. 4d., in unoquoque anno. Modo reddit £160. D. B., ii., 107.

CORFE, Dorset (Fig. 13).—Mr Eyton has shown that for the *castellum Warham* of Domesday Book we ought to read *Corfe*, because the castle was built in the manor of Kingston, four miles from Wareham.[1] And this is made clear by the *Testa de Nevill*, which says that the church of Gillingham was given to the nunnery of Shaftesbury in exchange for the land on which the castle of Corfe is placed.[2] Because King Edward the Martyr was murdered at Corfe, at some place where his stepmother Elfrida was residing, it has been inferred that there was a Saxon castle at Corfe; and because there is a building with some herring-bone work among the present ruins, it has been assumed that this building is the remains of that castle or palace. But the *Anglo-Saxon Chronicle*, the only contemporary authority for the event, says nothing of any castle at Corfe, but simply tells us that Edward was slain at Corfe Geat, a name which evidently alludes to a gap or passage through the chalk hills, such as there is at Corfe.[3] Nor is there any mention of Corfe as a fortress in Anglo-Saxon times; it is not named in the *Burghal Hidage*, and we do not hear of any sieges of it by the Danes. Nor is it likely that the Saxons would have had a fortress at Corfe, when they had a fortified town so near as Wareham.[4]

[1] Eyton, *Key to Domesday*, p. 43. This passage was kindly pointed out to me by Dr Round. The castle is not mentioned in Domesday under Wareham, but under Kingston. " De manerio Chingestone habet rex unam hidam, in qua fecit castellum Warham, et pro ea dedit S. Mariæ [of Shaftesbury] ecclesiam de Gelingeham cum appendiciis suis." D. B., i., 78b, 2.

[2] "Advocatio ecclesie de Gillingeham data fuit abbati [*sic*] de S. Edwardo in escambium pro terra ubi castellum de Corf' positum est." *Testa de Nevill*, 164b.

[3] It is by no means certain that Corfe was the scene of Edward's murder, as we learn from a charter of Cnut (*Mon. Ang.*, iii., 55) that there was a Corfe Geat not far from Portisham, probably the place now called Coryates.

[4] Called by Asser a *castellum;* but it has already been pointed out that *castellum* in early writers means a walled town and not a castle. (See p. 25.)

Kingston, the manor in which Corfe is situated, was not an important place, as it had no dependent soke. The language of Domesday absolutely upsets the idea of any Saxon castle or palace at Corfe, as it tells us that William obtained the land for his castle from the nuns of Shaftesbury, and we may be quite sure they had no castle there.[1]

Corfe Castle stands on a natural hill, which has been so scarped artificially that the highest part now forms a large motte. Three wards exist—the eastern or motte ward, the western, and the southern. The two former probably formed the original castle. On the motte (which possibly is not artificial, but formed by scarping) stands the lofty keep, of splendid workmanship, probably of the time of Henry I. In the ward pertaining to it are buildings of the time of John and Henry III.[2] The western ward has towers of the 13th century, but it also contains the interesting remains of an early Norman building, probably a hall or chapel, built largely of herring-bone work; this is the building which has been so positively asserted to be a Saxon palace. But herring-bone masonry, which used to be thought an infallible sign of Saxon work, is now found to be more often Norman.[3] The building is certainly

Wareham is a town fortified by an earthen vallum and ditch, and is one of the boroughs of the *Burghal Hidage*. (See Ch. II., p. 28.) A Norman castle was built there after the Conquest, and its motte still remains. D. B. says seventy-three houses were utterly destroyed from the time of Hugh the Sheriff. I., 75.

[1] Edred granted "to the religious woman, Elfthryth," supposed to be the Abbess of Shaftesbury, "pars telluris Purbeckinga," which would include Corfe. *Mon. Ang.*, ii., 478.

[2] Both these kings spent large sums on Corfe Castle. See the citations from the *Pipe Rolls* in Hutchins' *Dorset*, vol. i., and in Mr Bond's *History of Corfe Castle*.

[3] See Professor Baldwin Brown's paper in the *Journal of the Institute of British Architects*, Third Series, ii., 488, and Mr Micklethwaite's in *Arch.*

an ancient one, and may possibly have been contemporary with the first Norman castle; its details are
unmistakably Norman.   But very likely it was the only
Norman masonry of the 11th century at Corfe Castle.[1]
It is clear that the stone wall which at present surrounds
the western bailey did not exist when the hall (or
chapel) was built, as it blocks up its southern windows.
Probably there was a palisade at first on the edge of
the scarp.   Palisades still formed part of the defences of
the castle in the time of Henry III., when 62*l.* was
paid "for making two good walls in place of the
palisades at Corfe between the old bailey of the said
castle and the middle bailey towards the west, and
between the keep of the said castle and the outer bailey
towards the south."[2]   This shows that the present
wing-walls down from the motte were previously represented by stockades.   The ditch between the keep and
the southern bailey has been attributed to King John,
on the strength of an entry in the *Close Rolls* which
orders fifteen miners and stone-masons to work on the
banks of the ditch in 1214.[3] But we may be quite
certain that this ditch below the motte belonged to the
original plan of the castle; John's work would be either
to line it with masonry, or to enlarge it.   It is not
without significance for the early history of the castle
that Durandus the *carpenter* held the manor of
Mouldham near Corfe, by the service of finding a
carpenter to work at the keep whenever required.[4]

The area of Corfe Castle, if we include the large

Journ., liii., 338 ; also Professor Baldwin Brown's remarks on Corfe Castle
in *The Arts in Early England*, ii., 71.
    [1] There are other instances in which the chapel is the oldest piece of
mason-work about the castle, as, for example, at Pontefract.
    [2] Cited in Hutchins' *Dorset*, i., 488, from the *Close Rolls*.
    [3] *Close Rolls*, i., 178b.   [4] Hutchins' *Dorset*, i., 488.

southern bailey, is 3¾ acres; without it, 1½ acres.   This bailey was certainly in existence in the reign of Henry III. (as the extract from the *Close Rolls* proves) before the towers of superb masonry were added to it by Edward I.

The value of Kingston Manor had considerably increased at the date of the Survey.   After the Count of Mortain forfeited his lands (in 1105), the castle of Corfe was kept in the hands of the crown, and this increases the probability that the keep was built by Henry I.

About 400 yards S.W. of Corfe Castle is an earthwork which might be called a " Ring and Bailey." Instead of the usual motte there is a circular enclosure, defended by a bank and ditch of about the same height as those of its bailey, but having in addition an interior platform or berm.   This work is probably the remains of a camp thrown up by Stephen during his unsuccessful siege of Corfe Castle in 1139.

DOVER, Kent (Fig. 14).—The Norman historian, William of Poitiers, tells us that the castrum of Dover was built by Harold at his own expense.[1]   This comes from the celebrated story of the oath of Harold to William, a story of which Mr Freeman says that there is no portion of our history more entangled in the mazes of contradictory and often impossible statements.[2]   But let us assume the statement about the *castrum* to be true ; the question then to be answered is this : of what nature was that castrum?   We never are told by English chroniclers that Harold built any castles, though we do hear of his fortifying towns.   The present

[1] Castrum Doveram, studio atque sumptu suo communitum. P. 108. Eadmer makes Harold promise to William "Castellum Dofris cum puteo aquæ ad opus meum te *facturum.*" *Hist. Novorum*, i., d. The castle is not mentioned in Domesday Book.   [2] *Norman Conquest*, iii., 217.

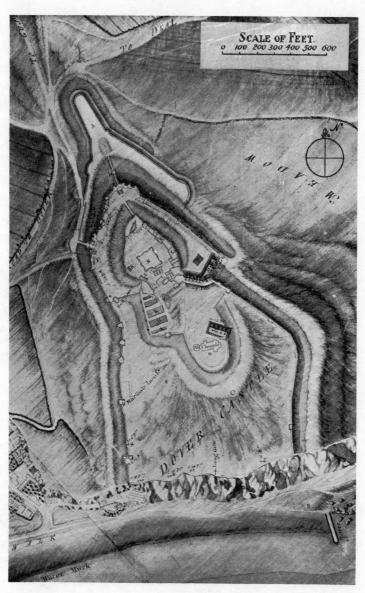

SCALE OF FEET.

0   100 200 300 400 500 600

DOVER.

(From a plan in the British Museum, 1756.)

FIG. 14.

writer would answer this question, tentatively indeed, and under correction, by the theory that the castrum constructed or repaired by Harold was the present outer rampart of Dover Castle, which encloses an area of about 34 acres, and may have enclosed more, if it was formerly complete on the side towards the sea.[1] The evidence in support of this theory is as follows :—

1. There certainly was a *burh* on the top of the cliff at Dover in Saxon times, as the *Anglo-Saxon Chronicle* tells us that in 1048 Eustace of Boulogne, after coming to Dover, and slaying householders there, went *up to the burh*, and slew people both within and without, but was repulsed by the burh-men.[2] There was then a burh, and valiant burh-men on the cliff at Dover in Edward the Confessor's reign. But the whole analogy of the word burh makes it certain that by the time of Edward it meant a fortified town.[3]

2. That the burh at Dover was of the nature of a town, with houses in it, is confirmed by the poem of Guy of Amiens, who says that when King William entered the *castrum*, he ordered the English to evacuate their houses.[4] William of Poitiers also states that there was an

---

[1] In 1580 an earthquake threw down a portion of the cliff on which the castle stands, and part of the walls. Statham's *History of Dover*, p. 287.

[2] "Wendon him tha up to thære burge-weard, and ofslogen ægther ge withinnan ge withutan, ma thanne 20 manna." Another MS. adds "tha burh-menn ofslogen 19 men on othre healfe, and ma gewundode, and Eustatius atbærst mid feawum mannum."   [3] See *ante*, pp. 17-19.

[4] His description is worth quoting :

> Est ibi mons altus, strictum mare, litus opacum,
> Hinc hostes citius Anglica regna petunt ;
> Sed castrum Doveræ, pendens a vertice montis,
> Hostes rejiciens, littora tuta facit.
> Clavibus acceptis, rex intrans mœnia castri
> Præcepit Angligenis evacuare domos ;
> Hos introduxit per quos sibi regna subegit,
> Unumquemque suum misit ad hospitium.

"Carmen de Bello Hastingensi," in *Monumenta Britannica*, p. 603.

innumerable multitude of people in the castle,[1] though he may refer to a multitude gathered there for safety.

3. Though the whole of the outer enceinte is generally credited to Hubert de Burgh in Henry III.'s reign, the truth probably is that he built the first stone walls and towers on the outer rampart ; but the existence of this earthen rampart shows that there was a wooden wall upon it previously. It is not improbable that it was for the repair of this wooden wall that so much timber was sent to Dover in the reigns of Richard I. and John.[2] Dering, who was lieutenant of the castle in 1629, records the tradition that the tower in the outer enceinte, called Canons' Gate, dates from Saxon times (of course this could only be true of a wooden prede-cessor of the stone tower), and that Godwin's Tower, on

---

[1] William's description is also of great interest : " Deinde dux contendit Doueram, ubi multus populus congregatus erat, pro inexpugnabile, ut sibi videtur, munitione ; quia id castellum situm est in rupe mari contigua, quæ naturaliter acuta undique ad hoc ferramentis elaborate incisa, in speciem muri directissima altitudine, quantum sagittæ jactus permetiri potest, consurgit, quo in latere unda marina alluitur." P. 140.

[2] The following entries in the *Pipe Rolls* refer to this :—

1194-5.	Three hundred planks of oak for the works of the castle	.	£2 0 0
1196-7.	Repair of the wall of the castle . . .	.	76 3 0
1208-9.	Timber for walling the castles of Dover and Rochester, also		
	rods and [wooden] hurdles and other needful things	.	76 13 4
1210-11.	Payment for the carpenters working the timber	.	24 9 5
1212-13.	For the carriage of timber and other things .	.	48 16 7
1214-15.	For the carriage of timber for the castle works	.	2 0 0
1214-15.	For timber and brushwood for the works, and for cutting		
	down wood to make hurdles, and sending them	.	sum not given,

but £100 entered same year for the works of the castle. There is no mention of stone for the castle during these two reigns, but after the death of John we find that works are going on at Dover for which kilns are required. (*Close Rolls*, i., 352, 1218.) This entry is followed by a very large expenditure on Dover Castle (amounting to at least £6000), sufficient to cover the cost of a stone wall and towers round the outer circuit. The orders of planks for joists must be for the towers, and the large quantities of lead, for roofing them. The order for timber "ad palum et alia facienda" in 1225 *may* refer to a stockade on the advanced work called the Spur, which is said to be Hubert's work. (*Close Rolls*, ii., 14.)

the east side of the outer vallum, existed as a postern before the Conquest.[1] Nearly all the towers on this wall were supported by certain manors held on the tenure of castle-guard, and eight of them still retain the names of eight knights to whom William is said to have given lands on this tenure. Mr Round has shown that the *Warda Constabularii* of Dover Castle can be traced back to the Conquest, and that it is a mere legend that it was given as a fief to a Fienes. He remarks that the nine wards of the castle named in the Red Book of the Exchequer are all reproduced in the names still attached to the towers. "This coincidence of testimony leads us to believe that the names must have been attached at a very early period; and looking at the history of the families named, it cannot have been later than that of Henry II."[2] May it not have been even earlier? Eight of these names are attached to towers on the outer circuit,[3] and five of them are found as landholders in Kent in Domesday Book.

4. William of Poitiers further tells us that when the duke had taken the castle, he remained there eight days, *to add the fortifications which were wanting*.[4] What was wanting to a Norman eye in Anglo-Saxon fortifications, as far as we know them, was a citadel; and without laying too much stress on the chronicler's eight days, we may assume that the short time spent by William at Dover was just enough for the construction of a motte and bailey, inside the *castrum* of Harold, but crowned by wooden buildings only.

---

[1] Cited by Statham, *History of Dover*, pp. 265, 313.

[2] *Commune of London*, pp. 278-81.

[3] The ninth name, Maminot, is attached to three towers on the curtain of the keep ward.

[4] "Recepto castro, quæ minus erant per dies octo addidit firmamenta." P. 140.

Taking these things together, we venture to assume that the inner court in which the keep of Dover stands, represents an original motte, or at any rate an original citadel, added to the castle by William I. Whether what now remains of this motte is in part artificial, we do not pretend to say; it may be that it was formed simply by digging a deep ditch round the highest knoll of ground within the ancient ramparts.[1] Anyhow, it is still in effect a motte, and a large one, containing not only the magnificent keep, but a small ward as well. That this keep was the work of Henry II. there can be no manner of doubt; the *Pipe Rolls* show that he spent more than £2000 on the *turris* or keep of Dover Castle between the years 1181 and 1187, and Benedict of Peterborough mentions the building of the keep at this date.[2] The curtain around the motte may also be reckoned to be his work originally, as the *cingulum* is spoken of along with the *turris* in the accounts. Modern alterations have left little of Norman character in this curtain which shows at a glance, and the gateways (one of which remains) belong to a later period.

Attached to this keep ward is another ward, whose rampart is generally attributed to Saxon times. We are not in a position positively to deny that the Saxons had an inner earthwork on the highest part of the ground within their *burh*. But considering that small citadels are unusual in Saxon earthworks : considering also that this bailey is attached to the motte in the

---

[1] Lyon says : "The keep [hill] was formed of chalk dug out of the interior hill. Cited by Statham, p. 245.

[2] "Per præceptum regis facta est apud Doveram turris fortissima." II. 8, R. S., anno 1187. The *Historia Fundationis* of St Martin's Abbey says that Henry II. built the high tower in the castle, and enclosed the donjon with new walls : "fit le haut tour en le chastel, et enclost le dongon de nouelx murs." *M. A.*, iv., 533.

usual manner of a Norman bailey, and that its size corresponds to the usual size of an original Norman bailey in an important place, it does not seem unreasonable to suppose that this was the original bailey attached to the Conqueror's motte. Its shape is singular, part of it being nearly square, while at the S.E. corner a large oval loop is thrown out, so as to enclose the Roman Pharos and the Saxon church. The outline of the bailey certainly suggests that it was built after the Pharos and the church, and was built with reference primarily to the keep or motte ward. The nature of the ground, and the necessity of enclosing the church and the Roman tower within the immediate bailey of the castle, which would otherwise have been commanded by them, were the other factors which decided the unusual shape of the bailey.

On this earthwork the foundations of a rubble wall were formerly to be traced,[1] probably built by Henry II., as considerable sums for "the wall of the castle" are mentioned in his accounts.[2] Whether there are still any remains of this curtain we are unable to say, but so many of the features of the middle ward have been swept away by modern alterations, and the difficulty of examining what remains, owing to military restrictions, is so great, that little can be said about it, and we find that most authorities observe a judicious silence on the subject. But as the carriage of stone is expressly mentioned in Henry II.'s accounts, we may with great probability assign to him the transformation of the original wooden castle of William into a castle of stone; while the transformation of the Anglo-Saxon borough

---

[1] Puckle's *Church and Fortress of Dover Castle*, p. 57.

[2] *Pipe Rolls*, 1178-80. "In operatione muri circa castellum de Doura, £165, 13s. 4d. The same, £94, 7s. 1d."

into a stone enceinte was the work of Henry III.'s reign.

We think the evidence suggests that this *burh* or outer rampart was in existence when the Conqueror came to Dover, crowned in all probability with a stockade and towers of wood. It may possibly have been a British or even a Roman earthwork originally (though its outline does not suggest Roman work); or it may have been built by Harold as a city of refuge for the inhabitants of the port.[1] The Saxon church which it encloses, and which has long been attributed to the earliest days of Saxon Christianity, is now pronounced by the best authorities to be comparatively late in the style.[2]

The size of the inner castle of Dover appears to be about 6 acres, reckoning the keep ward at 2, and the bailey at about 4.

The value of the town of Dover had trebled at the time of the Survey, in spite of the burning of the town at William's first advent.[3]

DUDLEY, Staffordshire (Fig. 15). — William Fitz Ansculf held Dudley at the time of the Survey, "and there is his castle."[4]   Mr Clark appears to accept the dubious tradition of a Saxon Dodda, who first built this castle in the 8th century, since he speaks of Dudley as "a great English residence."[5]   This tradition, however, is not supported by Domesday Book, which shows

[1] Mr Statham thinks the port of Dover, though a Roman station, was unwalled till the 13th century, and gives evidence. *History of Dover*, p. 56.

[2] See Professor Baldwin Brown, "Statistics of Saxon Churches" in the *Builder*, 20th October 1900; and in *The Arts in Early England*, ii., 338.

[3] D. B., i., 1.

[4] Istedem Willelmus tenet Dudelei, et ibi est castellum ejus.   T. R. E. valebat 4 libras, modo 3 libras."   D. B., i., 177.

[5] *M. M. A.*, i., 24.

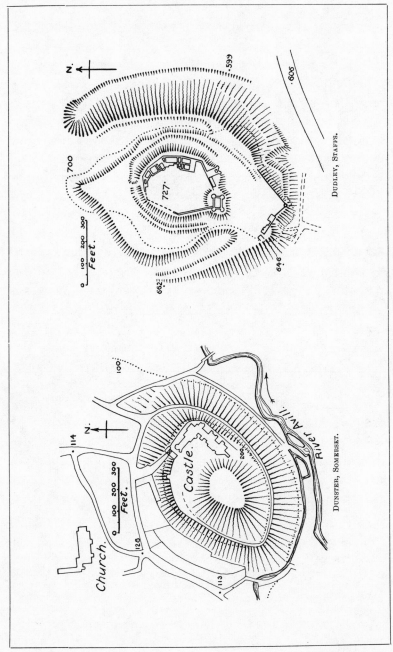

DUDLEY, STAFFS.

DUNSTER, SOMERSET.

FIG. 15.

[To face p. 144.

Dudley to have been only a small and unimportant manor before the Conquest. The strong position of the hill was no doubt the reason why the Norman placed his castle there. There is no Norman masonry in the present ruins. The earliest work is that of the keep on the motte, a rectangular tower with round corner turrets, attributed by Mr W. St John Hope to about 1320. The first castle was demolished by Henry II. in 1175,[1] and an attempt to restore it in 1218 was stringently countermanded.[2] The case of Dudley is one of those which proves that Henry II. destroyed some lawful castles in 1175 as well as the unlawful ones. In 1264 a license to restore it was granted to Roger de Somery, in consideration of his devotion to the king's cause in the Barons' War.[3] The whole area of the castle, including the motte, but not including the works at the base of the hill on which it stands, is 1¾ acres. The bailey is an irregular oval, following the hill top. Dudley is an instance in which the value of the manor has gone down instead of up since the erection of the castle ; this may perhaps be laid to the account of the devastation caused through the Staffordshire insurrection of 1069.

DUNSTER, Somerset (Fig. 15). — Called Torre in Domesday Book. "There William de Moion has his castle."[4] The motte here appears to be a natural rock or *tor*, whose summit has been levelled and its sides

---

[1] "Circa dies istos castellum de Huntinduna, de Waletuna, de Legercestria, et Grobi, de Stutesbers [Tutbury], de Dudeleia, de Tresc, et alia plura pariter corruerunt, in ultionem injuriarum quas domini castellorum regi patri frequenter intulerunt." *Diceto*, i., 404, R. S.

[2] *Close Rolls*, i., 380.

[3] Parker's *History of Domestic Architecture*, Licenses to Crenellate, 13th century, Part ii., p. 402. Godwin, "Notice of the Castle at Dudley," *Arch. Journ.*, xv., 47.

[4] D. B., i., 95b.

scarped by art. About 80 feet below the top is a (roughly) half-moon bailey, itself a shelf on the side of the hill; there is another and much smaller shelf at the opposite end.[1] Some foundations found in the S.W. corner of the upper ward appear to indicate a former stone keep.[2] Dunster was only a small manor of half a hide before the Conquest, but afterwards its value tripled. There was a borough as well as a castle.[3] The castle became the *caput baroniæ* of the De Moions, to whom the Conqueror gave fifty-six manors in different parts of the county. There is not the slightest reason to suppose that the site was fortified before the Conquest. Mr Clark remarks that " it is remarkable that no mouldings or fragments of Norman ornament have been dug up in or about the site, although there is original Norman work in the parish church." The simple explanation, probably, is that the first castle of De Moion was of wood, although on a site where it would have been possible to build in stone from the first, as it does not appear that any part of the motte is artificial. The area of the bailey is 1¾ acres. The value of Dunster had risen at the date of Domesday.[4]

DURHAM (Fig. 16). — The castle here was first built by the Conqueror, on his return from his expedition against Scotland in 1072.[5] It was intended as a strong residence for the bishop, through whom William

---

[1] Narrow terraces of this kind are found in several mottes, such as Mere, in Wilts. They are probably natural, and may have been utilised as part of the plan. The more regular terraces winding round the motte are generally found where the motte has become part of a pleasure-ground in later times.

[2] This is the only case in which I have had to trust to Mr Clark for the description of a castle. *M. M. A.*, ii., 24.

[3] Mentioned in *Close Rolls*, i., 518a.   [4] *D. B.*, i., 95b.

[5] Symeon of Durham, 1072. "Eodem tempore, scilicet quo rex reversus de Scotia fuerat, in Dunelmo castellum *condidit*, ubi se cum suis episcopus tute ab incursantibus habere potuisset."

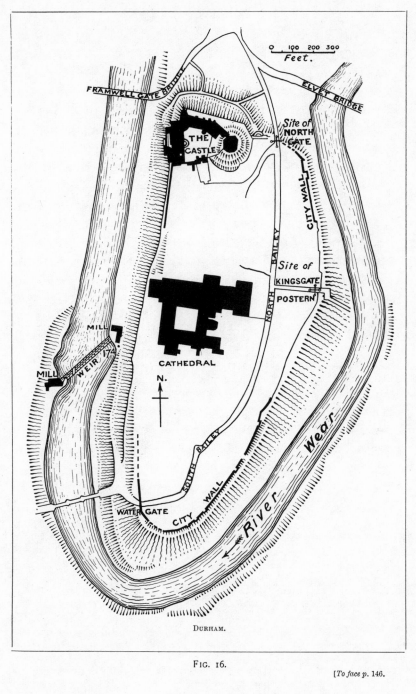

FRAMWELL GATE BRIDGE

ELVET BRIDGE

0   100   200   300
Feet.

Site of
NORTH
GATE

THE
CASTLE

CITY WALL

NORTH BAILEY

Site of
KINGSGATE

POSTERN

MILL

WEIR 17...

MILL

CATHEDRAL

N.

SOUTH BAILEY

CITY WALL

WATER GATE

River Wear

DURHAM.

FIG. 16.

[To face p. 146.

hoped to govern this turbulent part of the country. He placed it on the neck of the lofty peninsula on which the cathedral stands. The motte of the Conqueror still remains, and so does the chapel[1] which he built in the bailey; probably the present court of the castle, though crowded now with buildings, represents the outline of the original bailey.[2] The present shell keep on the motte was built by Bishop Hatfield in Edward III.'s reign,[3] but has been extensively modernised. There can be little doubt that up to 1345 there were only wooden buildings on the motte, as the writer was informed by Canon Greenwell that no remains of older stone-work than the 14th century had been found there. It is so seldom that we get any contemporary description of a castle, of this kind, that it seems worth while to translate the bombastic verse in which Laurence, Prior of Durham, described that of Durham in Stephen's reign :[4]

"Not far hence [from the north road into the city] a tumulus of rising earth explains the flatness of the excavated summit, explains the narrow field on the flattened vertex, which the apex of the castle occupies with very pleasing art. On this open space the castle is seated like a queen; from its threatening height, it holds all that it sees as its own. From its gate, the stubborn wall rises with the rising mound,[5] and rising still further, makes towards the comfort (amæna) of the keep. But the keep, compacted together, rises again

---

[1] This chapel is an instance of the honour so frequently done to the chapel, which was in many cases built of stone when the rest of the castle was only of timber, and was always the part most lavishly decorated.

[2] The bailey was twice enlarged by Bishops Flambard and Pudsey.

[3] Surtees, Durham, iv., 33.　　　　[4] Surtees Society, xx., 11-13.

[5] Evidently the southern wing wall up the motte ; but we need not suppose *murus* to mean a stone wall.

into thin air, strong within and without, well fitted for its work, for within the ground rises higher by three cubits than without—ground made sound by solid earth. Above this, a stalwart house[1] springs yet higher than the [shell] keep, glittering with splendid beauty in every part; *four posts are plain, on which it rests, one post at each strong corner.*[2] Each face is girded by a beautiful gallery, which is fixed into the warlike wall.[3] A bridge, rising from the chapel [in the bailey] gives a ready ascent to the ramparts, easy to climb; starting from them, a broad way makes the round of the top of the wall, and this is the usual way to the top of the citadel. . . . The bridge is divided into easy steps, no headlong drop, but an easy slope from the top to the bottom.   Near the [head of the] bridge, a wall descends from the citadel, turning its face westward towards the river.[4]   From the river's lofty bank it turns away in a broad curve to meet the field [*i.e.,* Palace Green].   It is no bare plot empty of buildings that this high wall surrounds with its sweep, but one containing goodly habitations.[5]   There you will find two vast palaces built with porches, the skill of whose builders the building

[1] *Domus,* a word always used for a *habitation* in mediæval documents, and often applied to a tower, which it evidently means here.

[2] This is the only indication which Lawrence gives that the keep was of wood.

[3] "Cingitur et pulchra paries sibi quilibet ala,
Omnis et in muro desinit ala fero."

The translation is conjectural, but *gallery* seems to make the best sense, and the allusion probably is to the wooden galleries, or *hourdes,* which defended the walls.

[4] Evidently the northern wing wall.

[5] This is the bailey; the two vast palaces must mean the hall and the lodgings of the men-at-arms, who did not share the bishop's dwelling in the keep.   These were probably all of wood, as the buildings of Durham Castle were burnt at the beginning of Pudsey's episcopate (1153) and restored by him.   Surtees Society, ix., 12.

well reveals.   There, too, the chapel stands out beauti-
fully raised on six pillars, not over vast, but fair enough
to view.   Here chambers are joined to chambers, house
to house, each suited to the purpose that it serves. . . .
There is a building in the middle of the castle which
has a deep well of abundant water. . . . The frowning
gate faces the rainy south, a gate that is strong, high-
reaching, easily held by the hand of a weakling or a
woman.   The bridge is let down for egress,[1] and thus
the way goes across the broad moat.   It goes to the
plain which is protected on all sides by a wall, where the
youth often held their joyous games.   Thus the
castellan, and the castle artfully placed on the high
ridge, defend the northern side of the cathedral.   And
from this castle a strong wall goes down southwards,
continued to the end of the church."[2]

The original bailey of this castle covers 1 acre.

ELY, Cambridgeshire (Fig. 17).—This castle was
built by William I. in 1070, when he was repressing the
last struggle of the English under the heroic Hereward.
The monks of Ely felt it a sore grievance that he placed
the castle within their own bounds.[3]   Both this castle
and the one built by William at Aldreth, to defend the
passage into the Isle of Ely, had a continuous existence,
as they were both refortified by Nigel, Bishop of Ely in
Stephen's reign, and Ely Castle was besieged and taken
by Stephen.[4]   The earthworks of this castle still exist,
to the south of the Minster.   There is a fine motte with

[1] "Hujus in egressu pons sternitur."   This seems a probable allusion to
a drawbridge, but if so, it is an early one.
[2] This describes the addition to the bailey made by Flambard. The
part of the peninsula to the S. of the church was afterwards walled in
by Pudsey, and called the South Bailey.
[3] *Liber Eliensis*, ii., 245 (Anglia Christiana). The part cited was written
early in the 12th century : see Preface.
[4] Stowe's *Annals*, 145, 1.

an oval bailey, of which the banks and ditches are traceable in parts. The area of the bailey is $2\frac{1}{2}$ acres. Of Aldreth or Aldrey there appear to be no remains.

The value of the manor of Ely was £33 in the Confessor's reign; it fell to £20 after the devastations of the Conquest, but had risen again to £30 at the time of the Survey.[1]

EWIAS, Herefordshire (Fig. 17).—The brief notice of this castle in Domesday Book throws some light on the general theory of castle-building in England.[2] William FitzOsbern, as the king's vicegerent, rebuilt this march castle, and committed it to the keeping of another Norman noble, and the king confirmed the arrangement. But in theory the castle would always be the king's. This is the only case in the Survey where we hear of a castle being *rebuilt* by the Normans. We naturally look to one of King Edward's Norman favourites as the first founder, for they alone are said by history to have built castles on the Welsh marches before the Conquest. Dr Round conjectures that Ewias was the "Pentecost's castle" spoken of in the (Peterborough) *Anglo-Saxon Chronicle* in 1052.[3] No masonry is now to be seen on the motte at Ewias, but Mr Clark states that the outline of a circular or polygonal shell keep is shown by

---

[1] D. B., ii., 192.

[2] "Alured de Merleberge tenet castellum de Ewias de Willelmo rege. Ipse rex enim concessit ei terras quas Willelmus comes ei dederat, qui hoc castellum refirmaverat, hoc est, 5 carucatas terræ ibidem. . . . Hoc castellum valet 10*l.*" D. B., i., 186a. As there is no statement of the value in King Edward's day, we cannot tell whether it had risen or fallen.

[3] *Feudal England*, p. 324. The present writer was led independently to the same conclusion. Pentecost was the nickname of Osbern, son of Richard Scrob, one of Edward's Norman favourites, to whom he had given estates in Herefordshire. Osbern fled to Scotland in 1052, but he seems to have returned, and was still holding lands in "the castelry of Ewias" at the time of the Survey, though his nephew Alured held the castle. See Freeman, *N. C.*, ii., 345, and *Florence of Worcester*, 1052.

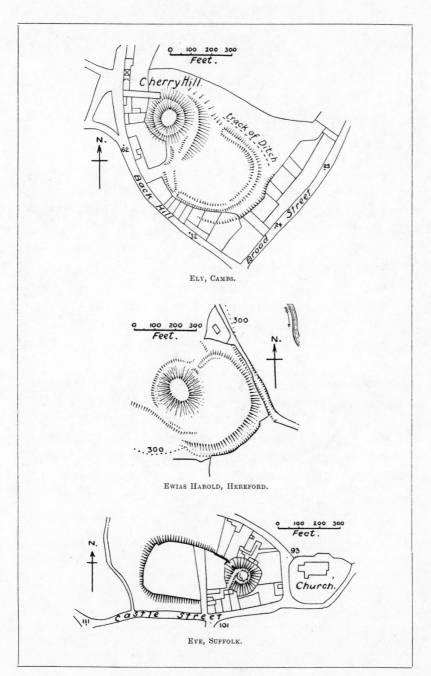

ELY, CAMBS.

EWIAS HAROLD, HEREFORD.

Church.

EYE, SUFFOLK.

FIG. 17.

[To face p. 150.

a trench out of which the foundations have been removed.
The bailey is roughly of half-moon shape and the mound
oval. The whole area of the castle, including the motte
and banks, is 2⅓ acres.

EXETER.—This castle is not mentioned in Domesday
Book, but Ordericus tells us that William *chose* a
site for the castle within the walls, and left Baldwin
de Molis, son of Count Gilbert, and other distinguished knights, to finish the work, and remain as
a garrison.[1] In spite of this clear indication that the
castle was a new thing, it has been obstinately held that
it only occupied the site of some former castle, Roman
or Saxon.[2] Exeter, of course, was a Roman castrum,
and its walls had been restored by Athelstan. In this
case William placed his castle inside instead of outside
the city walls, because, owing to the natural situation of
Exeter, he found in the north-west corner a site which
commanded the whole city. Although Domesday Book
is silent about the castle, it tells us that forty-eight
houses in Exeter had been destroyed since William
came to England,[3] and Freeman remarks that "we may
assume that these houses were destroyed to make room
for the castle, though it is not expressly said that they
were."[4]

Exeter Castle stands on a natural knoll, occupying
the north-west corner of the city, which has been

---

[1] Locum vero intra mœnia ad extruendum castellum delegit, ibique
Baldwinum de Molis, filium Gisleberti comitis, aliosque milites præcipuos
reliquit, qui necessarium opus conficerent, præsidioque manerunt." Ordericus,
ii., 181.

[2] Exeter is one of the few cities where a tradition has been preserved of
the site of the Saxon royal residence, which places it in what is now Paul
Street, far away from the present castle. Shorrt's *Sylva Antiqua Iscana*,
p. 7.

[3] "In hac civitate vastatæ sunt 48 domi postquam rex venit in Angliam."
D. B., i., 100.   [4] *Norman Conquest*, iv., 162.

converted into a sort of square motte by digging a great ditch round the two sides of its base towards the town.[1] That this ditch is no pre-Roman work is shown by the fact that it stops short at the Roman wall, and begins again on the outside of it, where, however, the greater part has been levelled to form the promenade of the *Northernhay* or north rampart of the city. On top of this hill, banks 30 feet high were thrown up, which still remain, and give to the courtyard which they enclose the appearance of a pit.[2] On top of these banks there are now stone walls ; but these were certainly no part of the work of Baldwin de Molis, who must have placed a wooden stockade on the banks which he constructed. One piece of stonework he probably did set up, the gatehouse, which by its triangle-headed windows and its long-and-short work is almost certainly of the 11th century. It has frequently been called Saxon, but more careful critics now regard it as "work that must have been done, if not by Norman hands, at Norman bidding and on Norman design."[3] It was no uncommon thing at this early period to have gatehouses of stone to walls of earth and wood. Of these gatehouses Exeter is the most perfect and the most clearly stamped with antiquity.

[1] The outer ditch may have been of Roman origin, but in that case it must have been carried all round the city, and we are unable to find whether this was the case or not. The banks on the north and east sides must also have been of Roman origin, and if we rightly understand the statements of local antiquaries, the Roman city wall stood upon them, and has actually been found *in situ*, cased with mediæval rubble. *Report of Devon Association*, 1895.

[2] This resemblance to a pit may be seen in every motte which still retains its ancient earthen breast-work, as at Castle Levington, Burton in Lonsdale, and Castlehaugh, Gisburne. Perhaps this is the reason that we so frequently read in the *Pipe Rolls* of "the houses *in* the motte" (domos in Mota) instead of *on* the motte. Devizes Castle is another and still more striking instance.

[3] Professor Baldwin Brown, *The Arts in Early England*, ii., 82.

One thing we look for in vain at Exeter, and that is
a citadel.   There is no keep, and there is no record that
there ever was one, though a chapel, hall, and other
houses are mentioned in ancient accounts.   Mr Clark
says that probably the Normans regarded the whole
court as a shell keep.   It certainly was, in effect, a
motte ; but it was altogether exceptional among Norman
castles of importance if it had no bailey.   And in fact a
bailey is mentioned in the *Pipe Roll* of 1 Richard I.,
where there is an entry for the cost of making a gaol in
the bailey of the castle.[1]   Now Norden, who published
a plan of Exeter in 1619, says that the prison which
formerly existed at the bottom of Castle Lane (on the
south or city front of the present castle) was " built upon
Castle grounde," and he states that the buildings and
gardens which have been made on this ground are
intrusions on the king's rights.[2]   The remarkably full
account of the siege of Exeter in the *Gesta Stephani*
speaks of an outer *promurale* which was taken by
Stephen, as well as the inner bridge leading from the
town to the castle, before the attack on the castle itself.
Unfortunately the word *promurale* has the same un-
certainty about it that attaches to so many mediæval
terms, and the description given of it would apply
either to the banks of a bailey, or to the *heriçon*
on the counterscarp of the ditch of the motte.   We
must, therefore, leave it to the reader's judgment
whether the evidence given above is sufficient to
establish the former existence of a bailey at Exeter,
and to place Exeter among the castles of the motte-
and-bailey type.

The description of the castle given by the writer of

---

[1] " In custamento gaiole in ballia castelli, £16, 15s. 8d."
[2] Cited by Dr Oliver, " The Castle of Exeter," in *Arch. Journ.*, vii., 128.

the *Gesta* has many points of interest.[1]   He describes
the castle as standing on a very high mound (*editissimo
aggere*) hedged in by an insurmountable wall, which
was defended by "Cæsarian" towers built with the very
hardest mortar.   This must refer to Roman towers
which may have existed on the Roman part of the wall.
Whether there was a stone wall on the other two sides,
facing the city, may be doubted, as the expenditure
entered to Henry II. in the *Pipe Rolls* suggests that he
was the first to put stone walls on the banks, and the
two ancient towers which still exist appear to be of his
time.[2]   The chronicler goes on to say that after Stephen
had taken the *promurale* and broken down the bridge,
there were several days and nights of fighting before he
could win the castle, which was eventually forced to
surrender by the drying-up of the wells.   The mining
operations which he describes were no doubt undertaken
with the view of shaking down the Roman wall at the
angle where it joins the artificial bank of Baldwin de
Molis.   Possibly the chamber in the rock with the
mysterious passages leading from it, which is still to be

[1] The whole of this passage is worth quoting : "Castellum in ea situm,
editissimo aggere sublatum, muro inexpugnabile obseptum, turribus
Cæsarianis inseissili calce confectis firmatum.   Agmine peditum instructis-
sime armato exterius promurale, quod ad castellum muniendum aggere
cumulatissimo in altum sustollebatur, expulsis constanter hostibus suscepit,
pontemque interiorem, quo ad urbem de castello incessus protendebatur,
viriliter infregit, lignorumque ingentia artificia, quibus de muro pugnare
intentibus resisteretur, mire et artificiose exaltavit.   Die etiam et noctu
graviter et intente obsidionem clausis inferre ; nunc cum armatis aggerem
incessu quadrupede conscendentibus rixam pugnacem secum committere ;
nunc cum innumeris fundatoribus, qui e diverso conducti fuerunt, intolerabile
eos lapidum grandine infestare ; aliquando autem ascitis eis, qui massæ
subterranæ cautius norunt venus incidere, ad murum diruendum viscera
terræ scutari præcipere : nonnunquam etiam machinas diversi generis, alias
in altum sublatis, alias humo tenus depressas, istas ad inspiciendam quidnam
rerum in castello gereretur, illas ad murum quassandum vel obruendum
aptare." *Gesta Stephani*, R. S., 23.

[2] *Pipe Rolls*, 1169-1186.

seen in the garden of Miss Owthwaite, at the point where the ditch ends, is the work of Stephen's miners.[1] The description of his soldiers scrambling up the *agger* on their hands and knees (*quadrupede incessu*) will be well understood by those who have seen the castle bank as it still rises from that ditch.

The present ward of Exeter Castle, which is rudely square in plan, covers an area of 2 acres, which is as large as the whole area of many of the smaller Norman castles. The castle was allowed to fall into decay as early as 1549,[2] and since then it has been devastated by the building of a Sessions House and a gaol. No plan has been preserved of the former buildings in this court, though the site of the chapel is known.

There is no statement in Domesday Book as to the value of Exeter.

EYE, Suffolk (Fig. 17).—This castle was built by William Malet, one of the companions of the Conqueror, who is described as having been half Norman and half English.[3] Eye, as its name implies, seems to have been an island in a marsh in Norman times, and therefore a naturally defensible situation. The references in the *Pipe Rolls* to the *palicium* and the *bretasches* of Eye Castle show that the outer defences of the castle at any rate were of wood in the days of Henry II.[4] That

---

[1] The difficulty about this, however, is that passages branch off from the central cave in every direction.

[2] Oliver's *History of Exeter*, p. 186.

[3] [Willelmus Malet] fecit suum castellum ad Eiam. D. B., ii., 379. For Malet, see Freeman, *N. C.*, 466, note 4.

[4] "In operatione castelli de Eya et reparatione veterarum bretascharum et 2 novarum bretascharum et fossatorum et pro carriagio et petra et aliis minutis operationibus 20*l*. 18*s*. 4*d*. *Pipe Rolls*, xix., 19 Henry II. The small quantity of stone referred to here can only be for some auxiliary work. The *bretasches* in this case will be mural towers of wood. "In emendatione palicii et 1 exclusæ vivarii et domorum castelli 20*s*." 28 Henry II.

there were works in masonry at some subsequent period is shown by a solitary vestige of a wing wall of flints which runs up the motte. A modern tower now occupies the summit. The bailey of the castle, the outline of which can still be traced, though the area is covered with buildings and gardens, was oval in shape, and covered 2 acres.

The value of the manor of Eye had gone up since the Conquest from £15 to £21. This must have been due to the castle and to the market which Robert Malet or his son William established close to the castle; for the stock on the manor and the number of ploughs had actually decreased.[1]   A proof that there is no deliberate register of castles in Domesday Book is furnished by the very careful inventory of the manor of Eye, where there is no mention of a castle, though it is noticed that there are now a park and a market; and it is only in the account of the lands of the bishop of Thetford, in mentioning the injury which William Malet's market at Eye had done to the bishop's market at Hoxne, that the castle of Eye is named.

GLOUCESTER.—"There were sixteen houses where the castle sits, but now they are gone, and fourteen have been destroyed in the *burgus* of the city," says Domesday Book.[2]   Gloucester was undoubtedly a Roman *chester*, and Roman pavements have been found there.[3] The description in the Survey would lead us to think that the castle was outside the ancient walls,[4] though

---

[1] D. B., ii., 319, 320.

[2] D. B., i., 162.   "Sedecim domus erant ubi sedet castellum, quæ modo desunt, et in burgo civitatis sunt wastatæ 14 domus."

[3] Rudge, *History of Gloucester*, p. 7. Haverfield, *Romanisation of Britain*, p. 204.

[4] It is, however, possible that by the *burgus* may be meant a later quarter which had been added to the city.

Speed's map places it on the line of the wall of his time, which may have been a mediæval extension. The castle of Gloucester is now entirely destroyed, but there is sufficient evidence to show that it was of the usual Norman type. There was a motte, which was standing in 1819, and which was then called the Barbican Hill ;[1] it appears to have been utilised as part of the works of the barbican. This motte must originally have supported a wooden keep, and Henry I. must have been the builder of the stone keep which Leland saw " in the middle of the area ; "[2] for in 1100 Henry gave lands to Gloucester Abbey " in exchange for the site where now the keep of Gloucester stands."[3] The bailey had previously been enlarged by William Rufus.[4] Possibly the *framea turris* or framework tower spoken of in Henry II.'s reign may refer to the wooden keep which had been left standing on the motte.[5] The walls of Gloucester Castle were frequently repaired by Henry II.,[6] but the word *murus* by no means implies always a stone wall, and it is certain that the castle was at that time surrounded by a wooden stockade, as a writ of a much later period (1225) says that the stockade which is around our castle of Gloucester has been blown down

---

[1] Fosbroke's *History of Gloucester*, pp. 125, 126. Stukeley, writing in 1721, says : " There is a large old gatehouse standing, and near it the castle, with a very high artificial mount or keep nigh the river." *Itin. Cur.*, i., 69.

[2] " Of al partes of yt the hy tower *in media area* is most strongest and auncient." Leland, *Itin.*, iii., 64.

[3] In excambium pro placea ubi nunc turris stat Gloucestriæ, ubi quondam fuit ortus monachorum." *Mon. Ang.*, i., 544. The document is not earlier than Henry II.'s reign.

[4] Round, *Studies in Domesday*, p. 123.

[5] " In operatione frame turris de Glouec, 20*l.* *Pipe Rolls*, i., 27. In the single *Pipe Roll* of Henry I. there is an entry " In operationibus turris de Glouec," 7*l.* 6*s.* 2*d.*, which *may* be one of a series of sums spent on the new stone keep.

[6] *Pipe Rolls*, 1177, 1180, 1181, 1184.

and broken by the wind, and must be repaired.[1]
Wooden bretasches on the walls are spoken of in the
Pipe Rolls of 1193, and even as late as 1222.[2]

The value of the city of Gloucester had apparently
risen at the time of the Survey, though the entry being
largely in kind, T. R. E., it is not easy to calculate.

HASTINGS, Sussex (Fig. 18).—In this case we have
positive contemporary evidence that the earthen mound
of the castle was thrown up by the Normans at the time
of the Conquest, for there is a picture in the Bayeux
Tapestry which shows them doing it. A number of
men with spades are at work raising a circular mound,
on the top of which, with the usual all-inclusiveness of
mediæval picturing, a stockade is already erected. A
man with a pick seems to be working at the ditch. The
inscription attached is : " He commands that a castle
be dug at Hestengaceastra."[3] There is no need to
comment on the significance of this drawing and its
inscription for the history of early Norman castles;
what is extraordinary is that it should have been entirely
overlooked for so long. In no case is our information
more complete than about Hastings. Not only does
Domesday Book mention the *castellaria* of Hastings,[4]
but the *Anglo-Saxon Chronicle* also tells us that
William built a castle there, while the chronicle of Battle
Abbey makes the evidence complete by telling us that
" having taken possession of a suitable site, he built
a *wooden castle* there."[5] This of course means the

---

[1] *Close Rolls*, ii., 88b.
[2] " In reparatione murorum et bretaschiarum," 20*l.* 7*s.* 11*d.* *Pipe Rolls*,
1193.   [3] " Jussit ut foderetur castellum ad Hestengaceastra."
[4] D. B., i., 18a, 2. " Rex Willelmus dedit comiti [of Eu] castellariam de
Hastinges."
[5] " Dux ibidem [at Pevensey] non diu moratus, haud longe situm, qui
Hastinges vocatur, cum suis adiit portum, ibique opportunum nactus locum,
ligneum agiliter castellum statuens, provide munivit." *Chron. Monast. de*

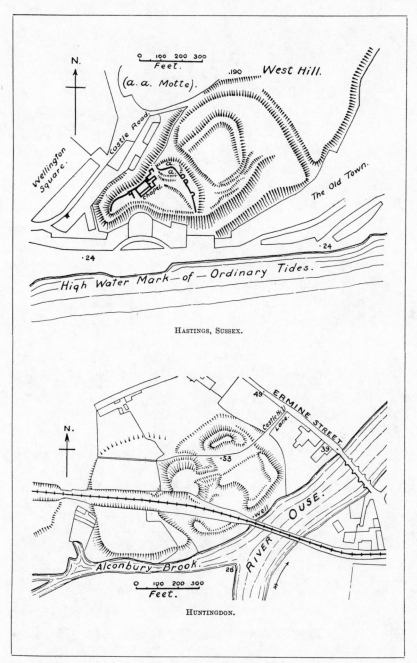

HASTINGS, SUSSEX.

HUNTINGDON.

FIG. 18.

[To face p. 158.

stockade on top of the motte, with the wooden tower or towers which would certainly be added to it. Wace states that this wooden castle was brought over in pieces in the ships of the Count of Eu.[1]

The masonry now existing at the castle is probably none of it older than the reign of Henry II. at the earliest, and most of it is certainly much later.[2] The *Pipe Rolls* show that Henry II. spent £235 on the castle of Hastings between the years 1160 and 1181, and it is indicated that some of this money was for stone, and some was for a keep (*turrim*).[3] There is no tower large enough for a keep at Hastings now, nor have any stone foundations been found on the motte, and Mr Harold Sands, who has paid particular attention to this castle, concludes that Henry II.'s keep has been carried away by the sea, which has probably torn away at least 2 acres from the area of the castle.[4] The beautiful

Bello, p. 3, ed. 1846. There is also the evidence of Ordericus, who says that Humphrey de Tilleul received the custody of Hastings Castle "from the first day it was built." iv., 4.

[1] Par conseil firent esgarder
Boen lieu a fort chastel fermer.
Donc ont des nes mairrien iete,
A la terre l'ont traine,
Que le quens d'Ou i out porte
Trestot percie e tot dole.
Les cheuilles totes dolees
Orent en granz bariz portees.
Ainz que il fust avespre
En ont un chastelet ferme ;
Environ firent une fosse,
Si i ont fait grant fermete.—Andresen's edition, p. 289.

[2] The north curtain is of ruder work than the other masonry.

[3] In attractu petre et calcis ad faciendam turrim de Hasting 6*l.* Idem 13*l.* 12*s.* Vol. xviii., p. 130. The work must have been extensive, as it is spoken of as "operatio castelli novi Hasting." 1181-1182. Though the sum given is not sufficient for a great stone keep, it may have been supplemented from other sources.

[4] See Mr Sands' paper on Hasting's Castle, in *Trans. of the South-Eastern Union of Scientific Societies*, 1908.

fragment of the Chapel of St Mary is probably of Henry II.'s reign; the walls and towers on the east side of the castle appear to be of the 13th century. The ditch does not run round the motte, but is cut through the peninsular rock on which the castle stands, the motte and its ward being thus isolated. The form of this bailey is now triangular, but it may have been square originally. Beyond the ditch is another bailey, defended by earthen banks and by a second ditch cut through the peninsula.[1] No exact estimate can be given of the original area of the castle, as so much of the cliff has been carried away by the sea.

Hastings itself had been a fortified town before the Norman Conquest, and is one of those mentioned in the *Burghal Hidage*. The name Hæstingaceaster, given to it in the *Anglo-Saxon Chronicle* (1050), is a proof that the Saxons used the name *chester* for constructions of their own, as no Roman remains have been found at Hastings. But the Norman castle is outside the town, on a cliff which overlooks it. As in the case of the other ports of Sussex, the castle was committed to an important noble, in this case the Count of Eu.

The manor of Bexley, in which Hastings Castle stood, had been laid waste at the Conquest; at the date of the Survey it was again rising in value, though it had not reached the figure of King Edward's days.[2]

[1] This bailey has been supposed to be a British or Roman earthwork, but no evidence has been brought forward to prove it, except the fact that discoveries made in one of the banks point to a flint workshop on the site.

[2] Totum manerium valebat T. R. E. 20 libras, et postea wastum fuit. Modo 18 libras 10 solidos. D. B., i., 18a, 2.

Since the above was written, Mr Chas. Dawson's large and important work on Hastings Castle has appeared, and to this the reader is referred for many important particulars, especially the passages from the *Pipe Rolls*, i., 56, and the repeated destructions by the sea, ii., 498-9. The reproduction of

HEREFORD.—There can be little doubt that the castle
of Hereford was built by the Norman Ralph, Earl of
Hereford, Edward the Confessor's nephew, about the
year 1048.[1] It was burnt by the Welsh in 1055, after
which Harold fortified the town with a dyke and ditch ;
but as Mr Freeman remarks, it is not said that he
restored the castle.[2] The motte of Earl Ralph is now
completely levelled, but it is mentioned several times in
documents of the 12th century,[3] and is described in a
survey of 1652, from which it appears that it had a stone
keep tower, as well as a stone breastwork enclosing a
small ward.[4] It stood outside the N.W. corner of
the bailey, surrounded by its own ditch ; the site is still
called Castle Hill. If the castle was not restored before
the Norman Conquest it was certainly restored afterwards, as in 1067 we find the "men of the castle"
fighting with Edric Child and the Welsh. The castle
appears to have had stone walls by the time of Henry II.,
as the mention of a kiln for their repair proves.[5] But
these walls had wooden towers.[6] The timber ordered in
1213 "ad hordiandum castellum nostrum de Hereford "[7]

Herbert's plan of 1824 (ii., 512) seems to show more than one bailey outside
the inner ward. The evidence for a great outer ditch, enclosing all these
works, and supposed to be prehistoric, is given on p. 515, vol. ii.

[1] See *Anglo-Saxon Chronicle*, 1048 (Peterborough) and 1052 (Worcester),
and compare with *Florence of Worcester*.

[2] *N. C.*, ii., 394.

[3] *Pipe Rolls*, 11 Henry II., p. 100, and 15 Henry II., p. 140. Stephen
granted to Miles of Gloucester "motam Hereford cum toto castello." Charter
cited by Mr Round, *Geoffrey de Mandeville*, Appendix O, p. 329.

[4] Cited by Grose, *Antiquities*, ii., 18. Stukeley saw the motte, and
mentions the well in it lined with stone. *Itin. Curiosum*, i., 71. See also
Duncombe's *History of Hereford*, i., 229.

[5] In custamento prosternandi partem muri castri nostri de Hereford, et
preparatione rogi ad reficiendum predictum murum, 26s. 6d. *Pipe Rolls*,
1181-1182.

[6] In operatione 5 bretaschiarum in castro de Hereford, £15, 3s. 9d. *Pipe
Rolls*, 1173-1174.

[7] *Close Rolls*, i., 134a.

refers to the wooden *alures* or machicolations which were placed on the tops of walls for the purpose of defending the bases.

Though Hereford was a private castle in the Confessor's reign, it was claimed for the crown by Archbishop Hubert, the Justiciary, in 1197, and continued to be a royal castle throughout the 13th century.[1]

The bailey of Hereford Castle still exists, with its fine banks; it is kite-shaped and encloses 5½ acres. The castle stood within the city walls, in the south-east angle.

The value of Hereford appears to have greatly increased at the date of the Survey.[2]

HUNTINGDON (Fig. 18).—"There were twenty houses on the site of the castle, which are now gone."[3] Ordericus tells us that the castle of Huntingdon was built by William on his return from his second visit to York in 1068.[4] Huntingdon had been a walled town in Anglo-Saxon times, and was very likely first fortified by the Danes, but was repaired by Edward the Elder. As in the case of so many other towns, the houses outside the walls had to pay geld along with those of the city, and it was some of the former which were displaced by the new Norman castle. Huntingdon was part of the patrimony of Earl Waltheof, and came to the Norman, Simon de Senlis, through his marriage with Waltheof's daughter and heiress. The line of Senlis ended in

---

[1] Hubertus Cantuariensis Archiepiscopus et totius Angliæ summus Justiciarius, fuit in Gwalia apud Hereford, et recepit in manu sua castellum de Hereford, et castellum de Briges, et castellum de Ludelaue, expulsis inde custodibus qui ea diu custodierant, et tradidit ea aliis custodibus, custodienda ad opus regis. *Roger of Howden*, iv., 35, R. S.

[2] D. B., i., 179.

[3] "In loco castri fuerunt 20 mansiones, quæ modo absunt." D. B., i., 203.

[4] *Ordericus*, ii., 185.

another heiress, who married David, afterwards the famous king of Scotland; David thus became Earl of Huntingdon. In the insurrection of the younger Henry in 1174, William the Lion, grandson of David, took sides with the young king, and consequently his castle was besieged and taken by the forces of Henry II.,[1] and the king ordered it to be destroyed. The *Pipe Rolls* show that this order was carried out, as they contain a bill for "hooks for pulling down the stockade of Huntingdon Castle," and "for the work of the new castle at Huntingdon, and for hiring carpenters, and crooks, and axes."[2] We learn from these entries that the original castle of the Conquest had just been replaced by a new one, very likely a new fortification of the old mounds by William, in anticipation of the insurrection. We also learn that the new castle was a wooden one; for a castle which has to be pulled down by carpenters with hooks and axes is certainly not of stone. It does not appear that the castle was ever restored, though "the chapel of the castle" is spoken of as late as the reign of Henry III.[3]

The motte of Huntingdon still exists, and has not the slightest sign of masonry. The bailey is roughly square, with the usual rounded corners; the motte was inside this enclosure, but had its own ditch. The whole area was $2\frac{1}{2}$ acres, but another bailey was subsequently added.

---

[1] *Benedict of Peterborough*, i., 70. The Justiciar, Richard de Lucy, threw up a siege castle against it.

[2] "Pro uncis ad prosternandum palicium de Hunted, 7s. 8d. In operatione novi castelli de Hunted, et pro locandis carpentariis et pro croccis et securibus et aliis minutis rebus, 21l." *Pipe Rolls*, 20 Henry II., pp. 50, 63. It is clear that the *operatio* was in this case one of pulling down. Giraldus (*Vita Galfredi*, iv., 368, R. S.) and *Diceto* (i., 404, R. S.), both say the castle was destroyed.

[3] *Mon. Ang.*, vi., 80.

The value of Huntingdon appears to have been stationary at the time of the Survey, the loss of the twenty houses causing a diminution of revenue which must have been made up from the new feudal dues of the castle.

LAUNCESTON, or Dunheved,[1] Cornwall (Fig. 19).— There, says Domesday Book, is the castle of the Earl of Mortain.[2]   In another place it tells us that the earl gave two manors to the bishop of Exeter "for the exchange of the castle of Cornwall," another name for Dunheved Castle. We have already had occasion to note that the "exchange of the castle," in Domesday language, is an abbreviation for the exchange of the site of the castle. The fact that the land was obtained from the church is a proof that the castle was new, for it was not the custom of Saxon prelates thus to fortify themselves. The motte of Launceston is a knoll of natural rock, which has been scarped and heightened by art. This motte now carries a circular keep, which cannot be earlier than the 13th century.[3]   There is no early Norman work whatever about the masonry of the castle, and the remarkably elaborate fortifications on the motte belong to a much later period.[4]   The motte rises in one corner of a roughly rectangular bailey, which covers 3 acres. It stands outside the town walls, which still exist, and join those of the castle, as at Totnes. Launceston was only a small manor of ten ploughs in the time of the Confessor. In spite of the building of

[1] Leland tells us that Launceston was anciently called Dunheved. *Itin.*, vii., 122.

[2] "Ibi est castrum comitis." D. B., i., 121b. "Hæc duo maneria [Hawstone et Botintone] dedit episcopo comes Moriton pro excambio castelli de Cornualia." D. B., i., 101b, 2.

[3] There are no entries for Launceston except repairs in the reigns of Henry II. and his sons.

[4] Murray's *Guide to Cornwall*, p. 203.

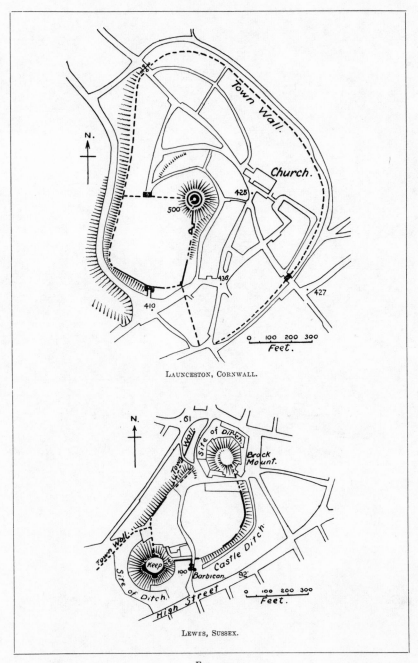

N.

Town Wall.

Church.

425

500

436

410

427

0   100   200   300
Feet.

LAUNCESTON, CORNWALL.

N.

.61

Site of Ditch.

Town Wall.

Brack Mount.

Town Wall.

Keep

Site of Ditch.

100

Barbican.

Castle Ditch.

92

High Street

0   100   200   300
Feet.

LEWES, SUSSEX.

FIG. 19.

[To face p. 164.

the castle, the value of the manor had greatly gone down in William's time.[1] The ten ploughs had been reduced to five.

LEWES, Sussex (Fig. 19).—The castle of Lewes is not mentioned in its proper place in Sussex by Domesday Book, and this is another proof that the Survey contains no inventory of castles; for that the castle was existing at that date is rendered certain by the numerous allusions in the Norfolk portion to "the exchange of the castle of Lewes."[2] It is clear that at some period, possibly during the revolt of Robert Curthose in 1079, William I. gave large estates in Norfolk to his trusty servant, William de Warenne, in exchange for the important castle of Lewes, which he may have preferred to keep in his own hands at that critical period. This bargain cannot have held long, at least as regards the castle, which continued to belong to the Warenne family for many generations. We cannot even guess now how the matter was settled, but the lands in Norfolk certainly remained in the hands of the Warennes.

Lewes is one of the very few castles in England which have two mottes.[3] They were placed at each end of an oval bailey, each surrounded by its own ditch, and each projecting about three-fourths beyond the line of the bailey. On the northern motte only the foundations

---

[1] "Olim 20*l.* ; modo valet 4*l.*" D. B., i., 121b.

[2] D. B., ii., 157, 163, 172. The first entry relating to this transaction says : "Hoc totum est pro escangio de 2 maneriis Delaquis." The second says : "Pertinent ad castellum Delaquis." It is clear that Lewes is meant, as one paragraph is headed "De escangio Lewes." I have been unable to find any explanation of this exchange in any of the Norfolk topographers, or in any of the writers on Domesday Book.

[3] Lincoln is the only other instance known to the writer. Deganwy has two natural mottes. It is possible that two mottes indicate a double owner-ship of a castle, a thing of which there are instances, as at Rhuddlan.

of a wall round the top remain ; on the other, part of
the wall which enclosed a small ward, and two mural
towers.   These towers have signs of the early Perpendicular period, and are very likely of the reign of Edward
III., when the castle passed into the hands of the Fitz
Alans.   The bailey, which enclosed an area of about
3 acres, is now covered with houses and gardens,
but parts of the curtain wall on the S.E. and E. stand
on banks, bearing witness to the original wooden fortifications.   The great interest of this bailey is its ancient
Norman gateway.   The entrance was regarded by
mediæval architects as the weakest part of the fortress,
and we frequently find that it was the first part to
receive stone defences.[1]   It is not surprising that at
such an important place as Lewes, which was then a
port leading to Normandy, and at the castle of so
powerful a noble, we should find an early case of stone
architecture supplementing the wooden defences.   But
the two artificial mottes have no masonry that can be
called early Norman.

Lewes is one of the boroughs mentioned in the
Burghal Hidage, and was a *burgus* at the time of the
Survey.[2]   The value of the town had increased by
£1, 18s. from what it had been in King Edward's
time.

LINCOLN (Fig. 20).—Domesday Book tells us that
166 houses were destroyed to furnish the site of the
castle.[3]   The *Anglo-Saxon Chronicle* says that William
built a castle here on his return from his first visit to

---

[1] Exeter and Tickhill are instances of early Norman gateways, and at
Ongar and Pleshy there are fragments of early gateways, though there are
no walls on the banks.   We have already seen that Arundel had a gateway
which cannot be later than Henry I.'s time.   [2] D. B., i., 26a, 1.

[3] "De predictis wastis mansionibus propter castellum destructi fuerunt
166." D. B., i., 336b, 2.

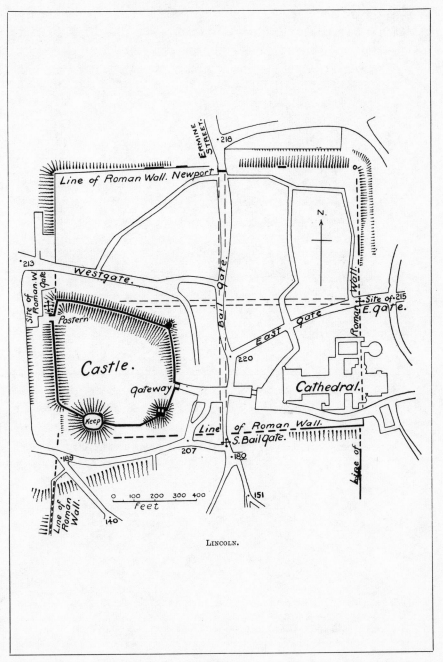

LINCOLN.

FIG. 20.

[To face p. 166.

York in 1068, and Ordericus makes the same statement.[1]
Lincoln, like Exeter, was a Roman *castrum*, and the
Norman castle in both cases was placed in one corner
of the castrum; but the old Roman wall of Lincoln,
which stands on the natural ground, was not considered
to be a sufficient defence on the two exterior sides,
probably on account of its ruinous condition. It was
therefore buried in a very high and steep bank, which
was carried all round the new castle.[2] This circumstance
seems to point to the haste with which the castle was
built, Lincoln being then for the first time subdued. The
fact that it was inside the probably closely packed Roman
walls explains why so many houses were destroyed for
the castle.[3]   Lincoln, like Lewes, has two mottes:
both are of about the same height, but the one in the
middle of the southern line of defence is the larger and
more important; it was originally surrounded with its
own ditch. It is now crowned with a polygonal shell
wall, which may have been built by the mother of
Ralph Gernon, Earl of Chester, in the reign of Henry I.[4]
The tower on the other motte, at the south-east corner,

---

[1] "In reversione sua Lincoliæ, Huntendonæ, et Grontebrugæ castra
locavit." Ordericus, 185 (Prévost).

[2] At present the bank is wanting on a portion of the south side, between
the two mottes.

[3] Mr Clark gravely argues that the houses were inside what he believes
to have been the Saxon castle.   There is not a vestige of historical evidence
for the existence of any castle in Lincoln in the Saxon period.

[4] Stephen gave Ralph the castle and city of Lincoln, and gave him leave
to fortify one of the towers in Lincoln Castle, and have command of it until
the king should deliver to him the castle of Tickhill; then the king was to
have the city and castle of Lincoln again, excepting the earl's own tower,
which his mother had fortified. His mother was Lucy, daughter of Ivo
Taillebois; and as the principal tower was known as the Luce Tower,
the masonry may have been her work. In that case the Norman work
on the smaller motte may be due to Ralph Gernon, and may possibly be
the *nova turris* which was repaired in John's reign. *Pipe Roll*, 2 John.
Stephen's charter is in Farrer's *Lancashire Pipe Rolls*.

has been largely rebuilt in the 14th century and added to in modern times, but its lower storey still retains work of Norman character. There is good reason to suppose that this bailey was first walled with stone in Richard I.'s reign, as there is an entry in the *Pipe Rolls* of 1193-1194 "for the cost of fortifying the bailey, £82, 16s. 4d."[1] The present wall contains a good deal of herring-bone work, and this circumstance led Mr Clark, who was looking for something which he *could* put down to William I.'s time, to believe that the walls were of that date. But the herring-bone work is all in patches, as though for repairs, and herring-bone work was used for repairs at all epochs of mediæval building. The two gateways (that is the Norman portions of them) are probably of about the same date as the castle wall. The whole area is 5¾ acres.

The total revenue which the city of Lincoln paid to the king and the earl had gone up from 30*l.* T. R. E. to 100*l.* T. R. W. For the sake of those who imagine that Saxon halls had anything to do with mottes, it is worth noting that the hall which was the residence of the chief landholder in Lincoln before the Conquest was still in existence after the building of the castle, but evidently had no connection with it.[2]

MONMOUTH (Fig. 21).—Domesday Book says that the king has four ploughs in demesne in the castle of

---

[1] "In custamento firmandi ballium castelli Lincoll." *Pipe Roll*, 5 Richard I. In an excavation made for repairs in modern times it was found that this wall rested on a timber frame-work, a device to avoid settling, the wall being of great height and thickness. Wilson, Lincoln Castle, *Proc. Arch. Inst.*, 1848.

[2] D. B., i. 336b, 2 : "Tochi filius Outi habuit in civitate 30 mansiones præter suam hallam, et duas ecclesias et dimidiam, et suam hallam habuit quietam ab omni consuetudine. . . . Hanc aulam tenuit Goisfredus Alselin et suus nepos Radulfus. Remigius episcopus tenet supradictas 30 mansiones ita quod Goisfredus nihil inde habet."

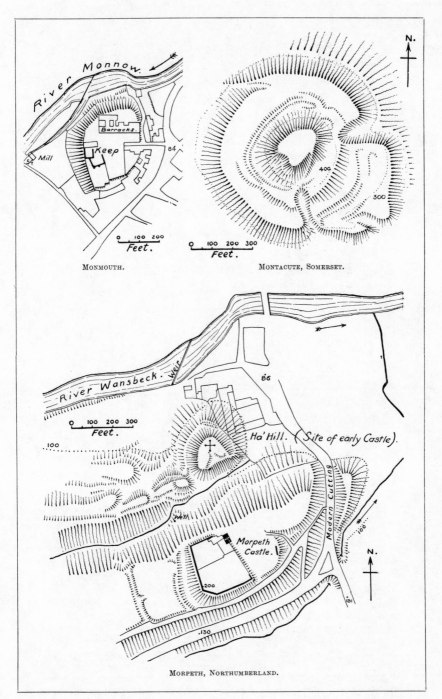

MONMOUTH.

MONTACUTE, SOMERSET.

MORPETH, NORTHUMBERLAND.

FIG. 21.

[*To face p.* 168.

Monmouth.[1] Dr Round regards this as one of the cases where *castellum* is to be interpreted as a town and not as a castle. However this may be, the existence of a Norman castle at Monmouth is rendered certain by a passage in the *Book of Llandaff*, in which it is said that this castle was built by William FitzOsbern, and a short history of it is given, which brings it up to the days of William Fitz Baderun.[2] Speed speaks of this castle as "standing mounted round in compasse, and within her walls another mount, whereon a Towre of great height and strength is built."[3] This sounds like the description of a motte and bailey; but the motte cannot be traced now. It is possible that it may have been swept away to build the present barracks; the whole castle is now on a flat-topped hill. The area is $1\frac{3}{4}$ acres.[4]

The value of the manor before the Conquest is not given.

MONTACUTE, Somerset (Fig. 21).—This is another instance of a site for a castle obtained by exchange from the church. Count Robert of Mortain gave the manor of Candel to the priory of Athelney in exchange for the manor of Bishopstowe, "and there is his castle, which is called Montagud."[5] The English name for

---

[1] "In castello Monemouth habet Rex in dominio 4 carucas. Willelmus filius Baderon custodit eas. Quod rex habet in hoc castello valet c solidos." D. B., 180b.

[2] *Liber Landavensis*, Evans' edition, pp. 277-278. See also Round's *Calendar of Documents Preserved in France*, p. 406.

[3] *Theatre of Britain*, p. 107.

[4] Speed's map shows the curtain wall surrounding the top of the hill and also a large round tower towards the N.E. part, but not standing on any "other mount." The square keep is not indicated separately. It must be remembered that Speed's details are not always accurate or complete.

[5] "Ipse comes tenet in dominio Bishopstowe, et ibi est castellum ejus quod vocatur Montagud. Hoc manerium geldabat T. R. E. pro 9 hidas, et erat de abbatia de Adelingi, et pro eo dedit comes eidem ecclesiæ manerium quod Candel vocatur." D. B., i., 93a, 1.

the village at the foot of the hill was Ludgarsburh, which does not point to any fortification on the hill itself, the spot where the wonder-working crucifix of Waltham was found in Saxon times.   Robert of Mortain's son William gave the castle of Montacute, with its chapel, orchard, and other appurtenances, to a priory of Cluniac monks which he founded close to it. The gift may have had something compulsory in it, for William of Mortain was banished by Henry I. in 1104 as a partisan of Robert Curthose.   Thus, as Leland says, " the notable castle partly fell to ruin, and partly was taken down to make the priory, so that many years since no building of it remained ; only a chapel was set upon the very top of the dungeon, and that yet standeth there." [1]   There is still a high oval motte, having a ditch between its base and the bailey ; the latter is semilunar in shape.   The hill has been much terraced on the eastern side, but this may have been the work of the monks, for purposes of cultivation.[2]   There is no masonry except a quite modern tower.   According to Mr Clark, the motte is of natural rock.   The French name of the castle was of course imported from Normandy, and we generally find that an English castle with a Norman-French name of this kind has a motte.[3]

Bishopstowe, in which the castle was placed, was not a large manor in Saxon times.   Its value T. R. E. is not given in the Survey, but we are told that it is

[1] *Itin.*, ii., 92.
[2] From a description communicated by Mr Basil Stallybrass.   The motte is shown in a drawing in Stukeley's *Itinerarium Curiosum.*   The "immense Romano-British camp" of which Mr Clark speaks (*M. M. A.*, i., 73) is nearly a mile west.
[3] Mountjoy, Monthalt (Mold), Beaumont, Beaudesert, Egremont, are instances in point.

worth 6*l.* to the earl, and 3*l.* 3*s.* to the knights who
hold under him.

MORPETH, Northumberland (Fig. 21).—There is
only one mention known to us of Morpeth Castle in the
11th century, and that is in the poem of Geoffrey Gaimar.[1]
He says that William Rufus, when marching to
Bamborough, to repress the rebellion of Mowbray, Earl
of Northumberland, "took the strong castle of Morpeth,
which was seated on a little mount," and belonged to
William de Morlei. Thus there can be no doubt that
the Ha' Hill, about 100 yards to the N. of the present
castle, was the motte of the first castle of Morpeth,
though the remains of the motte, which are mentioned
by Hodgson, have been destroyed.[2] A natural ridge
has been used to form a castle by cutting off its higher
end to form a motte, and making a court on the lower
part of the ridge. The great steepness of the slopes
rendered ordinary ditches unnecessary, nor are there
any traces now of banks or foundations. In the court
some Norman capitals and carved stones were found in
1830. This early castle was admirably placed for commanding the river and the bridge.[3] The present castle
of Morpeth was built in 1342-1349.[4]

NEWCASTLE, Northumberland.—The first castle here
was built by Robert, son of William I., on his return
from his expedition to Scotland in 1080.[5] It was of the

---

[1] *Gaimar*, 214, Wright's edition. Gaimar wrote in the first half of the
12th century; Wright states that his work is mainly copied from the *Anglo-
Saxon Chronicle*, but its chief value lies in the old historical traditions of
the north and east of England which he has preserved.

[2] Hodgson's *History of Northumberland*, Part II., ii., 384, 389.

[3] This account is taken from a description kindly furnished by Mr
D. H. Montgomerie.

[4] Bates' *Border Holds*, p. 11.

[5] *Simeon of Durham*, 1080. "Castellum Novum super flumen Tyne
condidit."

usual motte-and-bailey kind, the motte standing in a small bailey which was rectilinear and roughly oblong.[1] This motte was in existence when Brand wrote his *History of Newcastle*, but was removed in 1811. The castle was placed outside the Roman station at Monkchester, and commanded a Roman bridge over the Tyne, "and to the north-east overlooked a ravine that under the name of The Side formed for centuries a main artery of communication between England and Scotland."[2]   Henry II., when he built the fine keep of this castle, did not place it on the motte, but in the outer and larger ward, which was roughly triangular. The outer curtain appears to have stood on the banks of the former earthen castle, as the Parliamentary Survey of 1649 speaks of the castle as "bounded with strong works of stone and mud."[3]   The area of the whole castle was 3 acres and 1 rood.

NORHAM, Northumberland (Fig. 22).—The first castle here was built by Ranulf Flambard, Bishop of Durham, in the reign of William Rufus. It was built to defend Northumberland against the incursions of the Scots, and we are expressly told that no castle had existed there previously.[4]   This first castle, which we may certainly assume to have been of earth and wood, was destroyed by the Scots in 1138, and there does not seem to have been any stone castle until the time of

[1] See the map in an important paper on Newcastle by Longstaffe, *Arch. Æliana*, iv., 45.

[2] *Guide to the Castle of Newcastle*, published by Society of Antiquaries of Newcastle, 1901.

[3] Longstaffe, as above.

[4] "Condidit castellum in excelso preruptæ rupis super Twedam flumen, ut inde latronum incursus inhiberet, et Scottorum irruptiones. Ibi enim utpote in confinia regni Anglorum et Scottorum creber prædantibus ante patebat excursus, *nullo enim quo hujusmodi impetus repelleretur præsidio locato.*" *Symeon of Durham*, R. S., i., 140.

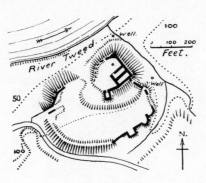

NORHAM.

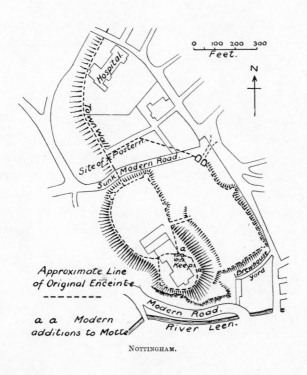

NOTTINGHAM.

Fig. 22.

[To face p. 172.

Bishop Puiset or Pudsey, who built the present keep by
command of King Henry II.[1] Mr Clark tried hard to
find some work of Flambard's in this tower, but found
it difficult, and was driven back on the rather lame
assumption that "the lapse of forty [really fifty at least]
years had not materially changed the style of architecture then in use."[2] In fact, the Norman parts of
this keep show no work so early as the 11th century,
but are advanced in style, for not only was the basement
vaulted, but the first floor also. The simple explanation
is that Flambard threw up the large square motte on
which the keep now stands, and provided it with the
usual wooden defences. It also had a strong tower, but
almost certainly a wooden one; hence it was easily
destroyed by the Scots when once taken.[3] The motte
was probably lowered to some extent when the stone
keep was built. It stands on a high bank overlooking
the Tweed, and is separated from its bailey by a deep
ditch. The bailey may be described as a segment of a
circle; its area is about 2 acres.

NORWICH (Fig. 23).—We find from Domesday
Book that no less than 113 houses were destroyed for
the site of this castle, a certain proof that the castle was
new.[4] It is highly probable that it was outside the
primitive defences of the town, at any rate in part.
Norwich was built, partly on a peninsula formed by a

---

[1] "Castellum di Northam, quod munitionibus infirmum reperit, turre
validissima forte reddidit." *Geoffrey of Coldingham*, 12 (Surtees Society).
Symeon says it was built "precepto regis." The keep was extensively
altered in the Decorated period.

[2] *M. M. A.*, ii., 331.   [3] *Richard of Hexham*, 319 (Twysden).

[4] "In illa terra de quâ Herold habebat socam sunt 15 burgenses et 17
mansuræ vastæ, quæ sunt in occupatione castelli; et in burgo 190 mansuræ
vacuæ in hoc quod erat in soca regis et comitis, et 81 in occupatione castelli."
D. B., ii., 116. This shows that the castle and its ditches occupied ground
partly within and partly without the ancient *burh*.

double bend of the river Wensum, partly in a district
lying south-west of this peninsula, and defended by a
ridge of rising ground running in a north-easterly
direction. The castle was placed on the edge of this
ridge, and all the oldest part of the town, including the
most ancient churches, lies to the east of it.[1] In the
conjectural map of Norwich in 1100, given in Woodward's *History of Norwich Castle*,[2] the street called
Burg Street divides the Old Burg on the east from the
New Burg on the west; this street runs along a ridge
which traverses the neck of the peninsula from south-
west to north-east, and on the northern end of this
ridge the castle stands.[3] There can be little doubt that
this street marks the line of the *burh* or enclosing bank
by which the primitive town of Norwich was defended.[4]
A clear proof of this lies in the fact that the castle of
Norwich was anciently not in the jurisdiction of the
city, but in that of the county; the citizens had no
authority over the houses lying beyond the castle ditches
until it was expressly granted to them by Edward III.[5]
The mediæval walls of Norwich, vastly extending the
borders of the city, were not built till Henry III.'s reign.[6]

The motte of Norwich Castle, according to recent

[1] Harrod's *Gleanings among Castles*, p. 142.

[2] The authorities from which this map is compiled are not given.

[3] The "new borough" at Norwich was the quarter inhabited by the
Normans. D. B., ii., 118. "Franci de Norwich: in novo burgo 36
burgenses et 6 Anglici." Mr Hudson says that Mancroft Leet corresponds
to the new burgh added to Norwich at the Conquest. See his map in
Arch. Journ., xlvi.

[4] Norwich was not a Roman town ; see Haverfield, *Vict. Hist. of
Norfolk*, i., 320. But the Roman road from Caistor passed exactly underneath the castle motte. *Brit. Arch. Assoc. Journ.*, xlvi., Rev. H. Dukin-
field Astley.

[5] Harrod's *Gleanings among Castles*, p. 137.

[6] *Mon. Ang.*, iv., 13. In 37 Henry III. the monks of Norwich Priory
received "licentiam includendi eandem villam cum fossis," and by doing
this they enclosed the lands of other fees.

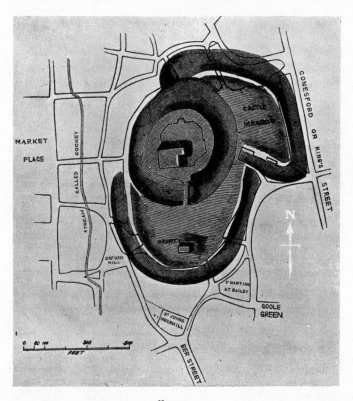

NORWICH.

(From Harrod's "Gleanings among the Castles and Convents of Norfolk," p. 133.)

FIG. 23.

[To face p. 174.

investigations, is entirely artificial;[1] it was originally square, and had "a prodigious large and deep ditch around it."[2] The fancy of the antiquary Wilkins that the motte was the centre of two concentric outworks[3] was completely disproved by Mr Harrod, who showed that the original castle was a motte with one of the ordinary half-moon baileys attached. Another ward, called the Castle Meadow, was probably added at a later date. The magnificent keep which now stands on the motte is undoubtedly a work of the 12th century.[4] The castle which Emma, wife of Earl Ralf Guader, defended against the Conqueror after the celebrated bride-ale of Norwich was almost certainly a wooden structure. As late as the year 1172 the bailey was still defended by a wooden stockade and wooden bretasches;[5] and even in 1225 the stockade had not been replaced by a stone wall.[6]

Norwich was a royal castle, and consequently always in the hands of the sheriff; it was never the property of the Bigods.[7] As the fable that extensive lands belonging to the monastery of Ely were held on the tenure of castle guard at Norwich *before the Conquest* is repeated by all the local historians,[8] it is worth while

---

[1] *Arch. Journ.*, xlvi., 445.

[2] Kirkpatrick's *Notes of Norwich Castle*, written about 1725. He states that the angles of the motte had been spoilt, and much of it fallen away.

[3] *Archæologia*, vol. xii.

[4] Mr Hartshorne thought it was built between 1120 and 1125. *Arch. Journ.*, xlvi., 260. It is certainly not as late as Henry II.'s reign, or the accounts for it would appear in the *Pipe Rolls*.

[5] *Pipe Rolls*, 19 Henry II., p. 117. In reparatione pontis lapidei et palicii et 3 bretascharum in eodem castello, 20*l*. 4*s*. 8*d*.

[6] *Close Rolls*, ii., 22. Order that the palicium of Norwich Castle, which has fallen down and is threatened with ruin, be repaired.

[7] Kirkpatrick, *Notes on Norwich Castle*.

[8] Except Kirkpatrick, who shows a judicious scepticism on the subject. *Ibid.*, p. 248.

to note that the charters of Henry I. setting the convent free from this service, make no allusion to any such ancient date for it,[1] and that the tenure of castle guard is completely unknown to the Anglo-Saxon laws. The area of the inner bailey is $3\frac{1}{4}$ acres, and that of the outer, $4\frac{1}{2}$ acres. The value of Norwich had greatly risen since the Conquest.[2]

NOTTINGHAM (Fig. 22).—This important castle is not mentioned in Domesday Book, but the *Anglo-Saxon Chronicle* says that William I. built the castle at Nottingham in 1067, on his way to repress the first insurrection in Yorkshire. Ordericus, repeating this statement, adds that he committed it to the keeping of William Peverel.[3] The castle was placed on a lofty headland at some distance from the Danish borough, and between the two arose the Norman borough which is mentioned in Domesday Book as the *novus burgus*. The two upper wards of the present castle probably represent William's plan. The upper ward forms a natural motte of rock, as it is 15 feet higher than the bailey attached to it, and has been separated from it by a ditch cut across the rocky headland, which can still be traced below the modern house which now stands on the motte. Such a site was not only treated as a motte, but was actually called by that name, as we read of the *mota* of Nottingham Castle in the *Pipe Rolls* of both John's and Richard I.'s reigns.

Mr Clark published a bird's-eye view of Nottingham Castle in his *Mediæval Military Architecture*, about which he only stated that it was taken from the *Illustrated London News*. It does not agree with the

---

[1] *Mon. Ang.*, i., 482.   [2] D. B., ii., 117.
[3] Ordericus, ii., 184.

plan made by Simpson in 1617,[1] and is therefore not quite trustworthy ; the position of the keep, for example, is quite different. The keep, which Hutchison in his Memoirs speaks of as " the strong tower called the Old Tower on the top of the rock," seems clearly Norman, from the buttresses. It was placed (according to Simpson's plan), on the north side of the small ward which formed the top of the motte, and was enclosed in a yet older shell wall which has now disappeared. The height of this motte is indicated in the bird's-eye view by the ascending wall which leads up it from the bailey. It had its own ditch, as appears by several mentions in the accounts of " the drawbridge of the keep," and " the bridge leading up to the dongeon."[2] It is highly probable that this keep was built by King John, as in a *Mise Roll* of 1212 there is a payment entered " towards making the tower which the king commanded to be built on the motte of Nottingham."[3] But the first masonry in the castle was probably the work of Henry II., who spent £1737, 9s. 5d. on the castle and houses, the gaol, the king's chamber, the hall, and in raising the walls and enclosing the bailey.[4] The castle has been so devastated by the 17th century spoiler, that the work of Henry and John has been almost entirely

[1] Published in a paper on Nottingham Castle by Mr Emanuel Green, in *Arch. Journ.* for December 1901.

[2] See Mr Green's paper, as above, p. 388.

[3] " Apud Rokingham liberavimus Philippo Marco ad faciendam turrim quam dominus Rex precepit fieri in Mota de Notingham 100 marcas quas burgenses de Notingham et Willelmus Fil. Baldwini dederunt domino Regi pro benevolencia sua habenda." In Cole's *Documents Illustrative of English History*, 235. There is some reason to think that John instead of building the cylindrical keeps which were then coming into fashion, reverted to the square form generally followed by his father.

[4] *Pipe Rolls*, 1170-1186. The *Pipe Roll* of 6 Richard I. mentions the making of " 1 posterne in mota," which may be the secret passage in the rock.

swept away, but the one round tower which still remains as part of the defences of the inner bailey, looks as though it might be of the time of Henry II. This bailey is semicircular ; the whole original castle covers only $1\frac{2}{3}$ acres. A very much larger bailey was added afterwards, probably in John's reign.[1] Probably this later bailey was at first enclosed with a bank and stockade, and this stockade may be the palitium of which there are notices in the records of Henry III. and Edward I.[2] The main gateway of this bailey, which still remains, is probably of Edward I. or Edward II.'s reign.[3]

The castle of Nottingham was the most important one in the Midlands, and William of Newburgh speaks of it as "so well defended by nature and art that it appears impregnable."[4] The value of the town had risen from £18 to £30 at the time of the Survey.[5]

OKEHAMPTON, Devon (Fig. 24).—Baldwin de Molis, Sheriff of Devon, held the manor of Okehampton at the time of the Survey, and had a castle there.[6] On a hill in the valley of the Okement River

---

[1] This is rendered probable by a writ of Henry III.'s reign, ordering that half a mark is to be paid annually to Isolde de Gray for the land which she had lost in King John's time "*per incrementum forinseci ballii Castri de Notinge.*" *Close Rolls,* i., 508.

[2] *Close Rolls,* i., 548b. "Videat quid et quantum mæremii opus fuerit ad barbecanas et palitia ipsius castri reparanda" (1223). *Close Rolls,* i., 531b : Timber ordered for the repair of the bridges, bretasches, and *palicium gardini* (1223). *Cal. of Close Rolls,* 1286, p. 390 : Constable is to have timber to repair the weir of the mill, and the *palings of the court* of the castle. Nottingham was one of eight castles in which John had baths put up. *Rot. Misæ.,* 7 John.

[3] The murage of the town of Nottingham was assigned "to the repair of the outer bailey of the castle there" in 1288. *Patent Rolls,* Edward I., i., 308.

[4] Chapter xlii.   [5] D. B., i., 280.

[6] "Ipse Baldwinus vicecomes tenet de Rege Ochementone, et ibi sedet castellum." D. B., i., 105b, 2.

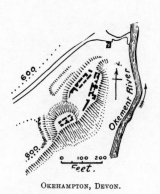

OKEHAMPTON, DEVON.

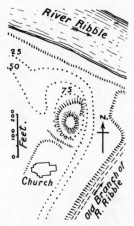

PENWORTHAM, LANCS.

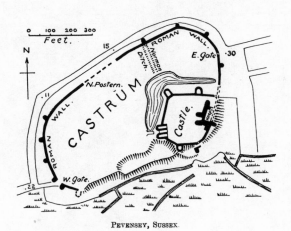

PEVENSEY, SUSSEX.

FIG. 24.

[To face p. 178.

stand the remains of a castle of the motte-and-bailey pattern. On the motte,.which is high and steep, are the ruins of a keep of late character, probably of the 14th century.[1] The oval bailey covers ½ an acre, and the whole castle is surrounded with a very deep ditch (filled up now on the east side) which is in part a natural ravine. The usual ditch between the motte and the bailey is absent here. This castle appears to have continued always in private hands, and therefore there is little to be learned about it from the public records. The value of Okehampton manor had increased since the Conquest from £8 to £10. As there is no *burgus* mentioned T. R. E., but four *burgenses* and a market T. R. W., Baldwin the Sheriff must have built a borough as well as a castle. Otherwise it was a small manor of thirty ploughs.

OSWESTRY, Shropshire. — Mr Eyton's identification of the Domesday castle of Louvre, in the manor of Meresberie, Shropshire, with Oswestry, seems to be decisive.[2] The name is simply L'Œuvre, the Work, a name very frequently given to castles in the early Norman period. Domesday Book says that Rainald de Bailleul built a castle at this place.[3] He had married the widow of Warin, Sheriff of Shropshire, who died in 1085. The castle afterwards passed into the hands of the Fitz Alans, great lords-marcher on the Welsh

---

[1] The late Mr Worth thought the lower part of the keep was early Norman. He was perhaps misled by the round arched loops in the basement. But round arches are by no means conclusive evidence in themselves of Norman date, and the size of these windows, as well as the absence of buttresses, and the presence of pointed arches, are quite incompatible with the early Norman period. The whole architecture of the castle agrees with a 14th century date, to which the chapel undoubtedly belongs.

[2] Eyton, *Antiquities of Shropshire*, vol. vii.

[3] "Ibi fecit Rainaldus Castellum Luure." D. B., i., 253b. Rainald was an under-tenant of Roger, Earl of Shrewsbury.

border.   As the Welsh annals give the credit of building the castle to Madoc ap Meredith, into whose hands it fell during the reign of Stephen, it is not impossible that some of the masonry still existing on the motte, which consists of large cobbles bedded in very thick mortar, may be his work, and probably the first stonework in the castle.   A sketch made in the 18th century, however, which is the only drawing preserved of the castle, seems to show architecture of the Perpendicular period.[1]   But probably the keep alone was of masonry in the 12th century, as in 1166, when the castle was in royal custody, the repair of the stockade is referred to in the *Pipe Rolls*.[2]   No plan has been preserved of Oswestry Castle, so that it is impossible to recover the shape or area of the bailey, which is now built over.   The manor of Meresberie had been unoccupied (*wasta*) in the days of King Edward, but it yielded 40s. at the date of the Survey.   Eyton gives reasons for thinking that the town of Oswestry was founded by the Normans.

OXFORD (Fig. 25).—This castle was built in 1071 by Robert d'Oilgi (or d'Oilly), a Norman who received large estates in Oxfordshire.[3]   Oxford was a burgus in Saxon times, and is one of those mentioned in the *Burghal Hidage*.   Domesday tells us that the king has twenty mural mansions there, which had belonged to Algar, Earl of Mercia, and that they were called mural mansions because their owners had to repair the city wall at the king's behest, a regulation probably as old as the days of Alfred.   The Norman castle was placed outside

[1] This sketch is reproduced in Mr Parry-Jones' *Story of Oswestry Castle*. Leland says, "Extat turris in castro nomine Madoci." *Itin.*, v., 38.

[2] "In operatione palicii de Blancmuster 2*l*. 6*s*. 8*d*."   XII., 124.   Oswestry was known as Blancmoustier or Album Monasterium in Norman times.

[3] *Abingdon Chronicle* and *Osney Chronicle*, which, though both of the 13th century, were no doubt compiled from earlier sources.

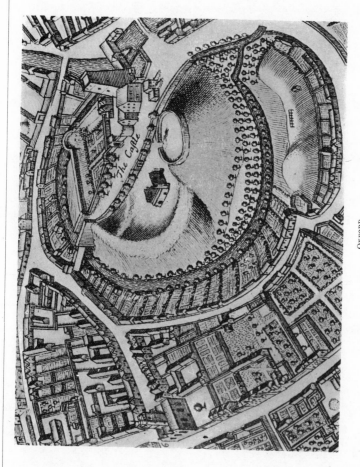

The Castle

OXFORD.

(From "Oxonia Illustrata," David Loggan, 1675.)

FIG. 25.

the town walls, but near the river, from which its trenches were fed.[1] It was without doubt a motte-and-bailey castle ; the motte still remains, and the accompanying bird's-eye view by David Loggan, 1675, shows that the later stone walls of the bailey stood on the earthen banks of D'Oilly's castle. The site is now occupied by a gaol. On the line of the walls rises the ancient tower of St George's Church, which so much resembles an early Norman keep that we might think it was intended for one, if the Osney chronicler had not expressly told us that the church was founded two years after the castle.[2] It is evident that the design was to make the church tower work as a mural tower, a combination of piety and worldly wisdom quite in accord with what the chronicler tells us of the character of Roger d'Oilly.

Henry II. spent some £260 on this castle between the years 1165 and 1173, the houses in the keep, and the well being specially mentioned. We may presume that he built with stone the decagonal [shell?] keep on the motte, whose foundations were discovered at the end of the 18th century.[3] There is still in the heart of the motte a well in a very remarkable well chamber, the masonry of which may be of his time. The area of the bailey appears to have been 3 acres.

The value of the city of Oxford had trebled at the time of the Domesday Survey.[4]

In the treaty between Stephen and Henry in 1153 the whole castle of Oxford is spoken of as the " Mota " of Oxford.[5]

---

[1] *Osney Chronicle*, 1071.

[2] See Ingram's *Memorials of Oxford* for an account of the very interesting crypt of this church, p. 8. The battlement storey of the tower is comparatively late.   [3] Mackenzie, *Castles of England*, i., 160.

[4] D. B., p. 154.   [5] Rymer's *Fœdera*, vol. i.

PEAK CASTLE, Derbyshire.—The Survey simply calls this castle the Castle of William Peverel, but tells us that two Saxons had formerly held the *land*.[1] There is no motte here, but the strong position, defended on two sides by frightful precipices, rendered very little fortification necessary. It is possible that the wall on the N. and W. sides of the area may be, in part at least, the work of William Peverel; the W. wall contains a great deal of herring-bone work, and the tower at the N.W. angle does not flank at all, while the other one in the N. wall only projects a few feet; the poor remains of the gatehouse also appear to be Norman. It would probably be easier to build a wall than to raise an earthbank in this stony country; nevertheless, behind the modern wall which runs up from the gatehouse to the keep, something like an earthbank may be observed on the edge of the precipice, which ought to be examined before any conclusions are determined as to the first fortifications of this castle. The keep, which is of different stone to the other towers and the walls, stands on the highest ground in the area, apparently on the natural rock, which crops up in the basement. It is undoubtedly the work of Henry II., as the accounts for it remain in the *Pipe Rolls*, and the slight indications of style which it displays, such as the nook-shafts at the angles, correspond to the Transition Norman period.[2] The shape of the bailey is a quadrant; its area scarcely exceeds 1 acre.

---

[1] "Terram castelli Pechefers tenuerunt Gerneburn et Hunding." D. B., i., 276a, 2.

[2] There are similar nook-shafts to Henry II.'s keep at Scarborough, and to Castle Rising. Mr Hartshorne (*Arch. Journ.*, v., 207) thought that there had been an earlier stone keep at Peak Castle, because some moulded stones are used in the walls, and because there is some herring-bone work in the basement. But this herring-bone work only occurs in a revetment wall to the rock in the cellar; and the moulded stones may be quite modern

The value of the manor had risen since the Conquest, and William Peverel had doubled the number of ploughs in the demesne. The castle only remained in the hands of the Peverels for two generations, and was then forfeited to the crown. The manor was only a small one ; and the site of the castle was probably chosen for its natural advantages and for the facility of hunting in the Peak Forest.

PENWORTHAM, Lancashire (Fig. 24).—" King Edward held Peneverdant. There are two carucates of land there, and they used to pay ten pence. Now there is a castle there, and there are two ploughs in the demesne, and six burghers, and three radmen, and eight villeins, and four cowherds. Amongst them all they have four ploughs. There is half a fishery there. There is wood and hawk's eyries, as in King Edward's time. It is worth £3." [1] The very great rise in value in this manor shows that some great change had taken place since the Norman Conquest. This change was the building of a castle. The *modo* of Domesday always expresses a contrast with King Edward's time, and clearly tells us here that Penwortham Castle was new. [2] It lay in the extensive lands between the Ribble and the Mersey, which were part of the Conqueror's enfeoffment of Roger the Poitevin, third son of Earl Roger de Montgomeri. [3] Since Penwortham is mentioned as demesne, and no

insertions for repairs, and may have come from the oratory in the N.E. angle, or from some of the ruined windows and doorways. The sums entered to this castle between the years 1172 and 1176 are less than half the cost of Scarborough keep, and do not appear adequate, though the keep was a small one. But there is some reason to think that the cost of castles was occasionally defrayed in part from sources not entered in the *Pipe Rolls*.

[1] Rex E. tenuit Peneverdant. Ibi 2 carucatæ terræ et reddebant 10 denarios. Modo est ibi castellum. . . . Valent 3 libras. D. B., i., 270.

[2] We need not resort to any fanciful British origins of the name Peneverdant, as it is clearly the effort of a Norman scribe to write down the unpronounceable English name Penwortham,   [3] See *ante*, under Clitheroe.

under-tenant is spoken of, we may perhaps assume that this castle, which was the head of a barony, was built by Roger himself.   He did not hold it long, as he forfeited all his estates in 1102.   At a later period, though we have not been able to trace when, the manor of Penwortham passed into the hands of the monks of Evesham, to whom the church had already been granted, at the end of the Conqueror's reign.[1]   Probably it is because the castle thus passed into the hands of the church that it never developed into a stone castle, like Clitheroe.   The seat of the barony was transferred elsewhere, and probably the timbers of the castle were used in the monastic buildings of Penwortham Priory.

The excavations which were made here in 1856 proved conclusively that there were no stone foundations on the Castle Hill at Penwortham.[2]   These excavations revealed the singular fact that the Norman had thrown up his motte on the site of a British or Romano-British hut, without even being aware of it, since the ruins of the hut were buried 5 feet deep and covered by a grass-grown surface, on which the Norman had laid a rude pavement of boulders before piling his motte.[3]

---

[1] Mr Halton's book (*Documents relating to the Priory of Penwortham*) throws no light on this point.

[2] *Transactions of the Historic Society of Lancashire and Cheshire*, vol. ix., 1856-1857, paper on "The Castle Hill of Penwortham," by the Rev. W. Thornber ; Hardwick's *History of Preston*, pp. 103-11.

[3] In a paper published in the *Trans. Soc. Ant. Scot.* for 1900, on "Anglo-Saxon Burhs and Early Norman Castles," the present writer was misled into the statement that this hut was the remains of the cellar of the Norman *bretasche*.   A subsequent study of Mr Hardwick's more lucid account of the excavations showed that this was an error.   There were two pavements of boulders, one on the natural surface of the hill, on which the hut had been built, the other 5 feet above it, and 12 feet below the present surface.   The hut appeared to have been circular, with wattled walls and a thatched roof.   Several objects were found in its remains, and were pronounced to be Roman or Romano-British.   The upper pavement would probably be the flooring of a Norman keep.

Among the objects found in the excavations was a Norman prick spur, a conclusive proof of the Norman origin of the motte.[1] No remains appear to have been found of the Norman wooden keep ; but this would be accounted for by the theory suggested above.

Penwortham is a double motte, the artificial hill rising on the back of a natural hill, which has been isolated from its continuing ridge by an artificial ditch cut through it. The double hill rises out of a bailey court which is rudely square, but whose shape is determined by the ground, which forms a headland running out into the Ribble. The whole area cannot certainly be ascertained. There was a ferry at this point in Norman times.[2] The castle defends the mouth of the Ribble and overlooks the town of Preston.

Penwortham was certainly not the *caput* of a large soke in Saxon times, as it was only a berewick of Blackburn, in which hundred it lay. It was the Norman who first made it the seat of a barony.

PETERBOROUGH.—The chronicler, Hugh Candidus, tells us that Abbot Thorold, the Norman abbot whom William I. appointed to the ancient minster of Peterborough, built a castle close to the church, "which in these days is called Mount Torold."[3] This mount is

---

[1] Mr Roach Smith pronounced this spur to be Norman. As its evidence is so important, it is to be regretted that its position was not more accurately observed. It was found in the lowest stratum of the remains, but Mr Hardwick says : "As it was not observed until thrown to the surface, a possibility remained that it might have fallen from the level of the upper boulder pavement, 5 feet higher." We may regard this possibility as a certainty, if the lower hut was really British.

[2] Mr Willoughby Gardner says the castle commands a ford, to which the ancient sunk road leads. *Victoria Hist. of Lancashire*, vol. ii.

[3] Hugh Candidus, *Cœnob. Burg. Historia*, in Sparke's *Scriptores*, p. 63. This passage was kindly pointed out to me by Mr Round. Hugh lived in Henry III.'s reign, but he must have had the more ancient records of the monastery at his disposal.

still existing, but it has lost its ancient name, and is now called Tout Hill. It stands in the Deanery garden, and has probably been largely ransacked for garden soil, as it has a decayed and shapeless look. Still, it is a venerable relic of Norman aggression, well authenticated.

PEVENSEY, Sussex (Fig. 24).—The Roman castrum of Pevensey (still so striking in its remains) was an inhabited town at the date of the Norman Conquest, and was an important port.[1] After taking possession of the castrum, William I. drew a strong bank across its eastern end, and placed a castle in the area thus isolated. This first castle was probably entirely of wood, as there was a wooden *palicium* on the bank as late as the reign of Henry II.[2] But if a wooden keep was built at first, it was very soon superseded by one of stone.[3] The remains of this keep have recently been excavated by Mr Harold Sands and Mr Montgomerie, and show it to have been a most remarkable building[4] (see Chapter XII., p. 355)—in all probability one of the few 11th century keeps in England. We may perhaps attribute this distinction to the fact that no less a man than the Conqueror's half-brother, the Count of Mortain, was made the guardian of this important port.

---

[1] Domesday Book mentions that the value of the burgus had greatly risen. It was one of the *burhs* mentioned in the *Burghal Hidage*.

[2] *Pipe Roll*, 1187-1188. William of Jumièges says, "Statim firmissimo vallo castrum condidit, probisque militibus commisit." VII., 34. Wace professes to give the account of an eye-witness, who saw the timber for the castle landed from the ships, and the ditch dug. But Wace was not a contemporary, and as he has made the mistake of making William land at Pevensey instead of Hastings, his evidence is questionable. *Roman de Rou*, p. 293 (Andresen's edition).

[3] The ruins of this keep, until 1908, were buried under so large a mound of earth and rubbish that Mr G. T. Clark mistook it for a motte, and the present writer was equally misled. It ought to be stated, before the date of this keep is finally settled, that the *Gesta Stephani* speaks of this castle as "editissimo aggere sublatum." P. 106.   [4] *Ibid.*

Pevensey is mentioned as a port in the *Close Rolls* of Henry III.'s reign, and was one of the important waterways to the Continent.[1] As has been already noted, the establishment of the castle was followed by the usual rise in the value of the *burgus*.[2] The area of the castle covers 1 acre.

PONTEFRACT, Yorkshire (Fig. 26).—This castle is not spoken of in Domesday by its French name, but there can be no doubt that it is "the Castle of Ilbert" which is twice mentioned and several times alluded to in the *Clamores*, or disputed claims, which are enrolled at the end of the list of lands in Yorkshire belonging to the tenants-in-chief.[3] The existence of Ilbert's castle at Pontefract in the 11th century is made certain by a charter (only an early copy of which is now extant) in the archives of the Duchy of Lancaster, in which William Rufus at his accession regrants to Ilbert de Lacy "the custom of the castelry of his castle, as he had it in the Conqueror's days and in those of the bishop of Bayeux."[4] As Mr Holmes remarks, this carries us back to four years before the compilation of Domesday Book, since Odo, Bishop of Bayeux, whom William had left as regent during his absence in Normandy, was arrested and imprisoned in 1082.[5]

Pontefract is called Kirkby in some of the earlier charters, and this was evidently the English (or rather the Danish) name of the place. It lay within the manor of Tateshall, which is supposed to be the same as Tanshelf, a name still preserved in the neighbourhood

---

[1] *Close Rolls*, i., 631a.   [2] D. B., i., 20b.
[3] D. B., i., 373b.   [4] Cited in Holmes' *History of Pontefract*, p. 62.
[5] Another charter, which is a confirmation by the second Ilbert de Lacy of the ecclesiastical gifts of Ilbert I. and Robert his son, states that the Chapel of St Clement in the castle of Pontefract was founded by Ilbert I. in the reign of William II. *Mon. Ang.*, v., 128.

of, but not exactly at, Pontefract.[1] Tanshelf claims to
be the Taddenescylf mentioned in the *Anglo-Saxon
Chronicle*, where King Edgar received the submission of
the Yorkshire Danes in 947. There is no proof that
the hill at Kirkby was fortified before the Conquest. It
was a steep headland rising out of the plain of the Aire,
and needing only to be scarped by art and to have a
ditch cut across its neck to be almost impregnable. It
lay scarcely a mile east of the Roman road from
Doncaster to Castleford and the north.

It is no part of our task to trace the fortunes of this
famous castle, which was considered in the Middle Ages
to be the key of Yorkshire.[2] In spite of the labels
affixed to the walls we venture to assert with confidence
that none of the masonry now visible belongs to the
days of Ilbert. The structural history of the castle was
probably this : Ilbert de Lacy, one of the greatest of the
Norman tenants-in-chief in Yorkshire,[3] built in this
naturally defensive situation a castle of earth and wood,
like other Norman castles. Whether he found the place
already defended by earthen banks we do not attempt to
decide, but analogy makes it fairly certain that the
motte was his work, and was crowned by a wooden
tower. This motte, which was at least partially scarped
out of the soft sandstone rock, is now disguised by the
remarkable keep which has been built up around it,
consisting at present of two enormous round towers and
the ruins of a third. As a fourth side is vacant, it may

[1] It is not necessary to discuss the meaning of the name Pontefract,
since for whatever reason it was given, it was clearly bestowed by the
Norman settlers.

[2] "Castrum de Pontefracto est quasi clavis in comitatu Ebor." Letter of
Ralph Neville to Henry III., *Fœdera*, i., 429, cited by Holmes, *Pontefract*,
194.

[3] The Conqueror had given him more than 200 manors in Yorkshire.
Yorks. Arch. Journ., xiv., 17.

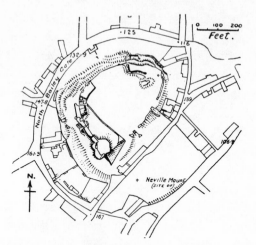

PONTEFRACT, YORKS.

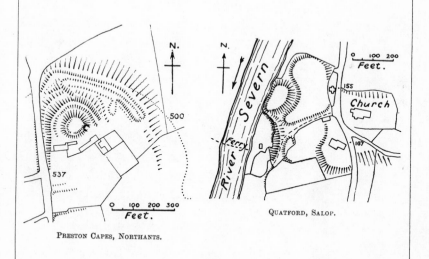

PRESTON CAPES, NORTHANTS.

QUATFORD, SALOP.

FIG. 26.

[To face p. 188.

reasonably be conjectured that there was a fourth roundel.[1] If the plan was a quatrefoil it resembled that of the keep of York, which is now ascertained to belong to the reign of Henry III.; and the very little detail that is left supports the view that Pontefract keep was copied from the royal experiment at York, though it differed from it in that it actually revetted the motte itself. There is no ditch now round the motte, but we venture to think that its inner ditch is indicated by the position of the postern in Piper's Tower, which seems to mark its outlet. It appears to have been partly filled up during the great siege of Pontefract in 1648.[2] The platform which is attached to the motte on the side facing the bailey is probably an addition of the same date, intended for artillery; its retaining wall shows signs of hasty construction. A well chamber and a passage leading both to it and to a postern opening towards the outer ditch appear to have been made in the rocky base of the motte in the 13th century.

The area of the inner and probably original bailey of this castle, including the motte, is 2⅓ acres. The Main Guard, and another bailey covering the approach on the S. side, were probably later additions, bringing up the castle area to 7 acres. The shape of the first bailey is an irregular oval, determined by the hill on which it stands.

The value of the manor of Tateshall had fallen at

[1] Four roundels are shown in the plate given in Fox's *History of Pontefract*, "from a drawing in the possession of the Society of Antiquaries." But the drawing is so incorrect in some points that it can hardly be relied upon for others. There were only three roundels in Leland's time.

[2] Drake's account of the siege says that there was a hollow place between Piper's Tower and the Round Tower all the way down to the well; the gentlemen and soldiers all fell to carrying earth and rubbish, and so filled up the place in a little space. Quoted in Holmes' *Manual of Pontefract Castle*.

the time of the Survey from £20 to £15, an unusual circumstance in the case of a manor which had become the seat of an important castle ; but the number of ploughs had decreased by half, and we may infer that Tateshall had not recovered from the great devastation of Yorkshire in 1068.[1]

PRESTON CAPES, Northants (Fig. 26).—That a castle of the 11th century stood here is only proved by a casual mention in the *Historia Fundationis* of the Cluniac priory of Daventry, which tells us that this priory was first founded by Hugh de Leycestre, Seneschal of Matilda de Senlis, close to his own castle of Preston Capes, about 1090. Want of water and the proximity of the castle proving inconvenient, the priory was removed to Daventry.[2] The work lies about 3 miles from the Watling Street. The castle stands on a spur of high land projecting northwards towards a feeder of the river Nesse, about 3 miles W. of the Watling Street. The works consist of a motte, having a flat top 80 to 90 feet in diameter, and remains of a slight breast-work. This motte is placed on the edge of the plateau, and the ground falls steeply round its northern half. About 16 feet down this slope, a ditch with an outer bank has been dug, embracing half the mound. Lower down, near the foot of the slope, is another and longer ditch and rampart. It is probable that the bailey occupied the flatter ground S.E. of the motte, but the site is occupied by a farm, and no traces are visible.[3]

---

[1] In the *English Historical Review* for July 1904, where this paper first appeared, the writer spoke of *two* mottes at Pontefract, having been led to this view by the great height of the east end of the bailey, where the ruins of John of Gaunt's work are found. This view is now withdrawn, in deference to the conclusions of Mr D. H. Montgomerie, F.S.A., who has carefully examined the spot.

[2] *Mon. Ang.*, iv., 178.

[3] From a description by Mr D. H. Montgomerie.

The value of the manor of Preston Capes had risen from 6s. to 40s. at the time of the Survey. It was held by Nigel of the Count of Mellent.[1]

QUATFORD, Shropshire (Fig. 26).—There can hardly be any doubt that the *nova domus* at Quatford mentioned in the Survey was the new castle built by Roger de Montgomeri, Earl of Shrewsbury. We have already suggested that the *burgus* which also existed there may have been his work, and not that of the Danes.[2] The manor belonged to the church before the Conquest.[3] The oval motte, which still remains, is described as placed on a bold rocky promontory jutting into the Severn ; it is not quite 30 feet high, and about 60 feet by 120 in diameter on top, and has a small bean-shaped bailey of 1 acre. It is near the church, which has Norman remains.[4] Robert Belesme, son of Earl Roger, removed the castle to Bridgenorth, and so the Quatford castle is heard of no more.[5] The manor of Quatford was paying nothing at the date of the Survey.

RAYLEIGH, Essex (Fig. 27).—"In this manor Sweyn has made his castle."[6] Sweyn was the son of Robert Fitz-Wymarc, a half English, half Norman favourite of Edward the Confessor. Robert was Sheriff of Essex under Edward and William, and Sweyn appears to have succeeded his father in this office.[7] Sweyn built his castle on land which had not belonged to his father, so Rayleigh cannot be the "Robert's Castle" of the *Anglo-*

---

[1] D. B., i., 224.   [2] See Chapter IV.

[3] Domesday Book says : "Ipse comes (Roger) tenet Ardinton. Sancta Milburga tenuit T. R. E. Ibi molinum et nova domus et burgus Quatford dictus, nil reddentes." I., 254.

[4] G. T. Clark, in *Arch. Cambrensis*, 1874, p. 264.

[5] *Ord. Vit.*, iv., 32.

[6] "In hoc manerio fecit Suenus suum castellum." D. B., ii., 33b.

[7] Freeman, *N. C.*, ii., 329, and iv., Appendix H.

Saxon Chronicle, to which some of the Norman adventurers fled on the triumph of Earl Godwin.[1] There is a fine motte at Rayleigh, and a semicircular bailey attached ; the ditch round the whole is still well marked. There is not a vestige of masonry on the surface, but some excavations made in 1910 revealed stone foundations. The inner bailey covers ¾ of an acre. The value of the manor had risen since the Conquest, but it was only a small one, with no villages in its soke.

RICHARD'S CASTLE, Herefordshire (Fig. 27).—There can be little doubt that this is the castle referred to in Domesday Book under the name of Avreton, as it is not far from Overton, on the northern border of Hereford.[2] Richard's Castle is almost certainly the castle of Richard, son of Scrob, one of the Normans to whom Edward the Confessor had granted large estates, and who probably fortified himself on this site. At the time of the Survey Richard was dead, and the castle was held by his son Osbern, and it is noted that he pays 10s., but the castle is worth 20s. to him. Its value was the same as in King Edward's time, a fact worth noting, as it coincides with the assumption that this was a pre-Conquest castle. There is a high and steep motte at Richard's Castle, and a small half-moon shaped bailey.[3] There are remains of a stone wing wall running down the motte, and on the top there is a straight piece of masonry which must be part of a tower keep. The area of the inner bailey is ⅔ of an acre. Avreton was

[1] Mr Round has suggested that this castle was at Canfield in Essex, where there is a motte and bailey.

[2] "Isdem Osbernus habet 23 homines in castello Avreton et reddit 10 solidos. Valet ei castellum hoc 20 solidos." D. B., i., 186b.

[3] Mr Clark's plan is strangely incorrect, as he altogether omits the bailey. Compare the plan in Mr Round's Castles of the Conquest, *Archæologia,* vol. lviii., and Mr Montgomerie's plan here, Fig. 27.

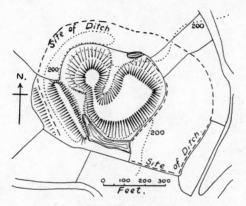

Site of Ditch

200

200

200

Site of Ditch

N.

0 100 200 300
Feet.

RAYLEIGH, ESSEX.

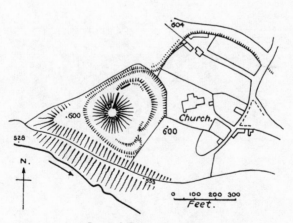

604

.600

Church.

528

600

553

N.

0 100 200 300
Feet.

RICHARD'S CASTLE, HEREFORD.

FIG. 27.

[To face p. 192.

not the centre of a soke, but appears to have lain in the manor of Ludeford.

RICHMOND, Yorks (Fig. 28).—As in the case of Pontefract, this other great Yorkshire castle is not mentioned by name in Domesday Book, nor is there any allusion to it except a casual mention in the *Recapitulation* that Earl Alan has 199 manors in his castelry, and that besides the castelry he has 43 manors.[1] The castle must have been built at the date of the Survey, which was completed only a year before William I.'s death ; for during William's lifetime Earl Alan, the first holder of the fief, gave *the chapel in the castle of Richmond* to the abbey of St Mary at York, which he had founded.[2] The name, of course, is French, and it seems impossible now to discover what English manor-name it has displaced.[3] It is certainly a case in which the Norman castle was not placed in the seat of the former Saxon proprietor, but in the site which seemed most defensible to the Norman lord. The lands of Earl Alan in the wapentake of Gilling had belonged to the Saxon Earl Edwin, and thus cannot have fallen to Alan's share before Edwin's death in 1071. The *Genealogia* published by Dodsworth (from an MS. compiled in the reign of Edward III.), says that Earl Alan first built Richmond Castle near his chief manor of Gilling, to defend his people against the attacks of

[1] "Comes Alanus habet in sua castellata 199 maneria. . . . Præter castellariam habet 43 maneria." D. B., i., 381a, 2.

[2] This is stated in a charter of Henry II., which carefully recapitulates the gifts of the different benefactors to St Mary's. *Mon. Ang.*, iii., 548. It is curious that the charter of William II., the first part of which is an inspeximus of a charter of William I., does not mention this chapel in the castle.

[3] Mr Skaife, the editor of the *Yorkshire Domesday*, thinks that it was at Hinderlag, but gives no reasons. Hinderlag, at the time of the Survey, was in the hands of an under-tenant. *Yorks. Arch. Journ.*, lii., 527, 530.

the disinherited English and Danes.[1]   The passage has been enlarged by Camden, who says that Alan "thought himself not safe enough in Gilling"; and this has been interpreted to mean that Alan originally built his castle at Gilling, and afterwards removed it to Richmond; but the original words have no such meaning.[2]

Richmond Castle differs from most of the castles mentioned in Domesday in that it has no motte.   The ground plan indeed was very like that of a motte-and-bailey castle, in that old maps show a small roundish enclosure at the apex of the large triangular bailey.[3] But a recent examination of the keep by Messrs Hope and Brakespear has confirmed the theory first enunciated by Mr Loftus Brock,[4] that the keep is built over the original gateway of the castle, and that the lower stage of its front wall is the ancient wall of the castle.   The small ward indicated in the old maps is therefore most likely a barbican, of later date than the 12th century keep, which is probably rightly attributed by the *Genealogia* cited above to Earl Conan, who reigned from 1148-1171.[5]   Some entries in the *Pipe Rolls* make it almost certain that it was finished by Henry II.,

[1] "Hic Alanus primo incepit facere castrum et munitionem juxta manerium suum capitale de Gilling, pro tuitione suorum contra infestationes Anglorum tunc ubique exhæredatorum, similiter et Danorum, et nominavit dictum castrum Richmond suo ydiomate Gallico, quod sonat Latine divitem montem, in editiori et fortiori loco sui territorii situatum." *Mon. Ang.*, v., 574.

[2] There are no remains of fortification at Gilling, but about a mile and a half away there used to be an oval earthwork, now levelled, called Castle Hill, of which a plan is given in M'Laughlan's paper, *Arch. Journ.*, vol. vi. It had no motte.   Mr Clark says, "The mound at Gilling has not long been levelled." *M. M. A.*, i., 23.   It probably never existed except in his imagination.

[3] See Clarkson's *History of Richmond.*

[4] *Journal of Brit. Arch. Ass.*, lxiii., 179.

[5] These are the dates given in Morice's *Bretagne.*

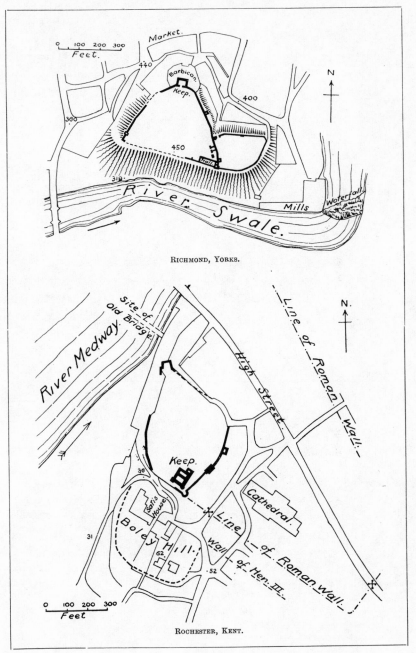

RICHMOND, YORKS.

ROCHESTER, KENT.

FIG. 28.

[To face p. 194.

who kept the castle in his own hands for some time after the death of Conan.[1] There are some indications at Richmond that the first castle was of stone and not of earth and wood. The walls do not stand on earthen banks; the Norman curtain can still be traced on two sides of the castle, and on the west side it seems of early construction, containing a great deal of herringbone work, and might possibly be the work of Earl Alan.

The whole area of the castle is $2\frac{1}{2}$ acres, including the annexe known as the Cockpit. This was certainly enclosed during the Norman period, as it has a Norman gateway in its wall.

As we do not know the name of the site of Richmond before the Conquest, and as the name of Richmond is not mentioned in Domesday Book, we cannot tell whether the value of the manor had risen or fallen. But no part of Yorkshire was more flourishing at the time of the Survey than this wapentake of Gilling, which belonged to Earl Alan; in no district, except in the immediate neighbourhood of York, are there so many places where the value has risen. Yet the greater part of it was let out to under-tenants.

ROCHESTER, Kent (Fig. 28).—Under the heading of Aylsford, Kent, the Survey tells us that "the bishop of Rochester holds as much of this land as is worth 17s. 4d. *in exchange for the land in which the castle sits.*"[2] Rochester was a Roman *castrum*, and portions of its Roman wall have recently been found.[3] The fact

---

[1] Henry spent 51*l.* 11*s.* 3*d.* in 1171 on "operationes domorum et turris," and 30*l.* 6*s.* in 1174 on "operationes castelli et domorum."

[2] "Episcopus de Rouecestre, pro excambio terræ in qua castellum sedet, tantum de hac terra tenet quod 17 sol. et 4 den. valet." D. B., i., 2b.

[3] See Mr George Payne's paper on *Roman Rochester,* in *Arch. Cantiana,* vol. xxi. Mr Hope tells me that parts of all the four sides are left.

that various old charters speak of the *castellum* of Rochester has led some authorities to believe that there was a castle there in Saxon times, but the context of these charters shows plainly that the words *castellum Roffense* were equivalent to *castrum Roffense* or *Hrofesceastre*.[1]   Otherwise there is not a particle of evidence for the existence of a castle at Rochester in pre-Norman times, and the passage in Domesday quoted above shows that William's castle was a new erection, built on land obtained by exchange from the church.

Outside the line of the Roman wall, to the south of the city, and west of the south gate, there is a district called Boley or Bullie Hill, which at one time was included in the fortifications of the present castle.   It is a continuation of the ridge on which that castle stands, and has been separated from it by a ditch. This ditch once entirely surrounded it, and though it was partly filled up in the 18th century its line can still be traced.   The area enclosed by this ditch was about 3 acres; the form appears to have been oblong.   In the grounds of Satis House, one of the villas which have been built on this site, there stills remains a conical artificial mound, much reduced in size, as it has been converted into a pleasure-ground with winding walks, but the retaining walls of these walks are composed of old materials; and towards the riverside there are still vestiges of an ancient wall.[2]   We venture to think that this Boley Hill and its motte formed the original site

[1] Thus Egbert of Kent, in 765, gives "terram intra castelli mœnia supra-nominati, id est Hrofescestri, unum viculum cum duobus jugeribus," *Kemble*, i., 138 ; and Offa speaks of the "episcopum castelli quod nominatur Hrofescester," Earle, *Land Charters*, p. 60.

[2] See an extremely valuable paper on *Mediæval Rochester* by the Rev. Greville M. Livett, *Arch. Cantiana*, vol. xxi.

of the (probably) wooden castle of William the Conqueror. Its nature, position, and size correspond to what we have already observed as characteristic of the first castles of the Conquest. It stands on land which originally belonged to the church of St Andrew, as Domesday Book tells us William's castle did.[1] The very name may be interpreted in favour of this theory.[2] And that there was no Roman or Saxon fortification on the spot is proved by excavations, which have shown that both a Roman and a Saxon cemetery occupied portions of the area.[3]

It is well known that between the years 1087 and 1089 the celebrated architect, Gundulf, Bishop of Rochester, built a new *stone* castle for William Rufus, "in the best part of the city of Rochester."[4] This castle, of course, was on the same site as the present one, though the splendid keep was not built till the next

[1] See the charter of Cœnulf, King of Mercia, giving to Bishop Beornmod three ploughlands on the southern shore of the city of Rochester, from the highway on the east to the Medway on the west. *Textus Roffensis*, p. 96.

[2] The name Boley may possibly represent the Norman-French *Beaulieu*, a favourite Norman name for a castle or residence. Professor Hales suggested that Boley Hill was derived from Bailey Hill (cited in Mr Gomme's paper on Boley Hill, *Arch. Cantiana*, vol. xvii.). The oldest form of the name is Bullie Hill, as in Edward IV.'s charter, cited below, p. 200.

[3] Roman urns and lachrymatories were found in the Boley Hill when it was partially levelled in the 18th century to fill up the castle ditch. *History of Rochester*, p. 281. At the part now called Watt's Avenue, Mr George Payne found "the fag-end of an Anglo-Saxon cemetery." *Arch. Cantiana*, vol. xxi.

[4] "In pulchriore parte civitatis Hrouecestre." *Textus Roffensis*, p. 145. Mr Freeman and others have noticed that the special mention of a *stone* castle makes it probable that the first castle was of wood. Mr Round remarks that the building of Rochester Castle is fixed, by the conjunction of William II. and Lanfranc in its history, to some date between September 1087 and March 1089. *Geoffrey de Mandeville*, p. 339. Probably, therefore, it was this new castle which Bishop Odo held against Rufus in 1088. Ordericus says that "cum quingentis militibus intra Rofensem urbem se conclusit." P. 272.

reign.[1] But if what we have maintained above be correct the castle of Gundulf was built on a different site from that of the castle of William. Nor are we without evidence in support of this. What remains of the original Norman wall of Gundulf's castle (and enough remains to show that the circuit was complete in Norman times) does not stand on earthen banks; and this, though not a proof, is a strong suggestion that there was no earthen bank belonging to some previous castle when Gundulf began his building.[2] But further, Mr Livett has shown in his paper on *Mediæval Rochester*[3] that in order to form a level plateau for the court of the castle the ground had to be artificially made up on the north and east sides, and in these places the wall rests on a foundation of gravel, which has been forcibly rammed to make it solid, and which goes through the artificial soil to the natural chalk below. Now what can this rammed gravel mean but an expedient to avoid the danger of building in stone on freshly heaped soil? Had the artificial platform been in existence ever since the Conquest, it would have been solid enough to build upon without this expense. It is therefore at least

[1] It is now attributed to Archbishop William of Corbeuil, to whom Henry I. gave the custody of the castle in the twenty-seventh year of his reign, with permission to make within it a defence or keep, such as he might please. *Continuator of Florence*, 1126. Gervase of Canterbury also says "idem episcopus turrim egregiam ædificavit." Both passages are cited by Hartshorne, *Arch. Journ.*, xx., 211. Gundulf's castle cost 60*l.* and can scarcely have been more than an enclosing wall with perhaps one mural tower. See Mr Round, *Geoffrey de Mandeville*, 340, and Mr Livett's paper, cited above.

[2] Two common friends of Rufus and Gundulf advised the king that in return for the grant of the manor of Hedenham and the remission of certain moneys, "episcopus Gundulfus, quia in opere cæmentario plurimum sciens et efficax erat, castrum sibi Hrofense *lapideum* de suo construeret." *Textus Roffensis*, p. 146. There was therefore an exchange of land in this affair also.

[3] *Arch. Cantiana*, vol. xxi.

probable that Bishop Gundulf's castle was built on an entirely new site.

It seems also to be clear that the Boley Hill was included as an outwork in Bishop Gundulf's plan, for the castle ditch is cut through the Roman wall near the south gate of the city.[1] Mr Livett remarks that King John appears to have used the hill as a point of vantage when he attacked the city in 1215, and he thinks this was probably the reason why Henry III.'s engineers enclosed it with a stone wall when they restored the walls of the city.[2] Henry III.'s wall has been traced all round the city, and at the second south gate it turns at right angles, or nearly so, so as to enclose Boley Hill.[3] It is probable, as Mr Livett suggests, that the drawbridge and *bretasche*, or wooden tower, ordered in 1226 for the southern side of Rochester Castle,[4] were intended to connect the Boley Hill court with the main castle. In 1722 the owner of the castle (which had then fallen into private hands) conveyed to one Philip Brooke, "that part of the castle ditch and ground, as it then lay unenclosed, on Bully Hill, being the whole breadth of the hill and ditch without the walls of the castle, extending from thence to the river Medway."[5]

The general opinion about the Boley Hill is that

[1] *Arch. Cantiana*, vol. xxi., p. 49.

[2] There are several entries in the *Close Rolls* relating to this wall of Henry III. in the year 1225.

[3] Mr Beale Poste says that this ancient wall was met with some years since in digging the foundations of the Rev. Mr Conway's house, standing parallel to the present brick walls and about 2 feet within them. "Ancient Rochester as a Roman Station," *Arch. Cantiana*, ii., 71. The Continuator of Gervase of Canterbury tells us (ii., 235) that at the siege of Rochester in 1265, Simon de Montfort captured the outer castle up to the keep (forinsecum castellum usque ad turrim), and Mr Livett thinks this outer castle must have been the Boley Hill.

[4] *Close Rolls*, ii., 98b.   [5] Hasted's *Kent*, iv., 163.

it is a Danish earthwork, thrown up by the Danes when they besieged the city in 885. But if our contention in Chapter IV. is just, the Danish fortifications were not mottes, nor anything like them ; and (as has already been pointed out) the *Anglo-Saxon Chronicle* indicates the nature of the fortress in this case by its expression, "they made a work around themselves";[1] that is, it was a circumvallation. Moreover, at Rochester the Danes would have had to pass under the bridge (which is known to have existed both in Roman and Saxon times) in order to get to the Boley Hill; and even if their ships were small enough to do this they would hardly have been so foolish as to leave a bridge in their possible line of retreat. It is therefore far more likely that their fastness was somewhere to the north or east of the city.[2]

It is a noteworthy fact that up till very recently the Boley Hill had a special jurisdiction of its own, under an officer called the Baron of the Bully, appointed by the Recorder of the city. This appears to date from a charter of Edward IV. in 1460, which confirms the former liberties of the citizens of Rochester, and ordains that they should keep two courts' leet and a court of pie-powder annually on the Bullie Hill. The anonymous historian of Rochester remarks that it was thought that the baron represented the first officer under the governor of the castle before the court leet was instituted, to whose care the security of the Bullie Hill was entrusted.[3] This is probably much nearer the truth than the theory which would assign such thoroughly feudal courts as those of court leet and

---

[1] "Ymb sætan tha ceastre and worhton other fæsten ymb hie selfe." See *ante*, p. 49, *note* 2.

[2] Mr Hope suggests the east side, as the north was a marsh.

[3] *History of Rochester* (published by Fisher, 1772), p. 285.

pie-powder to an imaginary community of Danes residing on the Boley Hill.   When we compare the case
of the Boley Hill with the somewhat similar cases
of Chester and Norwich castles we shall see that what
took place in Edward IV.'s reign was probably this :
the separate jurisdiction which had once belonged
to an abandoned castle site was transferred to the
citizens of Rochester, but with the usual conservatism of
mediæval legislation, it was not absorbed in the jurisdiction of the city.

The value of Rochester at the time of the Survey
had risen from 100s. to 20l.[1]   The increase of trade,
arising from the security of traffic which was provided
by William's castles on this important route, no doubt
accounts in great measure for this remarkable rise in
value.

ROCKINGHAM, Northants (Fig. 29).—Here, also,
the castle was clearly new in William's reign, as the
manor was uninhabited (wasta) until a castle was built
there by his orders, in consequence of which the manor
produced a small revenue at the time of the Survey.[2]
The motte, now in great part destroyed, was a large
one, being about 80 feet in diameter at the top ;
attached to it is a bailey of irregular but rectilateral
shape (determined by the ground) covering about 3
acres.   There is another large bailey to the S.
covering 4 acres, formed by cutting a ditch across the
spur of the hill on which the castle stands, which is
probably later.   The first castle would undoubtedly be
of wood, and it is probable that King John was the
builder of the "exceeding fair and strong" keep which

---

[1] D. B., i., 56.
[2] "Wasta erat quando Rex W. iussit ibi castellum fieri.   Modo valet
36 solidos."   D. B., i., 220.

stood on the motte in Leland's time,[1] as there is an entry in the *Pipe Roll* of the thirteenth year of his reign for 126*l*. 18*s*. 6*d*. for the work of the new tower.[2] This keep, if Mr Clark is correct, was polygonal, with a timber stockade surrounding it.

Rockingham was only a small manor of one hide in Saxon times, though its Saxon owner had sac and soke. It stands in a forest district, not near any of the great ancient lines of road, and was probably built for a hunting seat.

The value of the manor had risen at the time of the Survey.[3]

During the Civil War, the motte of Rockingham was fortified in an elaborate manner by the Parliamentarians, part of the defences being two wooden stockades :[4] an interesting instance of the use both of mottes and of wooden fortifications in comparatively modern warfare. Only the north and west sides of this mount now remain.

OLD SARUM, Wilts (Fig. 30).—Sir Richard Colt Hoare printed in his *Ancient Wiltshire* a document purporting to be an order from Alfred, "King of the English," to Leofric, "Earl of Wiltunshire," to maintain the castle of Sarum, and add another ditch to it.[5] The phraseology of the document suggests some doubts of its genuineness, and though there would be nothing

---

[1] "I markid that there is stronge Tower in the Area of the Castelle, and from it over the Dungeon Dike is a drawbridge to the Dungeon Toure." *Itin.*, i., 14.

[2] " In operatione nove turris et nove camere in cast. 126*l*. 18*s*. 6*d*."

[3] D. B., i., 120.

[4] See the plan reproduced in Wise's *Rockingham Castle and the Watsons*, p. 66.

[5] Vol. i., p. 224 : cited by Mr Irving in his valuable paper on Old Sarum in *Arch. Journ.*, xv., 1859. Sir Richard made a vague reference to an MS. in the Cottonian and Bodleian libraries, for which Mr Irving says he has searched in vain.

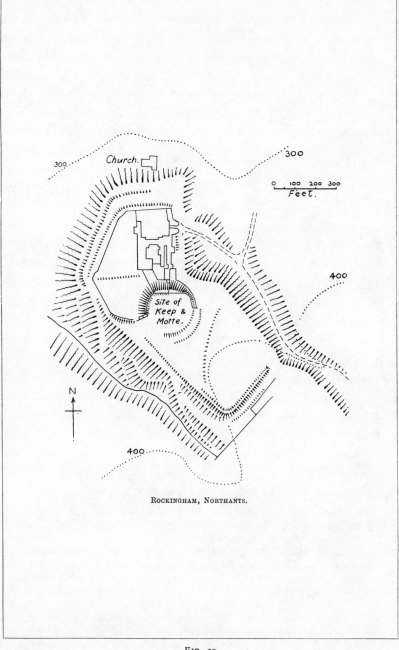

300

Church.

300

0   100 200 300
Feet.

400

Site of
Keep &
Motte.

N

400

ROCKINGHAM, NORTHANTS.

Fig. 29.

[To face p. 202.

improbable in the theory that Alfred reared the outer
bank of the fortress, recent excavations have shown that
the place was occupied by the Romans, and therefore
make it certain that its origin was very much earlier than
Alfred's time. Moreover, the convergence of several
Roman roads at this spot suggests the probability of a
Roman station,[1] while the form of the enclosure renders
an earlier origin likely. Domesday Book does not speak
of Salisbury as a *burgus*, and when the *burgus* of Old
Sarum is mentioned in later documents it appears to
refer to a district lying at the foot of the Castle Hill, and
formerly enclosed with a wall.[2] Nor is it one of the
boroughs of the *Burghal Hidage*. But that Sarum was
an important place in Saxon times is clear from the fact
that there was a mint there; and there is evidence of
the existence of at least four Saxon churches, as well as
a hospital for lepers.[3]

For more exact knowledge as to the history of this
ancient fortress we must wait till the excavations now
going on are finished, but in the meanwhile it seems
probable that the theory adopted by General Pitt-Rivers
is correct. He regarded Old Sarum as a British earthwork, with an inner castle and outer barbicans added by
the Normans. After building this castle in the midst of
it the Normans appear to have considered the outer and

---

[1] General Pitt-Rivers in his Address to the Salisbury meeting of the
Archæological Institute in 1887, says that traces of these roads may still
be seen. He adds that Old Sarum does not resemble the generality of ancient
British fortifications, in that the rampart is of the same height all round,
instead of being lower where the ground is steeper; this led him to think
that the original fortress had been modernised in later times. Sir Richard
Colt Hoare noticed that the ramparts of Sarum were twice as high as those
of the fine prehistoric camps with which he was acquainted. *Ancient
Wiltshire*, p. 226.

[2] Benson and Hatcher's *Old and New Sarum*, p. 604.

[3] *Cf.* Benson and Hatcher, 63, with *Beauties of England and Wales*, xv.,
78.

larger fortification too valuable to be given up to the public, but retained it under the government of the castellan, and treated it as part of the castle.

There is no mention of the castle of Salisbury in Domesday Book, but the bishop is named as the owner of the manor.[1] The episcopal see of Sherborne was transferred to Sarum in 1076 by Bishop Hermann, in accordance with the policy adopted by William I. that episcopal sees should be removed from villages to towns:[2] a measure which in itself is a testimony to the importance of Salisbury at that time. The first mention of the castle is in the charter of Bishop Osmund, 1091.[3] The bishop was allowed to lay the foundations of his new cathedral within the ancient fortress. As might be expected, friction soon arose between the castellans and the ecclesiastics; the castellans claimed the custody of the gates, and sometimes barred the canons, whose houses seem to have been outside the fortress, from access to the church. These quarrels were ended eventually by the removal of the cathedral to the new town of Salisbury at the foot of the hill.

The position of the motte of Old Sarum is exceptional, as it stands in the centre of the outer fortress. This must be owing to the position of the ancient vallum, encircling the summit of one of those round, gradually sloping hills so common in the chalk ranges, which made it necessary to place the motte in the centre, because it was the highest part of the ground. The

---

[1] D. B., i., 66. "Idem episcopus tenet Sarisberie." Part of the land which had been held under the bishop was now held by Edward the Sheriff, the ancestor of the earls of Salisbury. This in itself is a proof that the castle was new. See Freeman, *N. C.*, iv., 797.

[2] This policy had been dictated by an œcumenical council.

[3] He gives to the canons of the church two hides in the manor, "et ante portam castelli Seriberiensis terram ex utraque parte viæ in ortorum domorumque canonicorum necessitate." *M. A.*, vi., 1294.

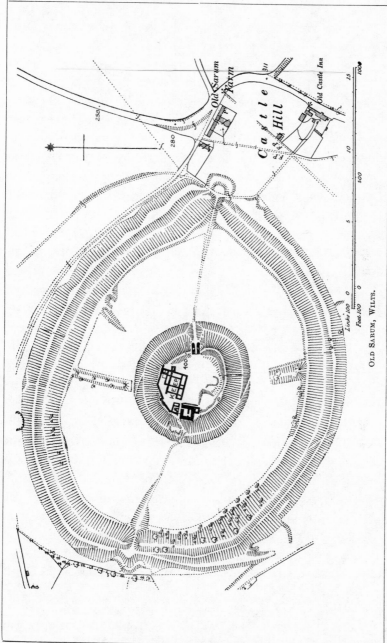

OLD SARUM, WILTS.

FIG. 30.

Old Sarum
Farm

Castle
Hill

Old Castle Inn

KEEP

present excavations have shown that it is in part artificial. But though the citadel was thus exceptionally placed, the principle that communication with the outside must be maintained was carried out; the motte had its own bailey, reaching to the outer vallum. The remains of three cross banks still exist, two of which must have enclosed the *magnum ballium* which is spoken of in the *Pipe Rolls* of Henry II. Probably this bailey occupied the south-eastern third of the circle, which included the main gateway and the road to the citadel. In the ditch on the north side of this enclosure, an arched passage, apparently of Norman construction, was found in 1795; it was doubtless a postern or sallyport.[1] The main entrance is defended by a separate mount with its own ditch, which is conjectured to be of later date than the vallum itself. The area of the top of the motte is about $1\frac{3}{4}$ acres, a larger size than usual, but not larger than that of several other important castles.[2] In Leland's time there was "much notable ruinous building" still remaining of this fortress, and the excavations have already revealed the lower portions of some splendid walls and gateways, and the basement of a late Norman keep which presents some unusual features.[3] The earthworks, however, bear witness to a former wooden stockade both to the citadel and the outer enclosure. The top of the motte is still surrounded by high earthen banks.

As that great building bishop, Roger of Salisbury

[1] *Gentleman's Magazine*, 1795.

[2] The area of the outer camp is $29\frac{1}{2}$ acres.

[3] It is unlikely that this is the *turris* mentioned in the solitary *Pipe Roll* of Henry I. "In unum ostium faciendum ad cellarium turris Sarum, 20s." This entry is of great interest, as entrances from the outside to the basement of keeps were exceptional in the 12th century; but the basement entrance of Colchester keep has every appearance of having been added by Henry I.

(1099-1139), is said to have environed the castle with a new wall,[1] it would seem likely that he was the first to transform the castle from wood tô stone. But in Henry II.'s reign, we find an entry in the *Pipe Rolls* for materials for enclosing the great bailey. An order for the destruction of the castle had been issued by Stephen,[2] but it is doubtful whether it was carried out. The sums spent by Henry II. on the castle do not amount to more than £266, 12s. 5d., but the work recently excavated which appears to be of his date is very extensive indeed.

The mention of a small wooden tower in Richard I.'s reign shows that some parts of the defences were still of wood at that date.[3] Timber and rods for *hoarding* the castle, that is, for the wooden machicolations placed at the tops of towers and walls, were ordered at the end of John's reign.[4]

It is not known when the castle was abandoned, but the list of castellans ceases in the reign of Henry VI., when it was granted to the Stourton family.[5] Though the earls of Salisbury were generally the custodians of Sarum Castle, except in the time of Bishop Roger, it was always considered a royal castle, while the manor belonged to the bishop.[6] It is remarked in the *Hundred Rolls* of Henry III., that no one holds fiefs for ward in

---

[1] William of Malmesbury, *Hist. Nov.*, ii., 91.

[2] In 1152 ; the writ is given by Benson and Hatcher, p. 32.

[3] "In operatione unius Bretesche in eodem Castro 50s." *Pipe Rolls*, 1193-4.

[4] "Virgam et mairemium ad hordiandum castrum." *Close Rolls*, i., 198b (1215).

[5] Benson and Hatcher, p. 704.

[6] "Dicunt quod castrum cum burgo Veteris Sarum et dominicus burgus domini Regis pertinent ad coronam cum advocatione cujusdam ecclesiæ quæ modo vacat." *Hundred Rolls*, Edward I., cited by Benson and Hatcher, p. 802.

this castle, and that nothing belonged to the castle outside the gate.[1]

The value of the manor of Salisbury appears to have risen very greatly since the Conquest.[2]

SHREWSBURY (Fig. 31).—The passage in Domesday Book relating to this town has been called by Mr Round one of the most important in the Survey, and it is of special importance for our present purpose. "The English burghers of Shrewsbury say that it is very grievous to them that they have to pay all the geld which they paid in King Edward's time, although the castle of the earl occupies [the site of] 51 houses, and another 50 are uninhabited."[3] It is incomprehensible how in the face of such a clear statement as this, that the new castle occupied the site of fifty-one houses, anyone should be found gravely to maintain that the motte at Shrewsbury was an English work; for if the motte stood there before, what was the clearance of houses made for? The only answer could be to enlarge the bailey. But this is exactly what the Norman would not wish to do; he would want only a small area for the small force at his disposal for defence. Shrewsbury was certainly a borough (that is, a fortified town) in Anglo-Saxon times; probably it was one of the towns fortified by Ethelfleda, though it is not mentioned by name in the list of those towns furnished by the *Anglo-Saxon Chronicle*.[4] Its

---

[1] Cited by Benson and Hatcher, p. 802.

[2] D. B., 66a, 1. The value T. R. E. is not, however, very distinctly stated.

[3] "Dicunt Angligenses burgenses de Sciropesberie multum grave sibi esse quod ipsi reddunt totum geldum sicut reddebant T. R. E. quamvis castellum comitis occupaverit 51 masuras et aliæ 50 masuræ sunt wastæ." D. B., i., 252.

[4] Some writers, such as Mr Kerslake and Mr C. S. Taylor, have supposed Sceargate to mean Shrewsbury.

ancient walls were certainly only of earth and wood, for a writ of 1231 says that the old stockade and the old bretasche of the old ditch of the town of Shrewsbury are to be granted to the burghers for strengthening the new ditch.[1]

The castle of Shrewsbury was built on the neck of the peninsula on which the town stands, and on the line of the town walls. The oval motte, which still remains, stands, as usual, on the line of the castle banks, and slopes steeply down to the Severn on one side. Its nearness to the river made it liable to damage by floods. Thus we find Henry II. spending 5*l.* on the repair of the motte,[2] and in Edward I.'s reign the abbot's mill is accused of having caused damage to the extent of 60 marks to the motte. But the men of the hundred exonerate the mill, and from another passage the blame appears to lie on the fall of a great wooden tower.[3] This can hardly have been other than the wooden keep on the motte, and thus we learn the interesting fact that as late as Edward I.'s reign the castle of Shrewsbury

---

[1] Mandatum est vicecomiti Salopie quod veterem palum et veterem bretaschiam de vetere fossato ville Salopie faciat habere probos homines ville Salopie ad novum fossatum ejusdem ville, quod fieri fecerant, efforciandum et emendendum. *Close Rolls*, 1231, p. 508. The honest men of the city are also to have "palum et closturam" from the king's wood of Lichewood "ad hirucones circa villam Salopie faciendas ad ipsam villam claudendam." *Ibid.* *Hirucones* are the same as *heritones* or *hericias*, a defence of stakes on the counterscarp of the ditch.

[2] "In op. castelli de Salop^be in mota 5*l.*" *Pipe Rolls*, 19 Henry II., p. 108.

[3] "Dampnum mote castri Salopp' ad valenciam 60 marcarum, sed non recolligunt totum evenisse propter molendinum abbatis Salopp', quia 30 annis elapsis mota castri fuit fere deteriorata sicut nunc est." *Hundred Rolls*, ii., 80. "Dicunt quod unus magnus turris ligneus (*sic*) qui ædificatur in castro Salopp' corruit in terram tempore domini Uriani de S. Petro tunc vicecomitis, et meremium ejus turris tempore suo et temporibus aliorum vicecomitum postea ita consumitur et destruitur quod nihil de illo remansit, in magnum damnum domini Regis et deteriorationem eiusdem castri." *Ibid.*, p. 105.

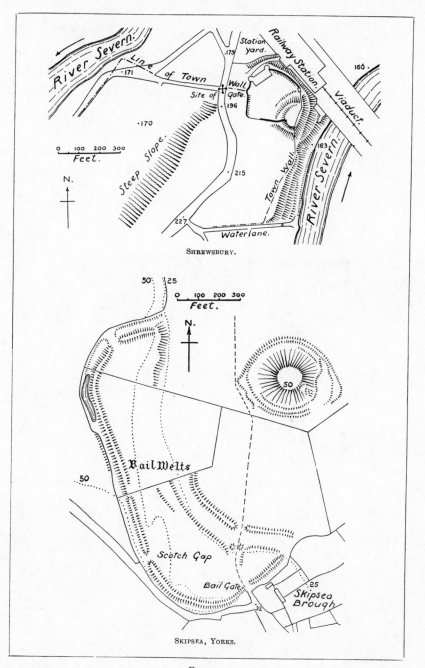

SHREWSBURY.

SKIPSEA, YORKS.

FIG. 31.

[*To face p.* 208.

had only a wooden keep. The present tower on the motte is the work of Telford.

The bailey of Shrewsbury Castle is roughly semi-lunar and covers nearly an acre. The walls stand on banks, which shows that the first wall was of timber. The Norman entrance arch seems to render it probable that it was in Henry II.'s reign that stone walls were first substituted for a wooden stockade, and the *Pipe Rolls* contain several entries of sums spent by Henry on this castle.[1] But the first mention of stone in connection with the castle is in the reign of Henry III.[2] In the reign of Edward I., a *jarola* or wooden wall, which had been raised above the outer ditch in the time of the Barons' War, was replaced by a stone wall.[3] This perhaps refers to the second bailey, now destroyed, which lay to the south of the castle. In the time of Charles I. the castle still had a wooden palisade on the counterscarp of the ditch.[4] The two large drum towers on the walls, and the building between them, now converted into a modern house, belong to a much later period than the walls. The area of the present castle, including the motte, is $\frac{4}{5}$ of an acre.

The value of the town of Shrewsbury had risen since the Conquest.

SKIPSEA, Yorks (Fig. 31).—There is no mention of this castle in Domesday Book, but the chronicle of Meaux Abbey tells us that it was built by Drogo de

[1] *Pipe Rolls*, 11 Henry II., p. 89; 12 Henry II., p. 59; 14 Henry II., p. 93; 15 Henry II., p. 108; 20 Henry II., p. 108.

[2] Payment to those who dig stone for the castle of Shrewsbury, *Close Rolls*, i., 622b. This is in 1224. There is also a payment of 50*l.* for works at the castle in 1223. *Ibid.*, 533b.

[3] *Hundred Rolls*, ii., 80. A *jarola* or garuillum is a stockade; apparently derived from a Gallic word for *oak*, and may thus correspond to an oak paling. See Ducange.

[4] Owen and Blakeway's *History of Shrewsbury*, i., 450.

Bevrère in the reign of William I.[1] This chronicle is
not indeed contemporary, but its most recent editor
regards it as based on some much earlier document.
It was the key of the great manor of Holderness, which
the Conqueror had given to Drogo, but which Drogo
forfeited by murdering his wife, probably on this very
site. The situation of Skipsea is remarkable, but the
original plan of Kenilworth Castle presented a close
parallel to it. The motte, which is 46 feet high, and
$\frac{1}{5}$ of an acre in space on top, is separated from
the bailey by a level space, which was formerly the
Mere of Skipsea, mentioned in documents of the 13th
century, which reckon the take of eels in this mere as a
source of revenue.[2] The motte thus formed an island in
the mere, but as an additional defence—perhaps when
the mere began to get shallow—it was surrounded by a
bank and ditch of its own. No masonry is to be seen
on the motte now, except a portion of a wing wall going
down it. It is connected with its bailey on the other
side of the mere by a causeway which still exists. This
bailey is of very unusual size, covering $8\frac{1}{4}$ acres; its
banks still retain the name of the Baile Welts, and
one of the entrances is called the Baile Gate.
Skipsea Brough, which no doubt represents the former
burgus of Skipsea, is outside this enclosure, and has
no defences of its own remaining. A mandate of
Henry III. in 1221, ordered the complete destruction
of this castle,[3] and it was no doubt after this
that the earls of Albemarle, who had succeeded
to Drogo's estates, removed their *caput baroniæ* to
Burstwick.[4]

[1] *Chronicon de Melsa*, R. S. See Preface, p. lxxii.
[2] *Yorks Inquisitions* (Yorks Rec. Ser.), i., 83.
[3] *Rot. Lit. Claus.*, i., 474b.
[4] Poulson's *History of Holderness*, i., 457.

The value of the manor of Cleeton, in which Skipsea lies, had fallen at Domesday.[1]

STAFFORD (Fig. 32).—The *Anglo-Saxon Chronicle* says that Ethelfleda of Mercia built the *burh* of Stafford; and consequently we find that both in King Edward and King William's time Stafford was a burgus, or fortified town. Florence of Worcester, who is considered to have used a superior copy of the *Chronicle* as the foundation of his work, says that Ethelfleda built an *arx* on the north bank of the Sowe in 914. *Arx*, in our earlier chronicles, is often only a bombastic expression for a walled town, as, for example, when Ethelwerd says that Ethelfleda's body was buried in St Peter's porch in the *arx* of Gloucester.[2] But the statement led many later writers, such as Camden, to imagine that Ethelfleda built a *tower* in the town of Stafford; and these imaginings have created such a tangled skein of mistake that we must bespeak our readers' patience while we attempt to unravel it.

Domesday Book only mentions Stafford Castle under the manor of Chebsey, a possession of Henry de Ferrers. Its words are: "To this manor *belonged* the land of Stafford, in which the king commanded a castle to be built, which is now destroyed."[3] Ordericus also says that the king placed a castle at Stafford, on his return from his third visit to the north, in 1070.[4] Now the language of Domesday appears to us to say very plainly that in the manorial rearrangement which followed the Conquest some land was taken out of the manor of Chebsey, which lies immediately to the south of the

---

[1] D. B., i., 323b.   [2] Ethelwerd, anno 910.

[3] "Ipse Henricus tenet Cebbeseio. Ad hoc manerium pertinuit terra de Stadford, in qua rex precepit fieri castellum, quod modo est destructum." D. B., i., 249a.

[4] "Apud Estafort alteram [munitionem] locavit." *Ord. Vit.*, p. 199.

borough of Stafford, to furnish a site for a royal castle.[1] It is exactly in this position that we now find a large oblong motte, similar to the other mottes of the Conquest, and having the usual bailey attached to it. It lies about a mile and a half south-west of the town, near the main road leading into Shropshire.

The position was an important one, as the castles of Staffordshire formed a second line of defence against the North Welsh, as well as a check to the great palatinate earls of Shropshire.[2] The motte itself stood on high ground, commanding a view of twenty or thirty miles round, and both Tutbury and Caus castles could be seen from it. Between it and the town lies a stretch of flat ground which has evidently been a swamp formerly, and which explains the distance of the castle from the town ; while the fact that it lies to the *south* of the Sowe shows that it has no connection with Ethelfleda's work. There is no dispute that this motte was the site of the later baronial castle of Stafford, the castle besieged and taken in the Civil War ; the point we have to prove is that it was also the castle of Domesday Book.[3]

[1] It should be said that Mr Eyton interprets the passage differently, and takes it to mean that the castle was built on land in the borough of Stafford belonging to the manor of Chebsey. But he himself says that "the site of Stafford Castle, within the liberties, though not within the borough of Stafford, would suggest a royal foundation" ; and he believes this castle (the one on the motte) to have been the one garrisoned by Henry I. and made a residence by Henry II. *Domesday Studies*, p. 21.

[2] *Salt. Arch. Soc. Trans.*, vol. viii., "The Manor of Castre or Stafford," by Mr Mazzinghi, a paper abounding in valuable information, to which the present writer is greatly indebted.

[3] In the addenda to Mr Eyton's *Domesday of Staffordshire* (p. 135) the learned editor says there are two Stafford castles mentioned in Domesday, in two different hundreds. We have carefully searched through the whole Stafford account, and except at Burton and Tutbury, there is no other castle mentioned in Staffordshire but this one at Chebsey.

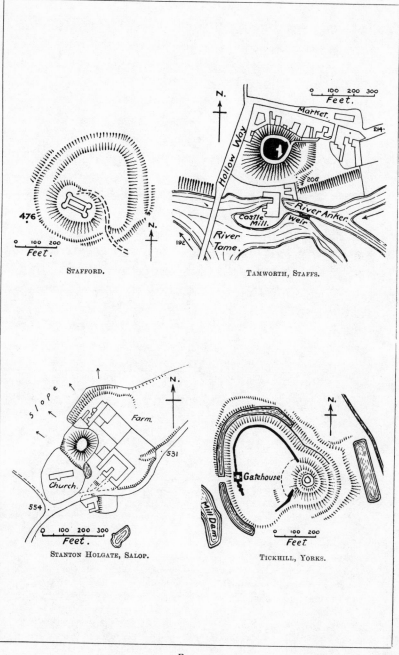

STAFFORD.

476

Feet.

TAMWORTH, STAFFS.

N.

Market.

Hollow Way

214.

206

River Anker.

Castle Mill.

Weir

192.

River Tame.

STANTON HOLGATE, SALOP.

Slope

Farm.

N.

531

Church.

554

Feet.

TICKHILL, YORKS.

N.

Gatehouse

Mill Dam.

Feet.

FIG. 32.

[To face p. 212.

If the first castle of Stafford was of earth and wood,
like most of William's castles, there would be nothing
wonderful in its having many destructions and many
resurrections.   This castle was clearly a royal castle,
from the language of Domesday Book.   As a royal
castle it would be committed to the custody of the sheriff,
who appears to have been Robert de Stafford,[1] ancestor
of the later barons of Stafford, and brother of Ralph de
Todeni, one of the great nobles of the Conquest.   Ralph
joined the party of Robert Curthose against Henry I. in
1101, and it is conjectured that his brother Robert was
involved in the same rebellion, for in that year we find
the castle held for the king by William Pantolf, a trusty
companion of the Conqueror.[2]   It is very unlikely that
this second castle of Stafford was on a different site from
the one which had been destroyed; and an ingenious
conjecture of Mr Mazzinghi's helps us to identify it with
the castle on the motte.   In that castle, when it again
emerges into light in the reign of Henry II., we find a
chapel dedicated to St Nicholas, which Robert de
Stafford gives to the abbey of Stone, and the king
confirms the gift.[3]   The worship of St Nicholas came
greatly into fashion after the translation of his remains
from Asia Minor to Bari, in Italy, in 1087.   William
Pantolf visited the shrine at Bari, got possession of
some of the relics of St Nicholas, and with great
reverence deposited them in his own church of Noron,
in Normandy.[4]   It is therefore extremely probable that
Pantolf founded the chapel of St Nicholas in Stafford

[1] Dugdale conjectures that Robert was sheriff of Staffordshire.   He had
large estates round the town of Stafford.   Eyton, *Staffordshire*, p. 61.

[2] Mazzinghi, *Salt Arch. Soc. Trans.*, viii., 6 ; Eyton, *Domesday Studies*,
p. 20.

[3] *Monasticon*, vi., 223 : "Ecclesiam S. Nicholai in castello de Stafford."

[4] Ordericus, vii., 12.   See also vii., 13, p. 220 (ed. Prévost).

Castle during the time that the castle was in his custody.[1]
But about the situation of the chapel of St Nicholas
there is no doubt, as its history is traceable down to the
16th century.   It stood in the bailey of the castle
outside the town.   This castle was therefore certainly
identical with that of Henry II., and most probably
with that of Henry I. and William I.

So far, as we have seen, Stafford Castle was a royal
castle.   It is true that in the reign of Henry II.'s
predecessor, Stephen, we find the castle again in the
hands of a Robert de Stafford, who speaks of it as
"castellum meum."[2]   Apparently the troubles of
Stephen's reign afforded an opportunity to the family of
the first Norman sheriff to get the castle again into their
hands.   But under the stronger rule of Henry II. the
crown recovered its rights, and the gift of the chapel in
the castle evidently could not be made without the
consent of the king.   The gaol which Henry II. caused
to be made in Stafford was doubtless in this castle.[3]
John repaired the castle,[4] and ordered *bretasches*, or
wooden towers, to be made in the forest of Arundel,
and sent to Stafford:[5] a statement which gives us an
insight into the nature of the castle in John's reign.
But it was the tendency of sheriffdoms to become
hereditary, as Dr Stubbs has pointed out,[6] and this
seems to have been the case at Stafford.   In the reign

---

[1] Mazzinghi, *Salt Arch. Soc. Trans.*, viii., 22.

[2] In a charter to Stone Abbey, *Salt Collections*, vol. ii.   That the castle
he speaks of was the one outside the town is proved by his references to
land "extra burgum."

[3] The *Pipe Roll* contains several entries relating to this gaol at Stafford.
It is clear from several of the documents given by Mr Mazzinghi that the
king's gaol of Stafford and the king's gaol of the castle of Stafford are
equivalent expressions.

[4] *Pipe Rolls*, 2 John.   [5] *Close Rolls*, i., 69.

[6] *Constitutional History*, i., 272.

of Edward I. a local jury decided that Nicholas, Baron of Stafford, held the castle of Stafford from the king *in capite*, by the service of three and a half knights' fees ;[1] and in 1348, Ralph, Baron of Stafford, obtained a license from Edward III. "to fortify and crenellate his *manses* of Stafford and Madlee with a wall of stone and lime, and to make castles thereof."[2] The indenture made with the mason a year previously is still extant, and states that the castle is to be built upon the *moële* in the manor, whereby the motte is evidently meant.[3] Besides, the deed is dated "at the Chastel of Stafford," showing that the new castle of stone and lime was on the site of an already existing castle.

We might spin out further evidence of the identity of the site of William's castle with that of the present one, from the name of the manor of Castel, which grew up around it, displacing the equally suggestive name of Montville, which we find in Domesday Book.[4] Against the existence of another castle in the town we have the absence of any such castle in William Smith's plan of 1588 ; the silence of Speed and Leland, who only mention the present castle ;[5] and the statement of Plot, who wrote about the end of the 17th century, that "he could not hear any footsteps remaining" of a castle in Stafford.[6] We may therefore safely conclude that it was only due to the fancy of some Elizabethan antiquary that in an old map of that time a spot to the south-

[1] Cited in *Salt Arch. Soc. Trans.*, vi., pt. i., 258.

[2] *Patent Rolls*, 22 Edward iii., cited by Mazzinghi, p. 80.

[3] *Salt Arch. Soc. Trans.*, viii., 122. It was undoubtedly at this time that the oblong stone keep on the motte, which is described in an escheat of Henry's VIII.'s reign, was built.

[4] *Salt Arch. Coll.*, viii., 14.

[5] Speed's *Theatre of Britain;* Leland, *Itin.*, vii., 26.

[6] The Stafford escheat of Henry VIII.'s reign, which describes the town, also makes no mention of any castle in the town. Mazzinghi, p. 105.

west of the town is marked with the inscription, "The old castle, built by Edward the Elder, and in memorie fortified with reel walls."[1]

The value of Stafford town had risen at the time of the Survey, as the king had 7*l.* for his share, which would make the whole revenue to king and earl 10*l.* 10*s.*, as against 9*l.* before the Conquest. The property of the canons of Stafford had risen from £1 to £3.[2]

The area of the bailey is 1⅜ acres.

STAMFORD, Lincoln and Northants.—This was one of the boroughs fortified by Edward the Elder, and consequently we find it a royal *burgus* at the time of the Survey. But Edward's borough, the *Chronicle* tell us, was on the south side of the Welland; the northern borough, on the other side, may have been the work of the Danes, as Stamford was one of the towns of the Danish confederacy of the Five Boroughs. The Norman castle and its motte are on the north side, and five *mansiones* were destroyed for the site.[3] There is at present no appearance of masonry on the motte, which is partly cut away, and what remains of the castle wall is of the 13th century. It is therefore probable that the *turris*, or keep, which surrendered to Henry II. in 1153, was of wood.[4] Henry gave the castle to Richard Humet, constable of Normandy, in 1155.[5] It was a

---

[1] *Salt Arch. Trans.*, viii., 231. The mistake may possibly have arisen from the fact that a fine castellated gateway, shown in W. Smith's map (*Description of England*), stood on the south-west wall of the town, close to the spot where Speed's map marks a Castle Hill.

[2] There must be some error in the first instalment of the Stafford revenue in Domesday, which says that the king and earl have 7*l.* between them, as it is contradicted by the later statement. D. B., i., 246a and 247b, 2.

[3] There were 141 *mansiones*, T. R. E., "et modo totidem sunt præter 5 quæ propter operationem castelli sunt wastæ." From a passage in the *Domesday of Nottingham* it would seem that a *mansio* was a group of houses.

[4] *Gervase of Canterbury*, i., 156, R. S.

[5] Peck's *Antiquarian Annals of Stamford;* he gives the charter, p. 17.

very exceptional thing that Henry should thus alienate a royal castle, and special circumstances must have moved him to this act. The castle was destroyed in Richard III.'s time, and the materials given to the convent of the Carmelite Friars. It appears to have been within the town walls, with a bailey stretching down to the river; this bailey is quadrangular. An inquisition of 1341 states that "the site of the castle contains 2 acres."[1]

Stamford had risen enormously in value since the Conquest. "In King Edward's time it paid 15*l.*; now, it pays for *feorm* 50*l.*, and for the whole of the king's dues it now pays 28*l.*[2]

STANTON, Stanton Long, in Shropshire (Fig. 32).— At the time of the Survey, the Norman Helgot was Lord of Corve Dale, and had his castle at Stanton.[3] The castle was afterwards known as Helgot's Castle, corrupted into Castle Holdgate. The site has been much altered by the building of a farmhouse in the bailey, but the motte still exists, high and steep, with a ditch round about half its circumference; there are some traces of masonry on the top. One side of the bailey ditch is still visible, and a mural tower of Edwardian style has been incorporated with the farmhouse. The exact area cannot now be calculated, but it can hardly have exceeded 2½ acres. The manor of Stanton was an

---

[1] Cited in Nevinson's " Notes on the History of Stamford," *Journ. Brit. Arch. Ass.*, xxxv.

[2] "T. R. E. dabat Stanford 15*l.*; modo dat ad firmam 50*l.* De omni consuetudine regis modo dat 28*l.*"

[3] "Ibi habet Helgot castellum, et 2 carucas in dominio, et 4 servos, et 3 villanos, et 3 bordarios, et 1 Francigenam cum 3½ carucis. Ibi ecclesia et presbyter. T. R. E. valebat 18 solidos; modo 25 solidos. Wastam invenit." D. B., i., 258b. There are some fragments of Norman work in the church, which is chiefly Early English, doubtless of the same date as the mural tower of the castle.

agglomeration of four small manors which had been held by different proprietors in Saxon times, so it was not the centre of a soke. The value of the manor had risen.

TAMWORTH, Stafford (Fig. 32).—Although Tamworth Castle is not mentioned in Domesday Book, it must have been in existence in the 11th century, as a charter of the Empress Matilda mentions that Robert le Despenser, brother of Urso d'Abetot, had formerly held this castle;[1] now Urso d'Abetot was a contemporary of the Conqueror, and so must his brother have been. Tamworth Castle stands on a motte 50 feet high, and 100 feet in diameter across the top, according to Mr Clark. It is an interesting instance of what is commonly called a shell keep, with a stone tower; one of the instances which suggest that the shell did not belong to a different type of castle to the tower, but was simply a ward wall, which probably at first enclosed a wooden tower. The tower and wall (or chemise) are probably late Norman, but the remarkable wing wall (there is only one, instead of the usual two) which runs down the motte is entirely of herring-bone work, and *may* be as old as Henry I.'s time.[2] A bailey court, which cannot have been large, lay between the motte and the river Tame, but its outline cannot now be determined, owing to the encroachments of buildings. Tamworth is about a mile from the great Roman road known as Watling Street. We have already referred to the fortification of the *burh* here by Ethelfleda;[3]

[1] Stapleton's Introduction to *Rot. Scac. Normanniæ*, vol. ii.

[2] It used to be supposed that herring-bone work was a Saxon sign, and this furnished an additional claim to the Saxon origin of this castle; but it is now known that herring-bone work only occurs in the later Saxon work, and is far more common in Norman. See *note*, p. 136.

[3] See *ante*, p. 34.

probably she only restored walls or banks which had existed before round this ancient capital of Mercia.

The value of the manor of Tamworth is not given in Domesday Book.

TICKHILL, Yorks (Fig. 32).—The name Tickhill does not occur in Domesday, but it is covered by that of Dadesley, the manor in which this castle was built: a name which appears to have gone out of use when the *hill* was thrown up. There can be no doubt that it was the castle of Roger de Busli, one of the most richly endowed of William's tenants-in-chief, as it is mentioned as such by Ordericus.[1] He calls it the castle of Blythe, a name which it probably received because Blythe was the most important place near, and Dadesley was so insignificant. Florence of Worcester, when describing the same events, calls the castle Tykehill. The remains furnish an excellent specimen of the earthworks of this class. The motte is 75 feet high, and its area on top about 80 feet in diameter; about a third of it is natural, the rest artificial. Only a slight trace remains of the ditch separating it from the oval bailey, which covers 2 acres. The foundations of a decagonal tower, built in the reign of Henry II., are still to be seen on the top.[2] The bailey retains its banks on the scarp, surmounted now by a stone curtain, which, along with the older part of the gatehouse, is possibly of the time of Henry I.[3] The outer ditch is about 30 feet broad, and is still full of water in parts. On the counterscarp a portion of the

---

[1] Ordericus, xi., ch. iii.

[2] There are three entries for the works of the *turris* at Tickhill in the *Pipe Rolls* of 1178 and 1179, amounting to £123, 12s. 5d.

[3] *Pipe Roll*, 31 Henry I., 33, 36. Expenses for work at the wall of the castle are mentioned. Ordericus says that Robert Belesme fortified the castle of Blythe at the time of his rebellion in 1101, but he also says that it had belonged to Roger de Busli. *Hist. Ecc.*, iv., 33; xi., 3.

bank remains.   This bank carried a wooden palisade when the castle was besieged by Cromwell.[1]   The site is not naturally defensible ; it is about three and a half miles from the northern Roman road.

The value of the manor of Dadesley had risen at the time of the Survey.[2]   The stone buildings which once stood in the bailey have been transformed into a modern house.

TONBRIDGE, Kent (Fig. 33).—This notable castle, the first English seat of the powerful family who afterwards took their name from Clare in Suffolk, is first mentioned in 1088, when it was stormed by William Rufus and his English subjects, who had adopted his cause against the supporters of his brother Robert.[3]   The castle was one of great importance at several crises in English history ; but it began as a wooden keep on a motte, and the stone shell which now crowns this motte cannot be earlier than the 12th century, and judging by its buttresses, is much later.   The castle stands outside the town of Tonbridge, separated from it by moats which were fed from the river.   The smaller bailey of $1\frac{1}{2}$ acres, probably the original one, is square, with rounded corners.   The palatial gatehouse, of the 13th or 14th century, is a marked feature of this castle.   There appears to have been only one wing wall down the motte to the bailey, but a second one was not needed, owing to the position of the motte with regard to the river.

The value of the manor of Hadlow, in which Tonbridge lay, was stationary at Domesday.[4]   It belonged to the see of Canterbury, and was held by

[1] Vicar's *Parliamentary Chronicle*, quoted by Hunter, *South Yorks*, ii., 235.
[2] D. B., i., 319a.   [3] *A.-S. C.* in *anno*.
[4] D. B., i., 76.

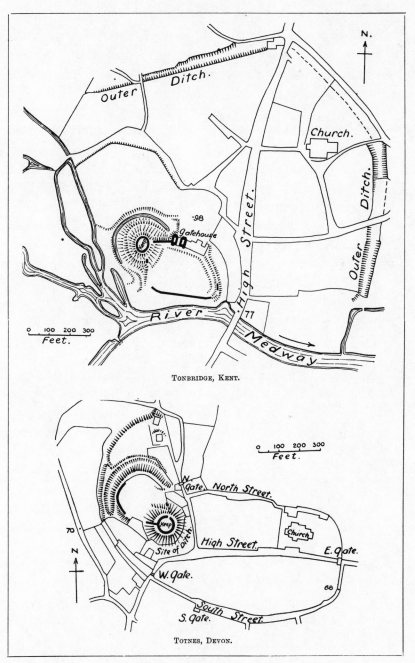

TONBRIDGE, KENT.

TOTNES, DEVON.

FIG. 33.

[To face p. 220.

Richard de Bienfaite, ancestor of the House of Clare, as a tenant of the see.

TOTNES, Devonshire (Fig. 33).—The castle of Totnes belonged to Judhael, one of King William's men, who has been already mentioned under Barnstaple. This castle is not noticed in Domesday Book, but its existence in the 11th century is made certain by a charter of Judhael's giving land *below his castle* to the Benedictine priory which he had founded at Totnes : a charter certainly of the Conqueror's reign, as it contains a prayer for the health of King William.[1] The site was an important one ; Totnes had been one of the boroughs of the *Burghal Hidage ;* it was at the head of a navigable river, and was the point where the ancient Roman (?) road from Devonshire to Bath and the North began its course.[2] The motte of the castle is very high and precipitous, and has a shell on top, which is perfect up to the battlements, and appears to be rather late Norman. This keep is entered in a very unusual way, by a flight of steps leading up from the bailey, deeply sunk in the upper part into the face of the motte, so as to form a highly defensible passage. Two wing walls run down to the walls of the bailey. There is at present no ditch between the motte and the bailey. The whole area of the work is ¾ acre. It stands in a very defensible situation on a spur of hill overlooking the town, and lies just outside the ancient walls.

The value of the town of Totnes had risen at Domesday.[3]

THE TOWER OF LONDON.—Here, as at Colchester, there is no motte, because the original design was that there should be a stone keep. Ordericus tells us that

---

[1] *M. A.,* iv., 630.   [2] Leland is responsible for this last statement.
[3] D. B., i., 108b.

after the submission of London to William the Conqueror he stayed for a few days in Barking while certain fortifications in the city were being finished, to curb the excitability of the huge and fierce population.[1]   What these fortifications were we shall never know, but we may imagine they were earthworks of the usual Norman kind.[2]   Certainly the great keep familiarly known as the White Tower was not built in a few days; it does not appear to have been even begun till some eleven years later, when Gundulf, a monk celebrated for his architectural skill, was appointed to the see of Rochester. Gundulf was the architect of the Tower,[3] and it must therefore have been built during his episcopate, which lasted from 1077-1108.[4]   In 1097 we read that " many shires which owe works to London were greatly oppressed in making the wall (weall) round the Tower."[5] This does not necessarily mean a stone wall, but probably it does, as Gundulf's tower can hardly have been without a bank and palisade to its bailey.

As the Tower in its general plan represents the type of keep which was the model for all succeeding

---

[1] " Egressus Lundoniæ rex *dies aliquot* in propinquo loco Bercingio morabatur, dum firmamenta quædam in urbe contra mobilitatem ingentis et feri populi perficerentur." P. 165.   Ordericus is quoting from William of Poitiers.   There was formerly a Roman camp at Barking, and the motte which William hastily threw up on its rampart to defend his sojourn still remains.   See *Victoria History of Essex.*

[2] Mr Harold Sands suggests to me that the first fortification may simply have been a bank and palisade across the angle of the Roman wall, with perhaps a wooden keep, and that the great fire in London in 1077 determined William to build a stone keep.

[3] Hearne's *Textus Roffensis*, 212.   " Idem Gundulfus, ex precepto Regis Willielmi Magni, præesset operi magnæ turris Londoniæ."

[4] The building of stone keeps was generally spread over several years, as we learn from the *Pipe Rolls*.   Richard I. built his celebrated keep of Chateau Gaillard in one year, but he himself regarded this as an architectural feat.   "Estne bella, filia mea de uno anno," he said in delight.

[5] *A.-S. C.* in *anno.*

stone keeps up to the end of the 12th century, it seems
appropriate here to give some description of its main
features.   Its resemblance to the keep of Colchester,
which also was a work of William I.'s reign, is very
striking.[1]   Colchester is the larger of the two, but
the Tower exceeds in size all other English keeps,
measuring 118 × 98 feet at its base.[2]   As it has
been altered or added to in every century, its details
are peculiarly difficult to trace, especially as the
ordinary visitor is not allowed to make a thorough
examination.[3]   Thus much, however, is certain : neither
of the two present entrances on the ground floor is
original ; the first entrance was on the first floor, some
25 feet above the ground, at the S.W. angle of the
south side, and has been transformed into a window.
There was no entrance to the basement, but it was
only reached by the grand staircase, which is enclosed
in a round turret at the N.E. angle.   There were
two other stairs at the N.W. and S.W. angles, but
these only began on the first floor.   The basement
is divided by a cross wall, which is carried up to
the third storey.   There are at present three storeys
above the basement.   The basement, which is now
vaulted in brick, was not originally vaulted at all,

[1] Round's *History of Colchester*, ch. iv.
[2] The keep of Norwich Castle measures 100 × 95 feet ; Middleham,
100 × 80 ; Dover, 95 × 90.   These are the largest existing keeps in England,
next to the Tower and Colchester.   The destroyed keep of Duffield
measured 99 × 93 feet ; that of Bristol is believed to have been 110 × 95.
[3] The reader will find little help for the structural history of the Tower
in most of the works which call themselves Histories of the Tower of
London.   The plan of these works generally is to skim over the structural
history as quickly as possible, perhaps with the help of a few passages from
Clark, and to get on to the history of the prisoners in the Tower.   For the
description in the text, the writer is greatly indebted to Mr Harold Sands,
F.S.A., who has made a careful study of the Tower, and whose monograph
upon it, it is hoped, will shortly appear.

except the south-eastern chamber, under the crypt of the chapel.

The first floor, like the basement, is divided into three rooms, as, in addition to the usual cross wall, the Tower has a branch cross wall to its eastern section, which is carried up to the top. This floor was formerly only lit by loopholes; Clark states that there were two fireplaces in the east wall, but there is some doubt about this. The S.E. room contained the crypt of the chapel, which was vaulted. It is commonly supposed that the rooms on the first floor were occupied by the guards of the keep. In the account which we have quoted from Lambert of Ardres, the first floor is said to be the lord's habitation, and the upper storey that of the guards; so that there seems to have been no invariable rule.[1] No special room was allotted to the kitchen, as in time of peace at any rate, the lord of the castle and all his retainers took their meals in a great hall in the bailey of the castle.[2] The ceilings of the two larger rooms of this floor are now supported by posts, an arrangement which is probably modern, as the present posts certainly are.[3]

The second floor contains the chapel, which in many keeps is merely an oratory, but is here of unusual size. Its eastern end is carried out in a round apse, a feature which is also found at Colchester, but is not usual in

[1] *Ante*, p. 89.

[2] Many of the larger keeps contain rooms quite spacious enough to have served as banqueting halls, and it is a point of some difficulty whether they were built to be used as such. But as late as the 14th century, Piers Ploughman rebukes the new custom which was growing up of the noble and his family taking their meals in private, and leaving the hall to their retainers. Every castle seems to have had a hall in the bailey.

[3] Mr Sands says the main floors are not of too great a span to carry any ordinary weight.

Norman keeps.[1] It is a singularly fine specimen of an early Norman chapel. This floor probably contained the royal apartments; it was lighted by windows, not loops. Both the eastern and western rooms had fireplaces; the eastern room goes by the name of the Banqueting Chamber.

The third storey is on a level with the triforium of the chapel.[2] This triforium is continued all round the keep as a mural passage, and it has windows only slightly smaller than those of the floor below. These mural galleries are found in most important keeps. As their windows were of larger size than the loops which lit the lower floors, it is possible that they may have been used for defence, either for throwing down missiles or for shooting with bows and arrows. But no near aim could be taken without a downward splay to the window, and the bows of the 11th and 12th centuries were incapable of a long aim. A plausible theory is that they were intended for the march of sentinels.[3]

The masonry of the Tower is of Kentish rag, with ashlar quoins. In mediæval times it had a forebuilding, with a round stair turret, which is shown in some old views; but it may reasonably be doubted whether this was an original feature.

As regards the ground plan of the castle as a whole,

[1] The keep of Pevensey Castle, the basement of which has been recently uncovered, has no less than four apsidal projections, one of which rests on the solid base of a Roman mural tower. But this keep is quite an exceptional building. See *Excavations at Pevensey*, Second Report, by H. Sands.

[2] Mr Sands has conjectured that the third floor may be an addition, and that the second storey was originally open up to the roof and not communicating with the mural passage except by stairs. This was actually the case at Bamborough keep, and at Newcastle and Rochester the mural gallery opens into the upper part of the second storey by inner windows.

[3] Until the end of the 12th century the roofs of keeps were gabled and not flat, but probably there was usually a parapet walk for sentinels or archers.

it is now concentric, but was not so originally.   The Tower was certainly placed in the S.E. angle of the Roman walls of London, and very near the east wall, portions of which have been discovered.[1]   The conversion of the castle into one of the concentric type was the work of later centuries, and the history of its development has still to be traced.[2]

TREMATON, Cornwall (Fig. 34).—"The Count [of Mortain] has a castle there and a market, rendering 101 shillings."[3]   Two Cornish castles are mentioned in Domesday, and both of them are only on the borders of that wild Keltic country; but while Launceston is inland, Trematon guards an inlet on the south coast. The position of this castle is extremely strong by nature, at the end of a high headland; on the extreme point of this promontory the motte is placed.   It carries a well-preserved shell wall, which may be of Norman date, from the plain round arch of the entrance.[4]   It has been separated by a ditch from the bailey, but the steepness of the hill rendered it unnecessary to carry this ditch all round.   The bailey, 1 acre in extent, in which a modern house is situated, still has an entrance gate of the 13th century, and part of a mediæval wall.   A second bailey, now a rose-garden, has been added at a later period. In spite of the establishment of a castle and a market

[1] Parts of these walls, running N. and S. have been found very near the E. side of the Tower.   No trace of the Roman wall has been found S. of the Tower, but in Lower Thames Street lines have been found which, if produced, would lead straight to the S. wall of the inner bailey.   Communicated by Mr Harold Sands.

[2] I have to thank Mr Harold Sands for kindly revising this account of the Tower.

[3] "Ibi habet comes unum castrum et mercatum, reddentes 101s." D. B., i., 122.

[4] It must be remembered that round arches, in castle architecture, are by no means a certain sign of date.   Of course the first castle on this motte must have been of wood.

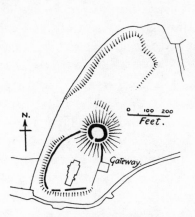

TREMATON, CORNWALL.

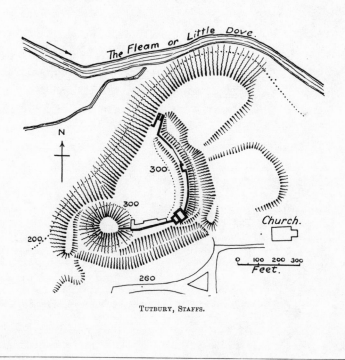

TUTBURY, STAFFS.

FIG. 34.

[To face p. 226.

the value of the manor of Trematon had gone down at the time of the Survey, which may be accounted for by the fact that there were only ten ploughs where there ought to have been twenty-four. It was only a small manor, and no burgus is mentioned.

TUTBURY, Staffordshire (Fig. 34).—In the magnificent earthworks of this castle, and the strength of its site, we probably see a testimony to the ability of Hugh d'Avranches; for we learn from Ordericus that in 1070 William I. gave to Henry de Ferrers the castle of Tutbury, which had belonged to Hugh d'Avranches,[1] to whom the king then gave the more dangerous but more honourable post of the earldom of Chester. Domesday Book simply states that Henry de Ferrers has the castle of Tutbury, and that there are forty-two men living by their merchandise alone in the borough round the castle.[2]

At Tutbury the keep was placed on an artificial motte, which itself stood on a hill of natural rock, defended on the N.W. side by precipices. There is no trace of any ditch between the motte and bailey. At present there is only the ruin of a comparatively modern tower on the motte, but Shaw states that there was formerly a stone keep.[3] A description of Elizabeth's reign says, "The castle is situated upon a round hill, and is circumvironed with a strong wall of astilar [ashlar] stone. . . . The king's lodging therein is fair and strong, bounded and knit to the wall. And a fair stage hall of timber, of a great length. Four chambers of timber, and other houses well upholden, within the walls of the

[1] *Ord. Vit.*, ii., 222 (Prévost).
[2] "Henricus de Ferrers habet castellum de Toteberie. In burgo circa castellum sunt 42 homines de mercato suo tantum viventes." D. B., i., 248b.
[3] Shaw's *History of Staffordshire*, i., 49.

castle."[1]   The king's lodging will no doubt be the closed gatehouse; the custom of erecting gatehouse palaces arose as early as the 13th century.   This account shows how many of the castle buildings were still of timber in Elizabeth's reign.

The bailey is quadrant-shaped, and has the motte at its apex.   Its area is 2½ acres.   Its most remarkable feature is that it still retains its ancient banks on the east side and part of the south, and the more recent curtain is carried on top of them.   This curtain is of the same masonry as the three remaining towers, which are of excellent Perpendicular work, and are generally attributed to John of Gaunt, who held this castle after his marriage with Blanche of Lancaster.   The first castle was undoubtedly of wood; it was pulled down by order of Henry I. in 1175,[2] nor does there seem to have been any resurrection till the time of Earl Thomas of Lancaster at the earliest.

Though Tutbury was the centre of the Honour of Ferrers, it does not seem to have been even a manor in Saxon times.   The borough was probably the creation of the castellan, who also founded the Priory.[3]   There is no statement in the Survey from which we can learn the value T. R. E., but T. R. W. it was 4*l.* 10*s.*

TYNEMOUTH, Northumberland.—Besieged and taken by William Rufus in 1095.[4]   There is no motte there, and probably never was one, as the situation is defended by precipitous cliffs on all sides but one, where a deep ditch has been cut across the neck of the headland.

WALLINGFORD, Berkshire (Fig. 35).—There is good

[1] Quoted in *Beauties of England and Wales*, Staffordshire, p. 1129.

[2] *Diceto*, i., 384.   The castle was then besieged on Henry's behalf by the vassal prince of South Wales, the Lord Rhys.

[3] The foundation charter is in *Mon. Ang.*, iii., 393.

[4] *A.-S. C.*

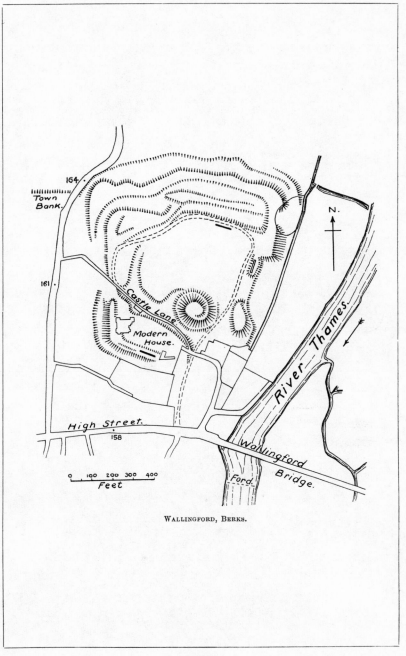

164.

Town
Bank.

161.

N.

Castle Lane.

Modern
House.

River Thames

High Street.

158

Wallingford
Bridge.

Ford.

0   100 200 300 400
Feet

Wallingford, Berks.

Fig. 35.

[To face p. 228.

reason to suppose that in the *vallum* of the town of
Wallingford we have an interesting relic of Saxon
times. Wallingford is one of the boroughs enumerated
in the *Burghal Hidage;* it was undoubtedly a fortified
town at the time of the Conquest,[1] and is called a *burgus*
in Domesday Book ; but there appears to be no evidence
to connect it with Roman times except the discovery of
a number of Roman coins in the town and its neighbourhood. No Roman buildings or pavements have ever
been found.[2] The Saxon borough was built on the
model of a Roman *chester:* a square with rounded
corners. The rampart of Wallingford, which still exists
in great part, is entirely of earth, and must have been
crowned with a wooden wall, such as was still existing
at Portsmouth in Leland's time.[3] The accounts of
Wallingford in the great Survey are very full and
important. "King Edward had eight virgates in the
borough of Wallingford, and in these there were 276
haughs paying 11*l.* of rent. Eight have been destroyed
for the castle."[4] This Norman castle was placed in the
N.E. corner of the borough. At present its precincts
cover 30 acres,[5] but this includes garden grounds, and
no doubt represents later enclosures. No ancient plan
of the castle has been preserved, but from Leland's
description there appear to have been three wards in his

[1] William of Poitiers calls it an *oppidum*, p. 141.

[2] Hedges, *History of Wallingford.*

[3] "The Towne of Portsmuth is murid from the Est Tower a forowgh
lenght with a Mudde Waulle armid with Tymbre." *Itin.*, iii., 113.

[4] "In burgo de Walingeford habuit Rex Edwardus 8 virgatas terræ ; et
in his erant 276 hagæ reddentes 11 libras de gablo. . . . Pro castello sunt
8 destructæ." D. B., i., 56. If we divide these 276 *haughs* by the 114 acres
enclosed by the town rampart, we get an average of about 1 rood 26 perches
for each haugh ; multiply this by 8 (the number destroyed for the castle)
and we get an area of 3 acres, which is about the average area of an early
Norman castle.

[5] Hedges, *History of Wallingford*, i., 139.

time, each defended by banks and ditches. The inner ward, which was doubtless the original one, is rudely oblong in shape; it covers $4\frac{1}{2}$ acres. Leland says, "All the goodly buildings, with the towers and dungeon, be within the third dyke." The motte, which still exists, was on the south-eastern edge of this ward; that is, it was so placed as to overlook both the borough and the ford over the Thames.[1] It was ditched around, and is said to have had a stone keep on the top; but no foundations were found when it was recently excavated. It was found to rest on a foundation of solid masonry several feet thick, sloping upwards towards the outside, so that it must have stood in a kind of stone saucer.[2] The masonry which remains in the other parts of the castle is evidently none of it of the early Norman period, unless we accept a fragment of wall which contains courses of tiles. Numerous buildings were added in Henry III.'s reign; the walls and battlements were repaired, and the *hurdicium*, which had been blown down by a high wind, was renewed.[3] But the motte and the high banks show clearly that the first Norman castle was of wood.

The value of the royal borough of Wallingford had considerably risen since the Conquest.[4]

WARWICK (Fig. 36).—Here again we have a castle built on land which the Conqueror obtained from a Saxon convent, a positive proof that there was no castle there previously. Only a small number of houses was

---

[1] Camden speaks of the motte as being in the middle of the castle, but this is a mistake.

[2] Such is the account in Hedges' *History of Wallingford*, p. 139, but it sounds odd. It is to be inferred from the same source that the fragment of a round building which stands on the top of the motte must be modern; it is thick enough to be ancient.

[3] *Close Rolls*, i., anno 1223.   [4] D. B., i., 56.

destroyed for the castle,[1] and this points to the probability, which is supported by some other evidence,
that the castle was built outside the town. Warwick, of
course, was one of the boroughs fortified by Ethelfleda,
and it was doubtless erected to protect the Roman road
from Bath to Lincoln, the Foss Way, against the Danes.
Domesday Book, after mentioning that the king's
barons have 112 houses in the borough, and the abbot
of Coventry 36, goes on to say that these houses
belong to the lands which the barons hold outside the
city, and are rated there.[2] This is one of the passages
from which Professor Maitland has concluded that the
boroughs planted by Ethelfleda and her brother were
organised on a system of military defence, whereby the
magnates in the country were bound to keep houses in
the towns.[3] Ordericus, after the well-known passage in
which he states that the lack of castles in England was
one great cause of its easy conquest by the Normans,
says : " The king *therefore* founded a castle at Warwick,
and gave it in custody to Henry, son of Roger de
Beaumont."[4] Putting these various facts together, we
may fairly assert that the motte which still forms part
of the castle of Warwick was the work of the Conqueror,
and not, as Mr Freeman believed, "a monument of
the wisdom and energy of the mighty daughter of
Alfred,"[5] whose energy was very much better employed

[1] "Abbas de Couentreu habet 36 masuras, et 4 sunt wastæ propter situm
castelli." D. B., i., 238a.

[2] "Hæ masuræ pertinent ad terras quas ipsi barones tenent extra
burgum, et ibi appreciatæ sunt." D. B., i., 238.

[3] Maitland, *Domesday Book and Beyond*, p. 189.

[4] Ordericus, p. 184. "Rex *itaque* castellum apud Guarevicum condidit, et
Henrico Rogerii de Bello Monte filio ad servandum tradidit." Mr Freeman
remarks that no authentic records connect Thurkil of Warwick with
Warwick Castle. *N. C.*, iv., 781.

[5] *N. C.*, iv., 190.

in the protection of her people.   Dugdale, who also put the motte down to Ethelfleda, was only copying Rous, a very imaginative writer of the 15th century.

The motte of Warwick is mentioned several times in the *Pipe Rolls* of Henry II. ; it then carried wooden structures on its top.[1]   In Leland's time there were still standing on this motte the ruins of a keep, which he calls by its Norman name of the Dungeon.   A fragment of a polygonal shell wall still remains.[2]   But there is not a scrap of masonry of Norman date about the castle. The motte, and the earthen bank which still runs along one side of the court, show that the first castle was a wooden one.   The bailey is oblong in shape, the motte being outside it; its area is about $2\frac{1}{2}$ acres.

The value of Warwick had doubled since the Conquest.

WIGMORE, Herefordshire (Fig. 36).—We have already referred to the absurdity of identifying this place with the *Wigingamere* of the *Anglo-Saxon Chronicle*.[3]   We have the strongest indication that the Norman castle at Wigmore was a new erection, since Domesday Book tells us that William FitzOsbern built it on waste land called Mereston.[4]   This express statement disposes of the fable in the *Fundationis Historia* of Wigmore Priory, that the castle of Wigmore had belonged to Edric the Wild, and was rebuilt by Ralph Mortimer.[5]   Wigmore had only been

---

[1] In operatione unius domus in mota de Warwick et unius bretaschie $5l.$ $7s.$ $11d.$ *Pipe Rolls,* 20 Henry II.   As *domus* is a word very commonly used for a keep, it is probable this expenditure refers to a wooden keep.

[2] From information received from Mr Harold Sands.   There appears to be no foundation whatever for the curious ground plan given by Parker.

[3] See *ante,* p. 42.

[4] "Willelmus comes fecit illud castellum in wasta terra quæ vocatur Mereston."   D. B., i., 183.

[5] *Mon. Ang.,* vi., 349.

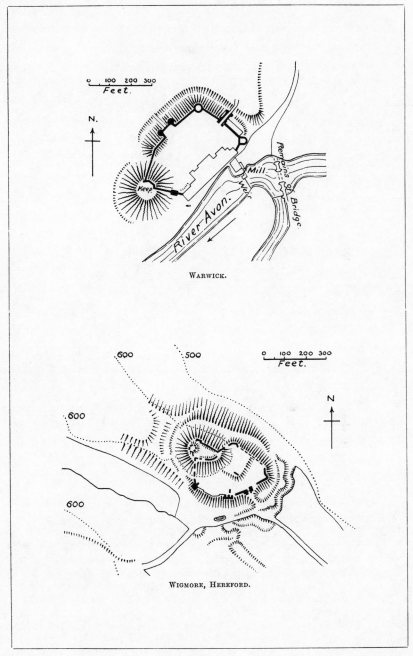

WARWICK.

WIGMORE, HEREFORD.

FIG. 36.

[To face p. 232.

a small manor of two taxable hides in Saxon times. Whereas it had then been unproductive, at the date of the Survey there were two ploughs in the demesne, and the borough attached to the castle yielded 7*l.* Here we have another instance of the planting of a borough close to a castle, and of the revenue which was thus obtained.

There is a very large and high motte at Wigmore Castle, of oval shape, on a headland which has been cut off by a deep ditch. The earthen banks of its first fortification still remain, enclosing a small ward, but on top of them is a wall in masonry, and the ruins of a polygonal keep ;[1] also the remains of two mural towers. Half-way down the end of the headland, below the motte, is a small square court, which *may* have been the original bailey ; below it, again, is a larger half-moon bailey furnished with walls and towers. But the whole area covered is only 1 acre. The masonry is none of it earlier than the Decorated period, except one tower in the bailey wall which may be late Norman.

WINCHESTER, Hants. — We include Winchester among the castles mentioned or alluded to in Domesday Book, because we think it can be proved that the *domus regis* mentioned under Alton and Clere is the castle built by William outside the west gate of the city, where the present County Hall is now almost the only remaining relic of any castle at all.[2] Under the head of "Aulton" we are told that the abbot of

---

[1] This keep rests on a broad extension of the earthen rampart, similar to what is still to be seen in the mottes of Devizes, Burton-in-Lonsdale, and William Hill, Middleham.

[2] Ordericus says : "Intra mœnia Guentæ, opibus et munimine nobilis urbis et mari contiguæ, validam arcem construxit, ibique Willelmum Osberni filium in exercitu suo precipuum reliquit." II., 166. The *intra mœnia* is not to be taken literally, any more than the *mari contiguæ*. It is strange that Mr Freeman should have mistaken Guenta for Norwich, since under 1067 Ordericus translates the Winchester of the *A.-S. C.* by Guenta.

Hyde had unjustly gotten the manor in exchange for the king's house, because by the testimony of the jurors it was already the king's house.[1]   That *excambio domus regis* should read *excambio terræ domus regis* is clear from the corresponding entry under Clere, where the words are *pro excambio terræ in qua domus regis est in civitate.*[2]   The matter is put beyond a doubt by the confirmatory charter of Henry I. to Hyde Abbey, where the king states that his father gave Aulton and Clere to Hyde Abbey *in exchange for the land on which he built his hall in the city of Winchester.*[3]   Where, then, was this hall, which was clearly new, since fresh land was obtained for it, and which must not therefore be sought on the site of the palace of the Saxon kings?   The *Liber Winton,* a roll of Henry I.'s time, says that twelve burgesses' houses had been destroyed and the land was now occupied by the king's house.[4]   Another passage says that a whole street *outside the west gate* was destroyed when the king made his ditch.[5]   These passages justify the conclusion of Mr Smirke that the king's house at Winchester was neither more nor less than the castle which existed until the 17th century outside the west gate.[6]   Probably the reason why it is spoken of so frequently in the earliest documents as the king's house or hall, instead of the castle, is that in this important city, the ancient capital of Wessex, where the

[1] "De isto manerio testatur comitatus quod injuste accepit [abbas] pro excambio domus regis, quia domus erat regis." D. B., i., 43a, 1.

[2] *Ibid.,* i., 43a, 2.

[3] "Sicut rex Willielmus pater meus ei dedit in excambium pro terra illa in qua ædificavit aulam suam in urbe Winton. *Mon. Ang.,* ii., 444.

[4] "Pars erat in dominio et pars de dominio abbatis ; hoc totum est post occupatum in domo regis." P. 534. This passage throws light on the fraud of the abbot of Hyde, referred to above.

[5] "Extra portam de Vuest . . . ibi juxta fuit quidam vicus ; fuit diffactus quando rex fecit facere suum fossatum." P. 535.

[6] *Arch. Inst.,* Winchester volume, p. 51.

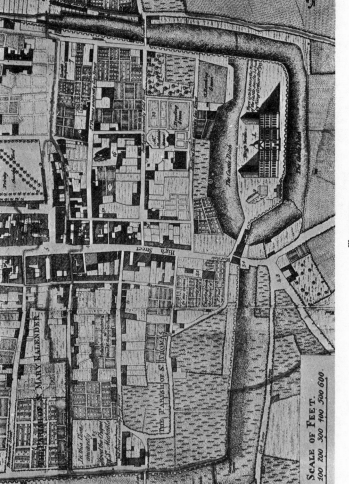

WINCHESTER.

(From a plan by W. Godson, 1750.)

SCALE OF FEET.
0 100 200 300 400 500 600.

FIG. 37.

[*To face p* 234.

king "wore his crown" once a year, William built, besides the usual wooden keep on the motte, a stone hall in the bailey, of size and dignity corresponding to the new royalty.[1] In fact, the hall so magnificently transformed by Henry III., and known to be the old hall of the castle, can be seen on careful examination to have still its original Norman walls and other traces of early Norman work.[2] The palace of the Saxon kings stood, where we might expect to find the palace of native princes, in the middle of the city; according to Milner it was on the site of the present Square.[3] William may have repaired this palace, but that he constructed two royal houses, a palace and a castle, is highly improbable. The castle became the residence of the Norman kings, and the Saxon palace appears to have been neglected.[4] We see with what caution the Conqueror placed his castle at the royal city of Wessex without the walls. Milner tells us that there was no access to it from the city without passing through the west gate.[5] The motte of the castle appears to have been standing in his time, as he speaks of "the artificial mount on which the keep stands."[6] It is frequently

[1] It should also be said that the word *domus* is frequently used for a keep in chronicles and ancient documents of the 11th and 12th centuries.

[2] The line of the more ancient roof gable can be traced in the north wall, and there is a vestige of a Norman doorway in the east wall.

[3] *History of Winchester*, ii., 210.

[4] Henry of Blois, Bishop of Winchester and brother of King Stephen, pulled down the royal palace close to the cathedral, which presumably was the old Saxon palace, and used the materials to build Wolvesey Castle. See Malmesbury, "De Vitis Sex Episcoporum," *Anglia Sacra*, ii., 421. He could hardly have dared to do this if the palace had still been used by the Norman kings.

[5] *History of Winchester*, ii., 210. See Fig. 37.

[6] *Ibid.*, p. 195. It is difficult, now that the area has been levelled, to say exactly where this motte stood. Woodward says that the keep stood in the N.E. corner; but he probably alludes to a mural tower whose foundations can still be seen, near the County Hall. *History of Hampshire*, i., 295-304.

mentioned in mediæval documents as the *beumont* or *beau mont*. It was surrounded by its own ditch.[1] The bailey, if Speed's map is correct, was triangular in shape. With its ditches and banks the castle covered 6 acres, according to the commissioners who reported on it in Elizabeth's reign; but the inner area cannot have been more than $4\frac{1}{2}$ acres. We may infer from the sums spent on this castle by Henry II., that he was the first to give it walls and towers of stone; the *Pipe Rolls* show entries to the amount of 1150*l.* during the course of his reign; the work of the walls is frequently specified, and stone is mentioned.

Domesday Book does not inform us whether the value of Winchester had risen or fallen since the Conquest.

WINDSOR (Fig. 38).—Here we have another of the interesting cases in which the geld due from the tenant of a manor is lessened on account of a castle having occupied a portion of the land.[2] The Survey tells us that the castle of Windsor sits in half a hide belonging to the manor of Clewer, which had become William's property as part of the spoils of Harold. It was now held of the king by a Norman tenant-in-chief, but whereas it was formerly rated as five hides it was *now* (that is, probably, since the castle was built) rated as four and a half hides. Of course we are not to suppose

---

[1] Turner, *History of Domestic Architecture.* He cites from the *Liberate Roll*, 35 Henry II., an order for the repair of the ditch between the great tower and the bailey.

[2] "Radulfus filius Seifrid tenet de rege Clivor. Heraldus comes tenuit. Tunc se defendebat pro 5 hidis, modo pro $4\frac{1}{2}$ hidis, et castellum de Windesores est in dimidia hida." D. B., i., 62b. The *Abingdon History* also mentions the foundation of Windsor Castle and gives some interesting details about castle guard. "Tunc Walingaforde et Oxenforde et Wildesore, cæterisque locis, castella pro regno servando compacta. Unde huic abbatiæ militum excubias apud ipsum Wildesore oppidum habendas regis imperio jussum." II., 3, R. S.

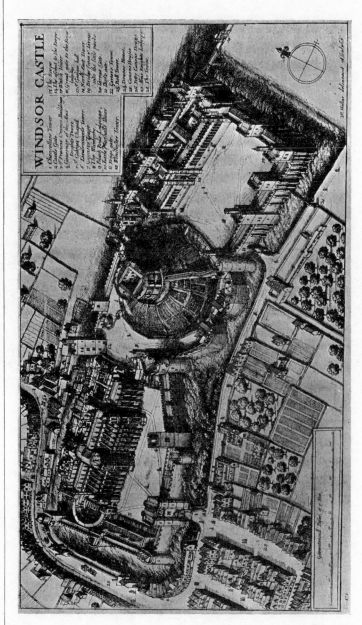

(From Ashmole's "Order of the Garter.")

FIG. 38.

[To face p. 286.

that the castle occupied the whole half hide, which might be some 60 acres; but it extinguished the liability of that portion.   At Windsor, however, we have no occasion to press this argument as a proof that the castle was new, since it is well established that the palace of the Saxon kings was at least 2 miles from the present castle and town, in the village long known as Old Windsor, which fell into decay as the town of Windsor sprang up under the Norman castle.¹   The manor of Windsor was given by Edward the Confessor to the convent of Westminster, but recovered by the Conqueror.²   But as the Survey shows us, he did not build his castle in the manor of Windsor, but in that of Clewer.   He built it for a hunting-seat,³ and it may have been for the purpose of recovering forest rights that he resumed possession of Old Windsor; but he placed his castle in the situation which he thought best for defence.   For even a hunting-seat in Norman times was virtually a castle, as many other instances show.

It is needless to state that there is no masonry at Windsor of the time of the Conqueror, or even of the time of his son Henry I., in spite of the statement of Stowe that Henry "new builded the castle of Windsor." This statement may perhaps be founded on a passage in the *Anglo-Saxon Chronicle* which says that Henry held his court for the first time in the New Windsor in

¹ *Leland,* iv., 1, 37. See also Tighe's *Annals of Windsor,* pp. 1-6. Until recently there was a farmhouse surrounded by a moat at Old Windsor, which was *believed* to mark the site of Edward's *regia domus.*

² Edward's grant of Windsor to Westminster is in *Cod. Dip.,* iv., 227. Domesday does not mention the rights of the church, but says the manor of Windsor was held of the crown T. R. E. and T. R. W.   Camden gives William's charter of exchange with the convent of Westminster. *Britannia,* i., 151.

³ This is stated in the charter given by Camden.

1110.   Perhaps the *Chronicle* here refers to the *borough* of New Windsor, as an entry in the *Pipe Roll* of Henry I. seems to show that he was the first to enclose the *burgus* of Windsor.[1]   For it is probable that the first stone castle at Windsor was built by Henry II., who spent £1670 on it in the course of his reign.   One of his first acts after his accession was an exchange of land at Windsor, which seems to have been for the purpose of a vineyard, and was possibly the origin of the second bailey.[2]   At present the position of the motte is central to the rest of the castle, but this is so unusual that it suggests the idea that the upper ward is the oldest, and that the motte stood on its outer edge. Henry II. surrounded the castle with a wall, at a cost of about 128*l*.[3]   The other entries in the *Pipe Rolls* probably refer to the first stone shell on the motte, and there is little doubt that the present Round Tower, though its height has been raised in modern times, and its masonry re-dressed and re-pointed so as to destroy all appearance of antiquity, is in the main of Henry II.'s building.   The frequent payments for stone show the nature of Henry's work.

Although so much masonry was put up in Henry II.'s reign, the greater part of what is now visible is not older than the time of Henry III.   The lower bailey seems to have been enlarged in his reign, as the castle

[1] In 1 virgata terræ quam Willelmus fil. Walteri habet in escambio pro terra sua quæ capta est ad burgum. P. 721.

[2] The *Red Book of the Exchequer*, which contains an abstract of the missing *Pipe Roll* of 1 Henry II., has an entry of 12s. paid to Richard de Clifwar for the exchange of his land, and regular payments are made later. There was another enlargement of the bailey in Henry III.'s reign, but the second bailey was then existing. See *Close Rolls*, i., 531b.

[3] "In operatione muri circa castellum 11*l*. 10s. 4*d*. Summa denariorum quos idem Ricardus [de Luci] misit in operatione predicta de ballia 128*l*. 9s." *Pipe Roll*, 20 Henry II., p. 116.

ditch was extended towards the town, and compensation given for houses taken down.[1] The upper (probably the original) ward is rectangular in shape, and with the motte and its ditches covers about $6\frac{1}{2}$ acres.[2] The state apartments, a chapel, and the Hall of St George, are in the upper ward, showing that this was the site of the original hall and chapel of the castle. The charter of agreement between Stephen and Henry in 1153 speaks of the *motte* of Windsor as equivalent to the castle.[3] Repairs of the motte are mentioned in the *Pipe Rolls* of Henry II.[4]

The value of the manor of Clewer had fallen since the Conquest; that of Windsor, which was worth 15*l.* T. R. E., but after the Conquest fell to 7*l.*, was again worth 15*l.* at the date of the Survey.[5]

WISBEACH, Cambridgeshire.—William I. built a castle here in 1072, after suppressing the revolt of Hereward, in order to hold in check the Cambridgeshire fen country.[6] There is an early mention of it in the Register of Thorney Abbey. This castle, after being several times rebuilt, is now completely destroyed, and "several rows of elegant houses built on the site." Nevertheless, there still remain distinct traces of the motte-and-bailey pattern in the gardens which now occupy the site of the original castle of King William; the present Crescent probably follows the line of the

---

[1] Tighe's *Annals of Windsor*, p. 21.

[2] There is a singular entry in the *Pipe Roll* of 7 Richard I., "pro fossato prosternando quod fuit inter motam et domos regis," clearly the ditch between the motte and the bailey. Mr Hope informs me that this can only refer to the northern part of the ditch, as the eastern portion was only filled up in 1824. Mr Hope thinks that the castle area has always included the lower bailey. I regret that Mr Hope's History of Windsor Castle did not appear in time to be used in this work.

[3] *Fœdera*, vol. i.   [4] *Pipe Rolls*, 30 Henry II.

[5] D. B., i., 62b, 2 ; 56b, 2.   [6] Roger of Wendover, in *anno*.

ditch. The meagre indications preserved in casual accounts confirm this. There was an inner castle of about 2 acres, just the area of the present garden enclosure, and an outer court, probably an addition, of some 4 acres.[1] Both areas were moated. Weston, a prisoner who was confined in the keep of this castle in the 17th century, has left an account of his captivity, in which he casually mentions that the keep or dungeon stood upon a high terrace, from which he could overlook the outer bailey, and was surrounded by a moat filled with water.[2]

The castle is not mentioned in Domesday, but as might be expected in a district which had been so ravaged by war, the value of the manor had fallen.

WORCESTER.—This borough, as we have seen, was fortified by Ethelfleda and her husband Ethelred in the 9th century. That the fortifications thus erected were those of a city and not of a castle is shown with sufficient clearness by the remarkable charter of this remarkable pair, in which they declare that they have built the *burh* at Worcester to shelter all the people, and the churches, and the bishop.[3] The castle is first mentioned in the *Anglo-Saxon Chronicle* in 1088, and it is to be noted that it is styled the king's castle. Urse d'Abitot, the Norman sheriff of Worcester, has the credit of having built the first castle, and Malmesbury relates that he seized part of the monks' cemetery for the bailey.[4] The monks, however, held on to their right,

---

[1] Walter and Cradock's *History of Wisbeach*, pp. 270-278.

[2] Morris' *Troubles of our Catholic Forefathers*, p. 223. This keep was one built by Bishop Morton in 1471.

[3] Birch's *Cartularium*, ii., 222.

[4] Ursus erat vicecomes Wigorniæ a rege constitutus, qui in ipsis pœne faucis monachorum castellum construxit, adeo ut fossatum cœmiterii partem decideret. *Gesta Pontif.*, p. 253.

and in the first year of Henry III. the bailey was restored to them by the guardians of the young king, the motte being reserved for the king's use.[1] The first wooden castle was burnt in 1113.[2] The tower or keep which succeeded it, and which was repaired by Henry II.,[3] may have been either of stone or wood; but in the order of John, that the gateway of the castle, which is of wood, is to be made of stone, we get a hint of the gradual transformation of the castle from a wooden to a stone fortress.[4]

Worcester Castle was outside the town, from Speed's map, and was near the Severn. The area now called College Green was no doubt the outer ward of the castle, which was restored to the convent by Henry III. The tower called Edgar's Tower was built by the monks as the gatehouse to their newly conceded close.[5] From the map given by Green, this outer bailey appears to have been roughly square; but there was also a small oblong inner ward, retained by the king, where the gaol was afterwards built. The area of the castle is said to have been between 3 and 4 acres.[6] The motte, which is mentioned several times in mediæval docu-

---

[1] "Castrum Wigorniæ nobis redditum est, tanquam jus noster, usquam motam turris." *Annales de Wigornia*, R. S., p. 407. "Rex Johanni Marescallo salutem: Mandamus vobis quod sine dilatione faciatis habere venerabili patri nostro domino Wigorniensi episcopo ballium castri nostri Wigorniæ, quod est jus ecclesiæ suæ; retenta ad opus nostrum mota ejusdem castri." *Patent Rolls*, 1 Henry III., p. 46.

[2] *Annales de Wigornia*, p. 375.

[3] "In reparatione turris Wigorniæ 8*l*." *Red Book of Exchequer*, ii., 656.

[4] "Precipimus tibi quod per visum liberorum et legalium hominum facias parari portam castri Wigorniæ, quæ nunc est lignea, lapideam, et bonam et pulchram." *Rot. de Liberate*, p. 93, 1204.

[5] Green's *History of Worcester*, i., 19.

[6] Allies' *Antiquities of Worcestershire*, p. 15. His words strictly apply to "the lofty mound called the keep, with its ditches, etc.," but probably the whole area was not more than 4 acres.

ments,[1] was completely levelled in 1848 ; it was then found out that it had been thrown up over some previous buildings, which were believed to be Roman, though this seems doubtful.[2]

The value of Worcester had risen since the Conquest.[3]

YORK (Fig. 39).—William the Conqueror built two castles at York, and the mottes of both these castles remain, one underneath Clifford's Tower, the keep of York Castle, the other, on the south side of the Ouse, still bearing the name of the Baile Hill, or the Old Baile.[4] The *Anglo-Saxon Chronicle* implies, though it does not directly state, that both these castles were built in 1068, on the occasion of William's first visit to York. The more detailed narrative of Ordericus shows that one was built in 1068, and the other at the beginning of 1069, on William's second visit.[5] Both were destroyed in September 1069, when the English and Danes captured York, and both were rebuilt before Christmas of the same year, when William held his triumphant Christmas feast at York.

This speedy erection, destruction, and re-erection is enough to prove that the castles of William in York were, like most other Norman castles, hills of earth with buildings and stockades of wood, especially as we find these hills of earth still remaining on the known sites of

[1] See the documents cited by Mr Round in his *Geoffrey de Mandeville*, Appendix O, and the *Pipe Rolls* of 1173. "In reparatione Mote et Gaiole de Wirecestra, £35, 13s. 8d."

[2] *Gentleman's Magazine*, i., 36, 1834. See Haverfield, "Romano-British Worcester," *Victoria County History of Worcestershire*, vol. i.

[3] D. B., i., 172.

[4] It is needless to remark that *baile* is the Norman word for an enclosure or courtyard ; Low Latin *ballia;* sometimes believed to be derived from *baculus*, a stick.

[5] Ordericus, ii., 188 (edition Prévost).

the castles. And we may be quite sure that the
Norman masonry, which Mr Freeman pictures as so
eagerly destroyed by the English, never existed.[1] But
the obstinate tendency of the human mind to make
things out older than they are has led to these earthen
hills being assigned to Britons, Romans, Saxons, Danes,
anybody rather than Normans. A single passage of
William of Malmesbury, in which he refers to the
castrum which the Danes had built at York in the
reign of Athelstan, is the sole vestige of basis for the
theory that the motte of Clifford's Tower is of Danish
origin.[2] The other theories have absolutely no foundation but conjecture. If Malmesbury was quoting from
some older source which is now lost, it is extremely
probable that the word *castrum* which he copied, did
not mean a castle in our sense of the word at all, but
was a translation of the word *burh*, which almost
certainly referred to a vallum or wall constructed round
the Danish suburb outside the walls of York. Such a
suburb there was, for there in 1055 stood the Danish
church of St Olave, in which Earl Siward was buried,
and the suburb was long known as the Earlsburgh or
Earl's Burh, probably because it contained the residence
of the Danish earls of Northumbria.[3] This suburb

---

[1] *Norman Conquest*, iv., 270. Mr Freeman has worked out the course
of events connected with the building and destruction of the castles with
his usual lucidity. But he never grasped the real significance of mottes,
though he emphatically maintained that the native English did not build
castles.

[2] "Ethelstanus castrum quod olim Dani in Eboraco obfirmaverant ad
solum diruit, ne esset quo se tutari perfidia posset." *Gesta Regum*, ii., 134.

[3] Widdrington, *Analecta Eboracensia*, p. 120. It was this suburb which
Alan, Earl of Richmond gave to the Abbey of St Mary at York, which he
had founded. "Ecclesiam sancti Olavii in quâ capud abbatiæ in honorem
sanctæ Mariæ melius constitutum est, et *burgum in quo ecclesia sita est.*"
Mon. Ang., iii., 547. For the addition of new boroughs to old ones see
ante, p. 174, under Norwich. Although Athelstan destroyed the fortifications

was not anywhere near Clifford's Tower, but in quite a different part of the city. To prove that both the mottes were on entirely new sites, we have the assurance of Domesday Book that out of the seven *shires* or wards into which the city was divided, one was laid waste for the castles ; so that there was clearly a great destruction of houses to make room for the new castles.[1]

What has been assumed above receives striking confirmation from excavations made recently (1903) in the motte of Clifford's Tower. At the depth of 13 feet were found remains of a wooden structure, surmounted by a quantity of charred wood.[2] Now the accounts of the destruction of the castles in 1069 do not tell us that they were burned, but thrown down and broken to pieces.[3] But the keep which was restored by William, and on the repair of which Henry II. spent 15*l.* in 1172,[4] was burnt down in the frightful massacre of the Jews at York Castle in 1190.[5] The excavations disclosed the interesting fact that this castle stood on a lower motte than the present one, and that when the burnt keep was replaced by a new one the motte was raised to its present height, "an outer crust of firmer and more clayey material being made round the older

of this borough, they were evidently renewed when the Danish earls took up their residence there, for when Earl Alan persuaded the monks from Whitby to settle there one inducement which he offered was the fortification of the site, "loci munitionem." *Mon. Ang.,* iii., 545.

[1] In Eboraco civitate T. R. E. præter scyram archiepiscopi fuerunt 6 scyræ ; una ex his est wasta in castellis. D. B., i., 298.

[2] *Notes on Clifford's Tower,* by George Benson and H. Platnauer, published by the York Philosophical Society.

[3] "Thone castel tobræcon and towurpan." *A.-S. C.* See Freeman, *N. C.,* iv., 270.

[4] "In operatione turris de Euerwick, 15*l.* 7*s.* 3*d.*" *Pipe Roll,* 19 Henry II., vol. xix., 2. We assume that William's second keep lasted till Henry II.'s reign.

[5] *Benedict of Peterborough,* ii., 107.

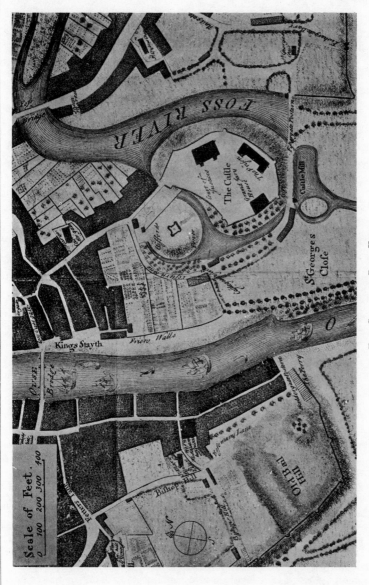

YORK CASTLE AND BAILE HILL.
(From a plan by P. Chassereau, 1750.)

Fig. 39.

[To face p. 244.

summit, and a lighter material placed inside this crater
to bring it up to the necessary level." This restoration
must have taken place in the third year of Richard I.,
when 28*l.* was spent "on the work of the castle."[1]
This small sum shows that the new keep also was of
wood; and remains of timber work were in fact found
on the top of the motte during the excavations, though
unfortunately they were not sufficiently followed up to
determine whether they belonged to a wooden tower or
to a platform intended to consolidate the motte.[2] It is
extremely likely that this third keep was blown down by
the high wind of 1228, when 2s. was paid "for collecting
the timber of York Castle blown down by the wind."[3]
In its place arose the present keep, one of the most
remarkable achievements of the reign of Henry III.[4]

---

[1] "In operatione castri 28*l.* 13*s.* 9*d.*" *Pipe Roll*, 3 Richard I.
Under the year 1193, after relating the tragedy of the Jews at York Castle,
Hoveden says: "Deinde idem cancellarius [William de Longchamp] tradidit
Osberto de Lunchamp, fratri suo, comitatum Eboracensem in custodia, et
precepit firmari castellum in veteri castellario quod Rex Willelmus Rufus
ibi construxerat." III., 34, R. S. The expression *vetus castellarium* would
lead us to think of the Old Baile, which certainly had this name from an
early period; and Hoveden, being a Yorkshireman as well as a very
accurate writer, was probably aware of the difference between the two
castles. But if he meant the Old Baile, then both the castles were restored
at about the same time. "Rufus" must be a slip, unless there was some
rebuilding in Rufus' reign of which we do not know.

[2] Messrs Benson and Platnauer are of the former opinion. "The
existence of a second layer of timber seems to show that the fortification
destroyed was rebuilt in wood." *Notes on Clifford's Tower*, p. 2.

[3] "Pro mairemio castri Ebor. prostrato per ventum colligendo, 2s."
Pipe Roll, 19 Henry III. It is, of course, a conjecture that this accident
happened to the keep; but the keep would be the part most exposed to the
wind, and the *scattering* of the timber, so that it had to be collected, is just
what would happen if a timber structure were blown off a motte.

[4] As the writer was the first to publish this statement, it will be well to
give the evidence on which it rests. The keep of York is clearly Early
English in style, and of an early phase of the style. It is, however, evident
to every one who has carefully compared our dated keeps, that castle
architecture always lags behind church architecture in style-development,
and must be judged by different standards. We should therefore be

The old ground-plan of the square Norman keep was now abandoned, and replaced by a quatrefoil. The work occupied thirteen years, from the 30th to the 43rd Henry III., and the total sum expended was 1927*l.* 8*s.* 7*d.*, equal to about 40,000*l.* of our money. This remarkable fact has slumbered in the unpublished *Pipe Rolls* for 700 years, never having been unearthed by any of the numerous historians of York.

The keep was probably the first work in stone at York Castle, and for a long time it was probably the only defensive masonry. The banks certainly had only a wooden stockade in the early part of Henry III.'s reign, as timber from the forest of Galtres was ordered for the repair of breaches in the *palicium* in 1225.[1] As late as Edward II.'s reign there was a *pelum*, or stockade, round the keep, on top of a *murus*, which was

prepared to find this and most other keeps to be of later date than their architecture would suggest. Moreover, the expenditure entered to York Castle in the reigns of Henry II., Richard I., and John, is quite insufficient to cover the cost of a stone keep. The *Pipe Rolls* of Henry III.'s reign decide the matter, as they show the sums which he expended annually on this castle. It is true they never mention the *turris*, but always the *castrum;* we must also admit that the *turris* and *castrum* are often distinguished in the writs, even as late as Edward III.'s reign. (*Close Rolls*, 1334.) On the other hand extensive acquaintance with the *Pipe Rolls* proves that though the mediæval scribe may have an occasional fit of accuracy, he is generally very loose in his use of words, and his distinctions must never be pressed. Take, for instance, the case of Orford, where the word used in the *Pipe Rolls* is always *castellum*, but it certainly refers to the keep, as there are no other buildings at Orford. Other instances might be given in which the word *castellum* clearly applies to the keep. It should be mentioned that in 1204 John gave an order for stone for the castle (*Close Rolls*, i., 4b), but the amounts on the bill for it in the *Pipe Rolls* show that it was not used for any extensive building operations.

[1] "Mandatum est Galterio de Cumpton forestario de Gauteris quod ad pontem et domos castri Eboraci et breccas palicii ejusdem castri reparandos et emendandos Vicecomitem Eboraci mæremium habere faciat in foresta de Gauteris per visum, etc." *Close Rolls*, ii., 61b.

undoubtedly an earthen bank.[1] At present the keep occupies the whole top of the motte except a small *chemin de ronde*, but the fact so frequently alluded to in the writs, that a stockade ran round the keep, proves that a small courtyard existed there formerly, as was usually the case with important keeps. Another writ of Edward II.'s reign shows that the motte was liable to injury from the floods of the River Fosse,[2] and probably its size has thus been reduced.

The present bailey of York Castle does not follow the lines of the original one, but is an enlargement made in 1825. A plan made in 1750, and reproduced here, shows that the motte was surrounded by its own ditch, which is now filled up, and that the bailey, around which a branch of the Fosse was carried, was of the very common bean-shaped form; it was about 3 acres in extent. The motte and bailey were both considerably outside what is believed to have been the Anglo-Saxon rampart of York,[3] but the motte was so placed as to overlook the city.

The value of the city of York, in spite of the sieges and sacks which it had undergone, and in spite of there being 540 houses "so empty that they pay nothing at all," had risen at the date of the Survey from 53*l.* in King Edward's time to 100*l.* in King William's.[4] This extraordinary rise in value can only be attributed to

[1] Order to expend up to 6 marks in repairing the wooden peel about the keep of York Castle, which peel is now fallen down. *Cal. of Close Rolls*, 17 Edward II., 25.

[2] *Cal. of Close Rolls*, 1313-1318, 262. *Mota* is wrongly translated *moat*.

[3] See Mr Cooper's *York: The Story of its Walls and Castles*. During Messrs Benson and Platnauer's excavations, a prehistoric crouching burial was found in the ground below the motte, 4 feet 6 inches under the present level. This raises the question whether William utilised an existing prehistoric barrow for the nucleus of his motte.

[4] D. B., i., 298a.

increased trade and increased exactions, the former being promoted by the greater security given to the roads by the castles, the latter due to the tolls on the high-roads and waterways, which belonged to the king, and the various "customs" belonging to the castles, which, though new, were henceforth equally part of his rights.

THE BAILE HILL, York (Fig. 39).—There can be no doubt whatever that this still existing motte was the site of one of William's castles at York, and it is even probable that it was the older of the two, as Mr Cooper conjectures from its position on the south side of the river.[1] The castle bore the name of the Old Baile at least as early as the 14th century, perhaps even in the 12th.[2] In 1326 a dispute arose between the citizens of York and Archbishop William de Melton as to which of them ought to repair the wall around the Old Baile. The mayor alleged that the district was under the express jurisdiction of the archbishop, exempt from that of the city ; the archbishop pleaded that it stood within the ditches of the city.[3] The meaning of this dispute can only be understood in the light of facts which have recently been unearthed by the industry and observation of Mr T. P. Cooper, of York.[4] The Old Baile, like so many of William's castles, originally stood outside the ramparts of the city. The original Roman walls of York (it is believed) enclosed only a small space on the eastern shore of the Ouse, and before the Norman

---

[1] *York : The Story of its Walls and Castles*, by T. P. Cooper, p. 222.

[2] See the passage from Hoveden already quoted, *ante*, p. 245.

[3] Drake's *Eboracum*, App. xliv.

[4] See Mr Cooper's *York: The Story of its Walls and Castles*, which contains a mass of new material from documentary sources, and sheds quite unexpected light on the history of the York fortifications. I am indebted to Mr Cooper's courtesy for some of the extracts cited above relating to York Castle.

Conquest the city had far outgrown these bounds, and therefore had been enlarged in Anglo-Saxon times. It appears that the Micklegate suburb was then for the first time enclosed with a wall, and as this district is spoken of in Domesday Book as "the shire of the archbishop," it was evidently under his jurisdiction. At a later period this wall was buried in an earthen bank, which probably carried a palisade on top, until the palisade was replaced by stone walls in the reign of Henry III.[1]

The evidence of the actual remains renders it more than probable that this rampart turned towards the river at a point 500 feet short of its present angle, so that the Old Baile, when first built, was quite outside the city walls.[2] This is exactly how we should expect to find a castle of William the Norman's in relation to one of the most turbulent cities of the realm ; and, as we have seen, the other castle at York was similarly placed. By the time of Archbishop Melton the south-western suburb was already enclosed in the new stone walls built in the 13th century, and these walls had been carried along the west and south banks of the Old Baile, so as to enclose that castle within the city. This was the archbishop's pretext for trying to lay upon the citizens the duty of maintaining the Old Baile. But probably on account of his ancient authority in this part of the city, the cause went against him; though he

[1] Cooper's *York*, chapters ii. and iv. 100*l.* was spent by the sheriff in fortifying the walls of York in the sixth year of Henry III. After this there are repeated grants for murage in the same and the following reign. There are some Early English buttresses in the walls, but the majority are later. No part of the walls contains Norman work.

[2] The details of this evidence, which consist mainly in (1) a structural difference in the extended rampart; (2) a subsidence in the ground marking the old line of the city ditch, will be found in Mr Cooper's work, p. 224.

stipulated that whatever he did in the way of fortification was of his own option, and was not to be accounted a precedent. A contemporary chronicler says that he enclosed the Old Baile first with stout planks 18 feet long, afterwards with a stone wall :[1] an interesting proof that wooden fortifications were still used in the reign of Edward III.

Though the base court of the Old Baile is now built over, its area and ditches were visible in Leland's time,[2] and can still be guessed at by the indications Mr Cooper has noted. The area of the bailey must have been nearly 3 acres, and its shape nearly square. This measurement includes the motte, which was placed in the south-west corner on the line of the banks ; it thus overlooked the river as well as the city.[3]

[1] " Locum in Eboraco qui dicitur Vetus Ballium, primo spissis et longis 18 pedum tabulis, secundo lapideo muro fortiter includebat." T. Stubbs, in Raine's *Historians of the Church of York*, ii., 417, R. S.

[2] " The plotte of this castelle is now caullid the Olde Baile, and the area and diches of it do manifestley appere." *Itin.*, i., 60.

[3] See the plan in Mr Cooper's *York*, p. 217.

CHAPTER VIII

MOTTE-CASTLES IN NORTH WALES

MOTTE-CASTLES are as common in Wales as they are in England, and in certain districts much more common. It is now our task to show how they got there. They were certainly not built (in the first instance at any rate) by the native inhabitants, for they do not correspond to what we know to have been the state of society in Wales during the Anglo-Saxon period.[1] The Welsh were then in the tribal condition, a condition, as we have shown, inconsistent with the existence of the private castle. The residence of the king or chieftain, as we know from the Welsh Laws, was a great hall, such as seems to have been the type of chieftains' residence among all the northern nations at that time. "It was adapted for the joint occupation of a number of tribesmen living together."[2]

Pennant describes the residence of Ednowen, a Welsh chieftain of the 12th century, as follows: "The remains are about 30 yards square; the entrance about 7 feet wide, with a large upright stone on each side for a doorcase; the walls were formed of large stones uncemented by any mortar; in short the structure shows

---

[1] "In the Wales of the Laws, the social system is tribal." Owen Edwards, *Wales*, p. 39.

[2] Vinogradoff, *Growth of the Manor*, pp. 15-16.

the very low state of Welsh architecture at this time; it may be paralleled only by the artless fabric of a cattle-house."[1] This certainly is a hall and not a castle.

The so-called Dimetian Code indeed tells us that the king is to have a man and a horse from every hamlet, with hatchets for constructing his castles (gestyll) at the king's cost; but the Venedotian Code, which is the older MS., says that these hatchet-men are to form encampments (uuesten); that is, they are to cut down trees and form either stockades on banks or rude *zerebas* for the protection of the host.[2] It is clearly laid down in the Codes what buildings the king's villeins are to erect for him at his residences: a hall, buttery, kitchen, dormitory, stable, dog-house, and little house.[3] In none of these lists is anything mentioned which has the smallest resemblance to a castle, not even a tower. We can imagine that these buildings were enclosed in an earthwork or stockade, but it is not mentioned.[4]

Wales was never one state, except for very short periods. Normally it was divided into three states, Gwynedd or North Wales, Powys or Mid-Wales, and Deheubarth, all almost incessantly at war with each

---

[1] Pennant's *Tour in Wales*, Rhys' edition, ii., 234.

[2] *Ancient Laws and Institutes of Wales*, pp. 238, 94. The MS. of the *Leges Wallicæ* is not earlier than the 13th century. The other editions of the Laws are even later. See Wade Evans, *Welsh Mediæval Law*, for the most recent criticism of the Laws of Howel Dda.

[3] The *Leges Wallicæ* say: "Villani regis debent facere novem domos ad opus regis; scilicet, aulam, cameram, coquinam, penu (capellam), stabulum, kynorty (stabulum canum), horreum, odyn (siccarium) et latrinam." P. 791.

[4] The word Din or Dinas, so often used for a fort in Wales, is cognate with the German *Zaun*, Anglo-Saxon *tun*, and means a fenced place. Neither it nor the Irish form *dun* have any connection with the Anglo-Saxon *dun*, a hill. See J. E. Lloyd, *Welsh Place-names*, "Y Cymmrodor," xi., 24.

other.[1]   Other subdivisions asserted themselves as
opportunity offered, so that the above rough division
into provinces must not be regarded as always accurate.
A Wales thus divided, and perpetually rent by internal
conflicts, invited the aggression of the Saxons, and it
is probable that the complete subjugation of Britain
would have been accomplished by the descendants of
Alfred, if it had not been for the Danish invasions.
The position of the Welsh kings after the time of
Athelstan seems to have been that of tributaries, who
threw off their allegiance whenever it was possible to do
so.   But still the Anglo-Saxon frontier continued to
advance.   Professor Lloyd has shown, from a careful
examination of Domesday Book, that even before the
Norman Conquest the English held the greater part of
what is now Flintshire and East Denbighshire, and
were advancing into the vale of Montgomery and the
Radnor district.[2]   The victories of Griffith ap Llywelyn,
an able prince who succeeded in bringing all Wales
under his sway, devastated these English colonies ; but
his defeat by Earl Harold in 1063 restored the English
ascendancy over these regions.   The unimpeachable
evidence of Domesday Book shows that a considerable
district in North Wales and a portion of Radnor were
held respectively by Earl Edwin and Earl Harold before
the Norman Conquest.   Moreover, the fact mentioned
by the *Anglo-Saxon Chronicle* in 1065, that Harold was
building a hunting-seat for King Edward at Portskewet,
after he had subdued it, suggests that the land between
Wye and Usk, which Domesday Book reckons under
Gloucestershire, was a conquest of Harold's.[3]

[1] It is doubtful whether Deheubarth ever included the small independent
states of Gwent, Brecknock, and Glamorgan.
[2] " Wales and the Coming of the Normans," *Cymmrodorion Trans.*, 1899
[3] There is an earthwork near Portskewet, a semicircular cliff camp with

The Norman Conqueror was not the man to slacken his hold on any territory which had been won by the Saxons. But there is no succinct history of his conquests in Wales; we have to make it out, in most cases, from notices that are scarcely more than allusive, and from the surer, though scanty, ground of documents. It is noteworthy that the *Anglo-Saxon Chronicle* is so hostile to the Norman kings that it discounts their successes in Wales. Thus we have only the briefest notice of William I.'s invasion of South Wales, which was very probably the beginning of the conquest of that region; and several expeditions of William II. are spoken of as entirely futile, though as we are told that the existing castles were still held by the Normans, or new ones were built, it is clear that this summing-up is not strictly correct.[1] Our Welsh authorities, the *Annales Cambriæ* and the *Brut y Tywysogion*,[2] seem to give a fairly candid account of the period, although the dates in the *Brut* are for the most part wrong (sometimes by three years), and they hardly ever give us a view of the situation as a whole. They tell us when the Welsh rushed down and burnt the castles built by the Normans

three ramparts and two ditches. It is scarcely likely that this can be Harold's work, as Roman bricks are said to have been found there. Willet's *Monmouthshire*, p. 244. Athelstan had made the Wye the frontier of Wales. *Malmesbury*, ii., 134.

[1] See *A.-S. C.*, anno 1097, and compare the entry for 1096 with the account in the *Brut* for 1093, which shows that the Norman castles had been restored, after being for the most part demolished by the Welsh.

[2] The *Brut y Tywysogion*, or *Story of the Princes*, exists in no MS. older than the 14th century. It and the *Annales Cambriæ* have been disgracefully edited for the *Rolls* Series, and the topographical student will find no help from these editions. See Mr Phillimore's criticism of them, in *Y Cymmrodor*, vol. xi. The Aberpergwm MS. of the *Brut*, known also as the *Gwentian Chronicle*, has been printed in the *Archæologia Cambrensis* for 1864; it contains a great deal of additional information, but as Mr Phillimore observes, so much of it is forgery that none of it can be trusted when unsupported.

in the conquered districts, but do not always tell when the Norman recovered and rebuilt them.

Fortunately we are not called upon here to trace the history of the cruel and barbarous warfare between Normans and Welsh. No one can turn that blood-stained page without wishing that the final conquest had come two hundred years earlier, to put an end to the tragedy of suffering which must have been so largely the portion of the dwellers in Wales and the Marches after the coming of the Normans.[1] Our business with both Welsh and Normans is purely archæological. We hold no brief for the Normans, nor does it matter to us whether they kept their hold on Wales or were driven out by the Welsh; our concern is with facts, and the solid facts with which we have to deal are the castles whose remains still exist in Wales, and whose significance we have to interpret.

"Wales was under his sway, and he built castles therein," says the *Anglo-Saxon Chronicle*, in summing up the reign of the Conqueror; a passage which is scarcely consistent with its previous almost complete silence about events in Wales. There can be little doubt that William aimed at a complete conquest of Wales, and that the policy he adopted was the creation of great earldoms along the Welsh border, endowed with special privileges, one of which was the right of conquering whatever they could from the Welsh.[2] To these earldoms he appointed some of his strongest men, men

[1] The barbarity on both sides was frightful, but in the case of the Welsh, it was often their own countrymen, and even near relations, who were the victims. And so little patriotism existed then in Wales that the Normans could always find allies amongst some of the Welsh chieftains. Patriotism, however, is a virtue of more recent growth than the 11th century.

[2] There is, however, no contemporary evidence for the existence of the Marcher lordships before the end of the 12th century. See Duckett "On the Marches of Wales," *Arch. Camb.*, 1881.

little troubled by scruples of justice or mercy, but capable leaders in war or diplomacy. It was an essential part of the plan that every conquest should be secured by the building of castles, just as had been done in England. And we have now to trace very briefly the outline of Norman conquest in Wales by the castles which they have left behind them.

We shall confine ourselves to those castles which are mentioned in the *Brut y Tywysogion*, the *Pipe Rolls*, or other trustworthy documents between 1066 and 1216, the end of King John's reign. Of many of these castles only the earthworks remain ; of many others the original plan, exactly similar to that of the early castles of Normandy and France, is still to be traced, though masked by the masonry of a later age. Grose remarked but could not explain the fact that we continually read of the castles of the Marches being burnt and utterly destroyed, and a few months later we find them again standing and in working order. This can only, but easily, be explained when we understand that they were wooden castles built on mottes, quickly restored after a complete destruction of the wooden buildings.

North Wales appears to have been the earliest conquest of the Normans, though not the most lasting. North Wales comprised the Welsh kingdoms of Gwynedd and Powys. Gwynedd covered the present shires of Anglesea, Carnarvon, and Merioneth, and the mountainous districts round Snowdon.[1] Powys stretched from the estuary of the Dee to the upper course of the Wye, and roughly included Flint, Denbigh, Montgomery, and Radnor shires. Hugh of Avranches, Earl of Chester, was the great instrument of Norman

---

[1] The districts of Cyfeiliog and Arwystli, in the centre of Wales, were also reckoned in Gwynedd.

conquest in Gwynedd, and in the northern part of Powys, which lay so near his own dominions. He was evidently a man in whose ability William had great confidence, as he removed him from Tutbury to the more difficult and dangerous position of Chester, and gave his earldom palatine privileges ; all the land in Cheshire was held under the earl, and he was a sort of little king in his county.

Hugh appears to have at once commenced the conquest of North Wales. As Professor Lloyd remarks, Domesday Book shows us Deganwy as the most advanced Norman post on the North Welsh coast, while on the Bristol Channel they had got no further than Caerleon.[1] In advancing to the valley of the Clwyd and building a castle at Rhuddlan, the Normans were only securing the district which had already been conquered by Harold in 1063, when he burnt the hall of King Griffith at Rhuddlan. Nearly the whole of Flintshire (its manors are enumerated by Domesday Book under Cheshire) was held by Earl Hugh in 1086, so that he commanded the entire road from Chester to Rhuddlan. His powerful vassal, Robert of Rhuddlan, who became the terror of North Wales, besides the lands which he held of Earl Hugh, held also directly of the King Rhos and Rhufeniog, districts which roughly correspond to the modern shire of Denbigh, and "Nort Wales" which Professor Lloyd takes to mean the remainder of the principality of Gwynedd, from which the rightful ruler, Griffith ap Cynan, had been driven as an exile to Ireland.

It does not appear that there was any fortification at RHUDDLAN[2] before the "castle newly erected" by

---

[1] "Wales and the Coming of the Normans," *Cymmrodorion Trans.*, 1899.
[2] In the descriptions of castles in this chapter, those which have not

Earl Hugh and his vassal Robert. They shared between them the castle and the *new borough* which was built near it.[1]   One word about this new borough, which will apply to the other boroughs planted by Norman castles. There were no towns in Wales of any importance before the Norman Conquest, and this civilising institution of the borough is the one great set-off to the cruelty and unrighteousness of the conquest. Mills, markets, and trade arose where castles were seated, and civilisation followed in their train.

The castle of Hugh and Robert was not the magnificent building which still stands at Rhuddlan, for that is entirely the work of Edward I., and there is documentary evidence that Edward made a purchase of new land for the site of his castle.[2]   More probably Robert and Hugh had a wooden castle on the now reduced motte which may be seen to the south of Edward's castle. In Gough's time this motte was still "surrounded with a very deep ditch, including the abbey." Nothing can be seen of this ditch now, except on the south side of the motte, where a deep ravine runs up from the river. As from Gough's description the

been specially visited for this work are marked with an asterisk. Those which have been visited by others than the writer are marked with initials : D. H. M. being Mr D. H. Montgomerie, F.S.A. ; B. T. S., Mr Basil T. Stallybrass ; and H. W., the Rev. Herbert White, M.A. This plan will be followed in the three succeeding chapters.

[1] "Hugo comes tenet de rege Roelent (Rhuddlan). Ibi T. R. E. jacebat Englefield, et tota erat wasta. Edwinus comes tenebat. Quando Hugo comes recipit similiter erat wasta. Modo habet in dominio medietatem castelli quod Roelent vocatur, et caput est hujus terræ. . . . Robertus de Roelent tenet de Hugone comite medietatem ejusdem castelli et burgi, in quo habet ipse Robertus 10 burgenses et medietatem ecclesiæ. Ibi est novus burgus et in eo 10 burgenses. . . . In ipso manerio est factum noviter castellum similiter Roeland appellatum." D. B., i., 269a, 1.

[2] Ayloffe's *Rotuli Walliæ*, p. 75. "De providendo indempnitati magistri Ricardi Bernard, Personæ Ecclesiæ de Rothelan', in recompensionem terræ suæ occupatæ ad placeam castri de Rothelan' elargandam."

hillock (called Tut Hill)[1] was within the precincts of the priory of Black Friars, founded in the 13th century, it is extremely probable that Edward gave the site of the old castle to the Dominicans when he built his new one.[2]

Another of the castles of Robert of Rhuddlan was DEGANWY, or Gannoc, which defended the mouth of the Conway.[3] Here it is said that there was an ancient seat of the kings of Gwynedd.[4] The two conical hills which rise here offer an excellent site for fortification, one of them being large enough on top for a considerable camp. The Norman Conqueror treated them as two mottes, and connected them by walls so as to form a bailey below them. The stone fortifications are probably the remains of the castle built by the Earl of Chester in 1211.[5] This castle was naturally a sorely contested point, and often passed from hand to hand;

[1] Tut or Toot Hill means "look-out" hill; the name is not unfrequently given to abandoned mottes. The word is still used locally. *Cf.* Christison, *Early Fortifications in Scotland*, p. 16.

[2] Such presentations of abandoned castle sites, and of old wooden castles, to the church, were not uncommon. We have seen how the site of Montacute Castle was given to the Cluniac monks (*ante*, p. 170). Thicket Priory, in Yorkshire, occupied the site of the castle of Wheldrake; and William de Albini gave the site and materials of the old castle of Buckenham, in Norfolk, to the new castle which he founded there. The materials, but not the site, of the wooden castle of Montferrand were given in Stephen's reign to Meaux Abbey, and served to build some of the monastic offices. *Chron. de Melsa*, i., 106.

[3] "Fines suos dilatavit, et in monte Dagannoth, qui mari contiguus est, fortissimum castellum condidit." *Ordericus*, iii., 284 (edition Prévost). The verb *condere* is never used except for a new foundation.

[4] The *Brut* says that in the year 823 the Saxons destroyed the *Castle* of Deganwy. This is one of the only two instances in which the word *castell* is used in this Welsh chronicle before the coming of the Normans. As the MS. is not earlier than the 14th century it would be idle to claim this as a proof of the existence of a castle at this period. *Castell*, in Welsh, is believed to have come straight from the Latin, and was applied to any kind of fortress. Lloyd, *Welsh Place-names*, "Y Cymmrodor," xi., 28.

[5] The "new castle of Aberconwy" mentioned by the *Brut* in 1211, undoubtedly means this new stone castle built by the earl at Deganwy, as the castle of Conway did not then exist.

but it was in English possession in the reign of Henry III. It was abandoned when Edward I. built his great castle at Conway.

With its usual indifference, the Survey mentions no castle in Flintshire, but we may be sure that the castle of MOLD, or Montalto (Fig. 40), was one of the earliest by which the Norman acquisitions in that region were defended,[1] though it is not mentioned in authentic history until 1147. The tradition that it was built by Robert de Monte Alto, one of the barons of the Earl of Chester, is no doubt correct, though the assumption of Welsh legend-makers that the *Gwydd Grug*, or great tumulus, from which this castle derives its Welsh name, existed before the castle, may be dismissed as baseless. The motte of Robert de Monte Alto still exists, and is uncommonly high and perfect; it has two baileys, separated by great ditches, and appears to have had a shell on top. [D. H. M.] The castle was regarded as specially strong, and its reduction by Owen Gwynedd in 1147 was one of the sweetest triumphs that the Welsh ever won.[2]

It is clear from the *Life of Griffith ap Cynan*[3] that the Earl of Chester had conquered and incastellated Gwynedd before the accession of William Rufus. This valuable document unfortunately gives no dates, but it mentions in particular the castle at Aberlleinog,[4] one at

[1] See Pennant, ii., 151 ; and *Arch. Camb.*, 1891, p. 321.

[2] *Brut of Tywysogion*, 1145.

[3] Published with a Latin translation in *Arch. Camb.*, 1866. "He built castles in various places, after the manner of the French, in order that he might better hold the country."

[4] The *Brut* also mentions the castle of Aberlleinog, and says it was built in 1096 ; *rebuilt* would have been more correct, as the "Life of Griffith ap Cynan" shows that it was built by the Earl of Chester, and burnt by Griffith, before the expedition of 1096 (really 1098), when Hugh, Earl of Shrewsbury, met with his death on the shore near this castle, from an arrow shot by King Magnus Barefoot, who came to the help of the Welsh.

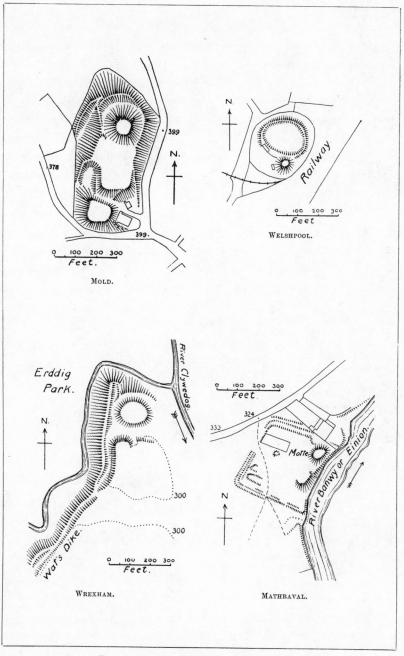

FIG. 40.—MOTTE-CASTLES OF NORTH WALES.

[To face p. 260.

Carnarvon, one at Bangor, and one in Merioneth. The motte at ABERLLEINOG, near Beaumaris, still exists, and the half-moon bailey is traceable, but the curious little round towers and revetting wall in masonry on the motte were probably built to carry guns at the time of the Civil War, when this castle was besieged by the Royalists. At CARNARVON the magnificent castle of Edward I. has displaced all former erections, yet some evidence for a motte-and-bailey plan may be found in the fact that the northern portion of the castle has evidently been once separated by a ditch from the southern, and is also much higher.[1] On the hills above BANGOR, Pennant thought he had discovered the remains of Earl Hugh's castle, but having carefully examined these walls, we are convinced that they never formed part of a castle at all, as they are much too thin; nor are there any vestiges of earthworks.[2] We are disposed to think that instead of at Bangor, the castle of Earl Hugh was at ABER, often spoken of as ABERMENAI in the *Chronicles*, and evidently the most important port on the Straits. At Aber there still remains a motte which must have belonged to an important castle, as it was afterwards one of the seats of Llywelyn ap Jorwerth, Prince of Gwynedd. The castle in Merioneth cannot be certainly identified.

In one of the invasions of William Rufus, which both the *Anglo-Saxon Chronicle* and the *Brut* describe as so unsuccessful, we hear that he encamped at MUR

---

[1] Mr Hartshorne in his paper on Carnarvon Castle (*Arch. Journ.*, vii.) cites a document stating that a wall 18 perches long had been begun *round the moat* [possibly *motam;* original not given]. He also cites from the *Pipe Rolls* an item for wages to *carriers of earth dug out of the castle.*

[2] This ruined wall runs in a straight line through the wood on the ridge to the east of the town; at one place it turns at right angles; at the back of the golf pavilion is a portion still erect, showing that it was a dry built wall of very ordinary character.

CASTELL, a place undoubtedly the same as what is now called TOMEN-Y-MUR, a motte standing just inside a Roman camp, on the Roman road leading from Shropshire into Merioneth and Carnarvon. This motte is surrounded by a ditch; there are traces of the usual earthen rampart round the top, now mutilated by landslips.[1] We may, with great probability, assume that this motte was thrown up by William Rufus, and that the Roman camp served as a bailey for his invading host. Whether it was garrisoned for the Normans we cannot say, but it evidently formed an important post on a route often followed by their invading armies, as Henry I. is said to have encamped there twice.[2] It is one of the few mottes which stand in a wild and mountainous situation, and its purpose no doubt was purely military.[3]

The earls of Chester did not retain the sovereignty of Gwynedd; on the death of Rufus, Griffith ap Cynan returned, and obtained possession of Anglesea. He was favourably received at the court of Henry I., and gradually recovered possession of the whole of Gwynedd. In 1114 Henry had to undertake a great expedition against him to enforce the payment of tribute;[4] from which, and from the peaceful manner in which Griffith seems to have acquired his principality, we may infer that this tribute was the bargain of his possession. It very likely suited Henry's policy better to have a tributary Welsh prince than a too powerful earl of Chester.

[1] Roman masonry has been exposed in the bank of the station.
[2] *Life of Griffith ap Cynan; Brut*, 1111.
[3] *Arch. Camb.*, iv., series 296 and 911.
[4] The *Anglo-Saxon Chronicle* dates this expedition in 1114, and says that Henry caused castles to be built in Wales. The *Brut* mentions the large tribute, 1111.

The reigns of the three first Norman kings were the time in which Norman supremacy in Wales made its greatest advances. With the accession of Stephen and the civil war which followed it came the great opportunity for the Welsh of throwing off the Norman yoke. Powys appears to have been the only province which remained faithful to the English allegiance, under Madoc ap Meredith.[1] The history of Norman conquest in Powys is more confused than that of Gwynedd, but Domesday shows us that Rainald, the Sheriff of Shropshire, a vassal of Earl Roger of Shrewsbury, was seated at Edeyrnion and Cynlle, two districts along the upper valley of the Dee.[2] Robert of Rhuddlan held part of his grant of "Nort Wales," namely the hundred of Arwystli, in the very centre of Wales, under Earl Roger. Professor Lloyd remarks, "Earl Roger claimed the same authority over Powys as Earl Hugh over Gwynedd, and the theory that the princes of this region were subject to the lords of Salop survived the fall of the House of Montgomery."[3]

We have already spoken of Earl Roger de Montgomeri and his brood of able and unscrupulous sons.[4] The palatine earldom of Shrewsbury lay along the eastern border of central Powys, and must soon have proved a menace to that Welsh kingdom. Domesday Book shows us that Earl Roger had already planted his castle of Montgomery well within the Welsh border at that date. But the ambition of Earl Roger and his

---

[1] *Brut*, 1149. Madoc ap Meredith, with the assistance of Ranulf, Earl of Chester, prepared to rise against Owen Gwynedd, son of Griffith ap Cynan.

[2] D. B., i., 255a. Professor Lloyd says, "Maelor Saesneg, Cydewain, Ceri, and Arwystli came under Norman authority, and paid renders of money or kine in token of subjection." "Wales and the Coming of the Normans," *Cymmrodor. Trans.*, 1899.

[3] *Ibid.*   [4] See page 130.

sons stretched beyond their immediate borders. It is probable that they used the upper Severn valley, which they fortified by the castle of Montgomery, and possibly by the castle of Welshpool, as their road into Ceredigion, for we find Earl Roger named by the *Brut* as the builder of the castle of Cilgerran,[1] and some say of Cardigan also. Possibly he was helping his son Arnolf in the conquest of Pembroke. In 1098 we find his successor, Earl Hugh, allied with the Earl of Chester in the invasion of Anglesea.

MONTGOMERY. — This castle is named from the ancestral seat of its founder.[2] The motte-and-bailey plan is still very apparent in the ruins, though the motte is represented by a precipitous rock, only a few feet higher than the baileys attached, and separated from them by a ditch cut through the headland. The masonry, the chief part of which is the shell wall and towers on this isolated rock, is none of it older than the reign of Henry III., when large sums were spent on this castle, and it is spoken of in a writ as "the new Castle of Montgomery."[3] Yet even then the whole of the defences were not remade in stone, as bretasches of timber are ordered in a *mandamus* of 1223.[4] The four wards are all roughly rectilateral. The castle was never recovered permanently by the Welsh, and after the forfeiture of Robert Belesme, the third Earl of Shrewsbury, in 1101, the Crown kept this important border fortress in its own hands throughout the Middle Ages.

Although Montgomery Castle is the only one mentioned in that region at the same date, there must have been many others, for in 1225 Henry III. ordered

---

[1] *Brut*, under 1107. The castle is called Dingeraint by this chronicler.

[2] "Ipse comes construxit castrum Muntgumeri vocatum." D. B., i., 254.

[3] *Montgomery Collections*, x., 56.   [4] *Close Rolls*, i., 558b.

all who had mottes in the valley of Montgomery to fortify them with good bretasches without delay;[1] and the remains of these mottes are still numerous in the valley. It is quite possible that the mottes at Moat Lane and Llandinam were thrown up to defend the road into Arwystli; but this is conjecture.[2]

WELSHPOOL, *alias* Pol or Pool (Fig. 40), is also called the Castle of Trallung.—In Powell's *History of Wales* (p. 137) it is stated that Cadwgan ap Bleddyn, when Henry I. took Cardigan from him, retired to Powys, and began to build a castle here. Powell's statements, however, have no authority when unconfirmed, and we are unable to find any confirmation of this statement in the more trustworthy version of the *Brut*. And as the House of Montgomeri was firmly established in the valley of Montgomery as early as 1086, it seems more probable that the two motte-and-bailey castles at Welshpool, lower down the Severn valley, are relics of the early progress of that family, especially as one of these castles is only about a mile east of Offa's Dyke, the ancient border. This latter motte is partly cut into by the railway, and diminished in size, but the bailey is nearly perfect. The other one is in the park of Powys Castle, and is an admirable specimen of its class. The breastwork round the top of the motte remains. [H. W.] It seems probable that this was the precursor of Powys Castle, and was abandoned at an early period, as the newer castle was known by the name of Castell Coch, or

---

[1] "Firmiter precipimus omnibus illis qui motas habent in valle de Muntgumeri quod sine dilatione motas suas bonis bretaschiis firmari faciant ad securitatem et defensionem suam et partium illarum." *Close Rolls*, ii., 42.

[2] Mr Davies Pryce has suggested that the Hen Domen, a very perfect motte and bailey within a mile of the present castle of Montgomery was the original castle of Montgomery, and that the one built by Henry III. was on a new site. This of course is quite possible, but I do not see that there is sufficient evidence for it. See *Eng. Hist. Rev.*, xx., 709.

the Red Castle, as early as 1233.[1] Leland states that there were formerly two castles of two different Lords Marchers at Welshpool;[2] possibly this throws some light on the existence of these two motte-castles.

When Henry II. came to the throne in 1154, one of the many questions which he had to settle was the Welsh question. His first expedition against North Wales was in 1157. Here he was one day placed in grave difficulties, and fortune was only restored by his personal courage. But in spite of this we learn even from the Welsh chronicler that he continued his advance to Rhuddlan, and that the object of the expedition, which was the restoration of Cadwalader, one of the sons of Griffith ap Cynan, to his lands, was accomplished. The English chronicler Roger of Wendover says that Henry recovered all the fortresses which had been taken from his predecessors, and rebuilt Basingwerk Castle; and when he had reduced the Welsh to submission, returned in triumph to England. The undoubted facts of the *Pipe Rolls* show us that in the year 1159 Henry had in his hands the castles of Overton, Hodesley, Wrexham, Dernio, Ruthin, and Rhuddlan, castles which would give him command of the whole of Flintshire and of East Denbigh and the valley of the Clwyd. Similarly, after the expedition of 1165, sometimes stated to have been only disastrous, we find him in possession of the castles of Rhuddlan, Basingwerk, Prestatyn, Mold, Overton, and Chirk;[3] so that after the battle of Crogen, or Chirk, he actually held the battlefield.

---

[1] *Brut y Tywysogion.*   [2] *Itin.*, vii., 16.
[3] *Pipe Rolls*, 1158-1164. It should be noted that the *Brut* does not claim the battle of Crogen as a Welsh victory.

We are thus introduced to an entirely new group of castles, Rhuddlan being the only one which we have heard of before.   But it is highly probable that most of these castles were originally raised by the earls of Chester or Shrewsbury, and were in Henry's hands by escheat.

*BASINGWERK.—The *werk* referred to in this name has probably nothing to do with the castle, but refers to Wat's Dyke, which reaches the Dee at this point.   The abbey at this place was founded by an earl of Chester,[1] which makes it probable that the castle also was originally his work, especially as Wendover says that Henry *rebuilt* it.   There is no trace of a castle near the abbey,[2] but less than a mile off, near Holywell Church, there is a headland called Bryn y Castell, with a small mound at the farther end, which has far more claim to be the site of Basingwerk Castle, especially as it is mentioned in John's reign (when it was retaken from the Welsh) as the castle of Haliwell.[3]

OVERTON, in East Denbigh, on the middle course of the Dee.   In custody of Roger de Powys for the king in 1159-1160.   As Leland speaks of the ditches and hill of the castle, it was probably a motte-castle of the usual type.   "One parte of the ditches and Hille of the castel yet remaynith; the residew is in the botom of Dee."[4] It is probably all there now, as not a vestige can be traced.   [B. T. S.]

DERNIO, or Dernant.—There can be no question that

---

[1] Lyttleton's *History of Henry II.*

[2] Pennant thought he saw vestiges of a castle "in the foundations of a wall opposite the ruins" [of the abbey]; but his accuracy is not unimpeachable.

[3] *Pipe Rolls*, 1211-1213.   "For the money expended in rescuing the castles of Haliwell and Madrael, £100."

[4] *Itin.*, p. 67.   Toulmin Smith's edition of Welsh portion.

Dernio is Edeyrnion, the valley stretching from Bala Lake to Corwen. Domesday Book tells us that Rainald the Sheriff, a "man" of Earl Roger of Shrewsbury, held two "fines" in Wales, Chenlei and Dernio, that is, Cynllaith and Edeyrnion.[1] Towards the end of the 11th century there must have been a Norman castle at Rug in Edeyrnion, as it was to this place that the earls of Chester and Shrewsbury enticed Griffith ap Cynan, the rightful ruler of Gwynedd; they then sent him prisoner to Chester for twelve years.[2] Very likely the castle of Dernio, which Henry II. was putting into a state of defence in 1159,[3] was at RUG, $1\frac{1}{2}$ miles from Corwen, where there is still a motte in some private grounds, and there was formerly a bailey also.[4] The place was the seat of an important family in later times. At any rate, the castle was in Edeyrnion, and shows that Henry was holding the northern part of Merionethshire.

HODESLEY; undoubtedly "The Rofts" near Gresford, a motte with remains of a bailey, on a headland above the river Alyn. It is in the former lordship of Hoseley.[5]

WREXHAM, the Wristlesham of the *Pipe Rolls* (Fig. 40).—Henry was paying for the custody of this castle and that of Hoseley in 1160 and 1161. Both castles are in the district of Bromfield, which was one of the early acquisitions of the earls of Chester. Mr Palmer remarks

---

[1] D. B., i., 255a.   [2] Life of Griffith.

[3] *Pipe Roll*, 1159-1160. £4, 3s. 4d. paid to Roger de Powys "ad custodiam castelli de Dernio"; "In munitione turris de Dermant £6, 4s. od." It cannot be doubted that these two names mean the same place.

[4] *Arch. Camb.*, iv., 1887.

[5] At the time of the Survey the manor of Gresford (Gretford) was divided between Hugh, Osbern, and Rainald. Osbern had $6\frac{1}{2}$ hides and a mill grinding the corn of *his court* (curiæ suæ). This probably is a reference to this castle. D. B., i., 268. It was waste T. R. E. but is now worth £3, 5s. od.

that this district was probably ceded to the princes of Powys, in return for the help which they often rendered to the English king against other Welsh princes, as it is found as part of Powys at a later period.[1] There are no remains of any castle at Wrexham itself, but about a mile off, in Erddig Park, there is a motte and bailey of considerable size (though the motte is reduced) showing that a castle of some importance once stood there. There were formerly some remains of masonry.[2] Wat's Dyke has been utilised to form one side of the bailey. It is probable that the importance of the two Bromfield castles, Wrexham and Hoseley, was lost when the princes of Powys built their castle on Dinas Bran.

*RUTHIN.—This important castle, defending the upper valley of the Clwyd, was probably in existence long before Henry II. repaired it in 1160, and may perhaps be attributed to Earl Hugh of Chester. The plan shows distinctly that it was once a motte and bailey, though the castle is now transformed into a modern house.[3]

CHIRK, or Crogen, in the valley of the Ceiriog.— Henry was paying for the custody of this castle in 1164, and was provisioning it in 1167.[4] King John paid for the erection of a bretasche there, possibly after some destruction by the Welsh.[5] Probably the first castle of Chirk did not stand in the commanding situation now occupied by the castle of Edward I.'s reign, but is

[1] "On the Town of Holt," by A. N. Palmer, *Arch. Camb.*, 1907.
[2] *Beauties of England and Wales, North Wales*, p. 589. I am glad to find that Mr Palmer, in the new edition of his *Ancient Tenures of Land in the Marches of Wales*, confirms the identifications which I have made of these two last castles, pp. 108, 116, 118.
[3] *Arch. Camb.*, 5th ser., iv., 352. Camden's statement that this castle was founded in Edward I.'s reign shows that he was unacquainted with the *Pipe Rolls*.
[4] *Pipe Rolls*, 1164-1165, and 1167-1168. [5] *Pipe Rolls*, 1212-1213.

represented by a small motte in a garden near the Ceiriog stream, and close to the church. An Anglo-Norman poem of the 13th century attributes the first building of this castle to William Peverel, Lord of Whittington and Ellesmere, and says he placed it "on the water of Ceiriog."[1] No doubt it defended the passage of the stream, and an important road into Shropshire.

PRESTATYN.—This castle defended the coast road from Chester to Rhuddlan. Henry II. granted it to Robert Banaster for his services in 1165.[2] It was destroyed by Owen Gwynedd in 1167, and does not appear to have been rebuilt. A low motte with a half-moon bailey, and a larger square enclosure, still remain. [B. T. S.]

Mr Davis has remarked that John was more successful in extending his authority over the British Isles than in anything else.[3] In 1211 he led an expedition into the heart of Wales, and reduced his son-in-law Llywelyn ap Jorwerth to complete submission. As usual, the expedition was marked by the building or repair of castles. The Earl of Chester restored Deganwy, which shows that the English frontier was again advanced to the Conway; he also repaired the castle of Holywell, which the *Pipe Roll* shows to have been recovered from the Welsh about this time.[4] These *Rolls* also show that in 1212-1213 John was paying for works at

---

[1] "Sur l'ewe de Keyroc," *History of Fulk Fitz Warine*, edited by T. Wright for Warton Club.

[2] *Victoria County History of Lancashire*, i., 369.

[3] *England under the Normans and Angevins.*

[4] "Ad recutienda castella de Haliwell et Madrael £100." *Pipe Rolls*, 1212-1213.

the castles of Carreghova, Ruthin, and Chirk, as well as at the following castles, which have not been mentioned before.

MATHRAVAL, Madrael in the *Pipe Rolls* (Fig. 40), near Meifod in Montgomeryshire, defending the valley of the Vyrnwy.—Here was the chief royal residence of Powys;[1] but the castle was built in John's reign by Roger de Vipont. It occupied 2¼ acres, and the motte is in one corner of the area, which is square,[2] and surrounded only by banks; though ruined foundations are found in parts of the castle. John himself burned the castle in 1211, when the Welsh were besieging it,[3] but the *Pipe Roll* (1212-1213) shows that he afterwards repaired it. [D. H. M.]

EGLOE, or Eulo, called by Leland Castle Yollo.—On the Chester and Holywell road, about 8 miles from Holywell. The mention in the *Pipe Roll* of pikes and ammunition provided for this castle in 1212-1213 is the first ancient allusion to it with which we are acquainted. It is a motte-and-bailey castle, with additions in masonry which are probably of the reign of Henry III. The keep is of the "thimble" plan, a rare instance.[4] [B. T. S.]

*YALE.—The *Brut* tells us that in 1148 (read 1150) Owen Gwynedd built a castle in Yale. Powell identified this with Tomen y Rhodwydd, a motte and bailey on the road between Llangollen and Ruthin. Yale, however, is the name of a district, and there can be little doubt that the castle of Yale was the motte and

---

[1] Wade Evans, *Welsh Mediæval Law*, vol. xii.

[2] It has in fact every appearance of a Roman camp.

[3] *Brut*, 1211.

[4] The castle of Hawarden, which is only about 2¼ miles from that of Euloe, is not mentioned in any records before 1215; but it is believed to have been a castle of the Norman lords of Mold. It also is on a motte.

bailey at Llanarmon, which for a long period was the *caput* of Yale.[1] Yale undoubtedly belonged to the Normans when Domesday Book was compiled,[2] and it is therefore not unlikely that these earthworks were first thrown up by the Earl of Chester. The castle was burnt by Jorwerth Goch in 1158, but restored by John in 1212. One of the expenses entered for that year is "for iron mallets for breaking the rocks in the ditch of the castle of Yale."[3] This ditch cut in the rock still remains, as well as some foundations on the motte,[4] which is known as Tomen y Vardra, or the Mount of of the demesne.[5]

How long the two last-mentioned groups of castles continued in Anglo-Norman hands we do not attempt to say. North Wales, as is well known, reaped a harvest of new power and prosperity through the civil war of the end of John's reign, and the ability of Llywelyn ap Jorwerth. Our task ends with the reign of John. We have only to remark that until the *Pipe Rolls* of Henry III.'s reign have been carefully searched, it is impossible to say with certainty what castles of North Wales, or if any, were still held by the English king.

[1] I am indebted for this identification to the kindness of Mr A. N. Palmer of Wrexham.

[2] D. B., i., 254. The manor is called Gal. It had been waste T. R. E., but was now worth 40s.

[3] *Pipe Roll* (unpublished), 1212-1213.

[4] Whereas there is no rock in the ditch of the neighbouring motte of Tomen y Rhodwydd. Pennant (and others following him) most inaccurately describe Tomen y Rhodwydd as *two* artificial mounts, whereas there is only one, with the usual embanked court. See Appendix K.

[5] "The Maer dref [which Vardra represents] may be described as the home farm of the chieftain." Rhys and Brynmor Jones, *The Welsh People*, p. 401.

CHAPTER IX

MOTTE-CASTLES IN SOUTH WALES

It is not possible to fix certain dates for all the Norman conquests of the several provinces of South Wales. These conquests proceeded from various points, under different leaders. We might have expected that the earliest advances would have been on the Herefordshire border, the earldom of Hereford having been given by William I. to William FitzOsbern, one of his most trusted and energetic servants. Ordericus tells us that FitzOsbern and Walter de Lacy first invaded the district of Brecknock, and defeated three kings of the Welsh.[1] This looks as though the conquest of Brecknock was then begun. But it was not completed till the reign of Rufus; in 1093 Bernard of Neufmarché defeated and slew Rhys ap Tudor, King of South Wales, in a battle which the Welsh chronicler speaks of as the fall of the kingdom of the Britons.[2] William Fitz-Osbern died in 1071, and he had scarcely time to accomplish more than the building of the border castles of Wigmore, Clifford, Ewias, and Monmouth, and the incastellation of Gwent, that is the country between the Wye and the Usk, which had already been conquered by Harold.

It seems probable that Pembrokeshire was one

[1] Ordericus, ii., 218, 219 (edition Prévost).   [2] *Brut y Tywysogion*, 1091.

of the earliest Norman conquests in South Wales, as in 1073 and 1074 the *Brut* tells of two expeditions of "the French" into Dyfed, a region which included not only what we now call Pembrokeshire, but also Strath Towy, which comprised an extensive district on both sides of the valley of the Towy.[1] The *Annales Cambriæ* name Hugh de Montgomeri, Earl Roger's eldest son, in connection with the second of these expeditions, seven years before the expedition of King William into Wales in 1081.[2] The House of Montgomeri certainly took the most conspicuous part in the conquest of Dyfed and Cardigan, which was completed, according to the *Brut*, in 1093.[3] Arnulf of Montgomeri, fifth son of Earl Roger, was the leader of this conquest. But his father must at the same time have been operating in Cardigan, as the building of the castle of Cilgerran, which is on the very borders of Pembroke and Cardigan, is attributed to him.

How far Earl Roger made himself master of Ceredigion it is impossible to say. Later writers say that he built the castle of Cardigan, but we have not been able to find any early authority for this statement, which in itself is not improbable. Powell's *History* makes him do homage to William Rufus for the lordship of Cardigan, but here again the authority is doubtful.[4] The fact

[1] *Brut*, 1071. "The French ravage Ceredigion (Cardigan) and Dyfed"; 1072, "The French devastated Ceredigion a second time.

[2] *A.-S. C.*, 1081. "This year the king led an army into Wales, and there he set free many hundred persons"—doubtless, as Mr Freeman remarks, captives taken previously by the Welsh. The *Brut* treats this expedition as merely a pilgrimage to St David's !

[3] "Then the French came into Dyfed and Ceredigion, *which they have still retained*, and fortified the castles, and seized upon all the land of the Britons." *Brut*, 1091 = 1093.

[4] Powell's *History of Wales* professes to be founded on that of Caradoc, a Welsh monk of the 12th century ; but it is impossible to say how much of it is Caradoc, and how much Powell, or Wynne, his augmentor.

that a castle in or near Aberystwyth was not built until 1109 may indicate that the conquest of Northern Cardigan was not completed till it became the portion of the De Clares. This took place in 1109, when Henry I. deposed Cadwgan, a Welsh prince whom he had made Lord of Cardigan, and gave the lordship to Gilbert de Clare, who immediately proceeded to build the above-mentioned castle, and to restore Earl Roger's castle at Cilgerran (Dingeraint).[1] From this time the castle and district of Cardigan continued to be an appanage of the House of Clare (of course with frequent interruptions from Welsh invasions), and of the family of William Marshall, to whom the Clare lands came by marriage. The authority of these earls was suspended during the reign of Henry II., when he made Rhys ap Griffith, who had possessed himself of Ceredigion by conquest, Justiciar of South Wales, but in the reigns of John and Henry III., the *Close Rolls* show that Cardigan Castle and county were generally in the hands of the Marshalls.

The conquest of Pembrokeshire must have been closely followed by that of what is now Carmarthenshire, which was then reckoned as part of Dyfed.[2] We first hear of the castle of Rhyd y Gors in 1094,[3] but it evidently existed earlier. This castle we believe to have been the important castle of Carmarthen (see *post*). It was founded by William, son of Baldwin, sheriff of Devon, and cousin of the Gilbert de Clare who at a later period was made Lord of Cardigan by

[1] *Brut*, 1107.

[2] "In the *Brut*, Ystrad Towy does not only mean the vale of Towy, but a very large district, embracing most of Carmarthenshire and part of Glamorganshire. *Welsh Historical Documents*, by Egerton Phillimore, in *Cymmrodor*, vol. xi.

[3] *Brut*, 1092.

Henry I. We thus see at what an early date this important family made its appearance in Welsh history.

The conquest of Brecknock (Brecheiniog) we have already briefly referred to. It must have begun as early as 1088, for in that year Bernard de Neufmarché gave to St Peter's Abbey at Gloucester the church and manor of Glasbury. The inheritance of Bernard passed by marriage to the De Braoses, and from them to the Mortimers. It is convenient to mention in this connection the Norman conquest of Radnor, of which the De Braoses and Mortimers were the heroes. A charter of Philip de Braose, not later than 1096, is dated at " Raddenoam."[1] Even during the anarchy of Stephen's reign, the Mortimers were able to maintain their hold on this district, for the *Brut* relates that in 1145, Hugh, son of Ralph Mortimer, conquered Malienydd and Elvael the second time.[2] These two districts properly belong to Powys, though geographically in South Wales.

We leave to the last the conquest of Glamorgan, which may possibly have been one of the earliest, but whose date is still a matter of dispute, owing to the legendary nature of the Aberpergwm version of the *Brut*, the only one which even alludes to this conquest. We have, however, an initial date given us in the year 1082, when the *Brut y Tywysogion* tell us of the building of Cardiff Castle.[3] The conquest of "Morgannwg," that is the country between the Usk and the Neath, was the most permanent of any of those accomplished by the Normans in Wales, but its details

[1] Lloyd, "Wales and the Coming of the Normans," *Cymmrodor. Trans.*, 1899 : refers to Marchegay, *Chartes du Prieurie de Monmouth.*

[2] *Brut*, 1143.

[3] The date given is 1080, but as the dates in the *Brut* at this period are uniformly two years too early, we alter them accordingly throughout this chapter.

are the most obscure of any. The earlier version of the *Brut* takes no notice of the conquest of Glamorgan; the later version which goes by the name of the *Gwentian Chronicle*[1] tells us that the Norman Robert Fitz Hamon, being called in to the help of one Welsh prince against another, conquered Glamorgan for himself, and divided it amongst his followers, who built castles in all parts of the country. The date given is 1088. It seems to be agreed by historians that while the facts of Robert Fitz Hamon's existence and of his conquest of Glamorgan are certain, the details and the list of followers given in this chronicle are quite untrustworthy.[2]

The district called Gower did not then form part of Glamorgan, as it does now, though it is still ecclesiastically separate. If we are to believe the Aberpergwm *Brut*, it must have been conquered in 1094, when William de Londres, one of the "knights" of Robert Fitz Hamon, built a strong castle in Cydweli (Kidwelly).[3]

We will now briefly notice such of the castles of these various districts as are mentioned in the sources to which we have already referred in our last chapter, taking them in the order of the modern counties in which they are found.

[1] Now more often called the Aberpergwm *Brut*, from the place where the MS. is preserved.

[2] See Freeman, *Norman Conquest*, v., 820; William Rufus, ii., 79; and Prof. Tout, in *Y Cymmerodor*, ix., 208. For this reason we do not use the list of castles given in this chronicle, but confine ourselves to those mentioned in the more trustworthy *Brut y Tywysogion*.

[3] The same MS. says, under the year 1099, "Harry Beaumont came to Gower, against the sons of Caradog ap Jestin, and won many of their lands, and built the castle of Abertawy (Swansea) and the castle of Aberllychor (Loughor), and the castle of Llanrhidian (Weobley), and the castle of Penrhys (Penrice), and established himself there, and brought Saxons from Somerset there, where they obtained lands; and the greatest usurpation of all the Frenchmen was his in Gower."

Castles of Pembrokeshire.

PEMBROKE.—Giraldus says that Arnulf de Montgomeri first built this castle of sods and wattles, a
scanty and slender construction, in the reign of Henry
I.[1] This date, however, must certainly be wrong, for
the castle sustained a siege from the Welsh in 1094, and
in 1098 Arnulf gave the chapel of St Nicholas in his
castle of Pembroke to the abbey of St Martin at Sées.[2]
There is no motte at Pembroke Castle; the magnificent
keep (clearly of the 13th century or later) stands in a
small ward at the edge of a cliff,[3] separated by a former
ditch from the immense encircling bailey whose walls
and towers are clearly of Edwardian date. The words
of Giraldus "a castle of wattles and turf" might lead us
to think that the first castle was a motte of the usual
type, but the use which he makes of the same expression
in his work on Ireland leads one to think that he means
a less defensible fort, a mere bank and fence.[4] There is
some reason, moreover, to doubt whether the present
castle of Pembroke stands on the same site as Arnulf's,
as after the banishment of the latter, Gerald, the royal
Seneschal of Pembroke "built the castle anew in the
place called Little Cengarth."[5]

But however this may be, the castle of Pembroke
was certainly strong enough in 1094 to resist a great

---

[1] "Primus hoc castrum Arnulphus de Mongumeri sub Anglorum rege
Henrico primo ex virgis et cespite, tenue satis et exile construxit." *Itin.
Cambriæ*, R. S., 89.

[2] Quoted from Duchesne in *Mon. Ang.*, vol. vi.

[3] See Mr Cobbe's paper on Pembroke Castle in *Arch. Camb.*, 1883,
where reasons are given for thinking that the present ward was originally,
and even up to 1300, the whole castle.

[4] A motte-castle of earth and wood was certainly not regarded as "a
weak and slender defence" in the time of Giraldus.

[5] *Brut y Tywysogion*, 1095.

insurrection of the Welsh, when all the castles of south-west Wales were destroyed, except Pembroke and Rhyd y Gors. And it continued to be one of the chief strong-holds of English power in South Wales until Edward I. completed the conquest of the country. Its splendid situation on a high cliff at the mouth of an excellent harbour, to which supplies could be brought by sea, was one of the secrets of its strength. A passage cut in the rock led from the castle to a cave below opening on to the water.

*NEWPORT, or Trefdaeth, was the head of the Barony of Keymes, an independent lordship founded at the time of the first Norman advance, by Martin of Tours.[1] There is no mention of it before 1215. The present ruined castle of Newport is not earlier than the 13th century, but about $1\frac{1}{2}$ miles higher up the river, at Llanhyfer, is a fine motte and bailey, which probably mark the site of the first castle of Martin of Tours.[2]

WISTON, *alias* Gwys or Wiz.—First mentioned in 1148, when it was taken by the Welsh.[3] At a later period we find it one of the castles of the Earl of Pembroke. There is a motte still remaining, with a shell wall on top, 6 feet thick, having a plain round arched entrance. This masonry is probably the work of William Marshall, Earl of Pembroke, as he restored the castle in 1220 after it had been razed to the ground by Llywelyn ap Jorwerth.[4] The bailey is large and bean-shaped.

LAWHADEN, or Llanyhadein, or Lauwadein.—First

---

[1] Bridgeman's *Hist. of South Wales*, 17.
[2] *Arch. Camb.*, 3rd ser., v., a paper on Newport Castle, in which the writer says that there are *two* mottes at Llanhyfer, the larger one ditched round. The Ordnance Map only shows one.
[3] *Brut y Tywysogion*, 1146.
[4] *Patent Rolls of Henry III.*, 255 ; *Fœdera*, i., 161.

mention in 1192.[1]   It afterwards became a palace of the
bishops of St David's.   There is no motte, though the
circular outline of the platform on which the fine ruins
of the castle stand, very much suggests a lowered motte.

HAVERFORDWEST.—First mentioned in the *Pipe
Roll* of 1214-1215, when it was in the custody of the Earl
of Pembroke.   Although this castle is now a gaol, and
the whole site masked with gaol buildings, the motte
can still be seen distinctly from one side, though the
keep which stands upon it is blocked by buildings.   The
ditch which went round the motte can also be traced.
[H. W.]

NARBERTH.—This castle is first mentioned in 1115,
when it was burnt by the Welsh.   Said to have been
the castle of Stephen Perrot.[2]   The present ruins are
entirely of the 13th century, and there is no motte; but
Lewis states that the first castle was in another site,
between the present town and Templeton; about which
we have no information.

TENBY.—First mention in 1152.   An important coast
station.   The small and curious round keep is placed on
the highest point of a small island; it is a miniature
copy of the keep of Pembroke, and was probably built
by one of the earls Marshall, not earlier than the 13th
century.   There is no motte, nor was one needed in
such a situation.

CASTLES OF CARDIGAN.

CARDIGAN Castle, or Aberteifi, has been so much
transformed by the incorporation of the keep into a
modern house that nothing decisive can be said about

---

[1] *Brut y Tywysogion*, 1192.

[2] Bridgeman says that Narberth was given to Stephen Perrot by Arnulf
de Montgomeri, but gives no authority for this statement.

its original plan, but there is nothing to foreclose the idea of a previous motte, and Speed's plan of 1611 seems to show that the keep and the small ward attached to it were on a higher elevation than the bailey. That the first castle was a wooden one is rendered almost certain by the fact that Rhys ap Griffith, after having demolished the previous castle, rebuilt it *with stone and mortar*, in the reign of Henry II.[1] The Welsh chronicler speaks of this castle as the key of all Wales, an exaggeration certainly, but it was undoubtedly the most important stronghold of South Ceredigion. [H. W.]

CILGERRAN, or Dingeraint (Fig. 41).—This castle was certainly built by Earl Roger;[2] a castle of great importance, in a magnificent situation. Like nearly all the castles in our Welsh list, it was repeatedly taken by the Welsh and retaken from them. The present masonry is of the 13th century, but the original motte-and-bailey plan is quite discernible. [H. W.] It was a connecting link between the castles of Pembrokeshire and those of Cardigan, and stands near a road leading directly from Tenby and Narberth to Cardigan.

ABERYSTWYTH, also Lampadarn Vaur, also Aber-rheiddiol.[3] In 1109 Henry I. deposed Cadwgan, a Welsh prince who had purchased from the king the government of Cardigan, and gave that country to Gilbert, son of Richard, Earl of Clare, who took possession, and built a castle "opposite to Llanbadarn, near the mouth of the river Ystwyth."[4] This was

---

[1] *Brut*, 1171.

[2] *Ibid.*, 1107. "Earl Gilbert built a castle at Dingeraint, where Earl Roger had before founded a castle."

[3] The castle of Aberrheiddiol is probably the name of the present castle of Aberystwyth when it was first built, as Lewis Morris says that the river Rheiddiol formerly entered the sea near that point. Quoted by Meyrick, *History of Cardigan*, p. 488.

[4] *Brut*, 1107.

undoubtedly the precursor of the modern castle of Aberystwyth, but it is doubtful whether it was on the same site; the present ruins are not opposite Llanbadarn. The castle was as important for the defence of N. Cardigan as Cardigan Castle for the south. It was taken at least seven times by the Welsh, and burnt at least five times. The present ruins are not earlier than the time of Edward I., and there is no motte or keep. [H. W.]

*BLAENPORTH, or Castell Gwythan (Fig. 41).—Also built by Gilbert de Clare, and evidently placed to defend the main road from Cardigan to Aberystwyth. The motte and bailey are still remarkably perfect, as shown by the 25-inch Ordnance Map.

YSTRAD PEITHYLL.—Another of Gilbert de Clare's castles, as it was inhabited by his steward. It was burnt by the Welsh in 1115,[1] and is never mentioned again, but its motte and ditch still survive, with some signs of a bailey, close to the little stream of the Peithyll, near Aberystwyth. [H. W.]

CHASTELL GWALTER, or Llanfihangel, in Pengwern (Fig. 41).—Castle of Walter de Bec, probably one of the barons of Gilbert de Clare. First mentioned in 1137, when it was burned by the Welsh.[2] There is a small but well-made motte and part of an adjoining bailey standing in a most commanding position on a high plateau. The ditch of the motte is excavated in the rock. [D. H. M.]

*DINERTH.—Also burnt in 1137; restored by Roger, Earl of Clare, in 1159, after which it underwent many vicissitudes.[3] Probably originally a castle of the Clares. "In the grounds of Mynachty, in the parish of

---

[1] *Brut*, 1113.   [2] *Ibid.*, 1135.
[3] *Ibid.*, 1135, 1157, 1199, 1203, 1207.

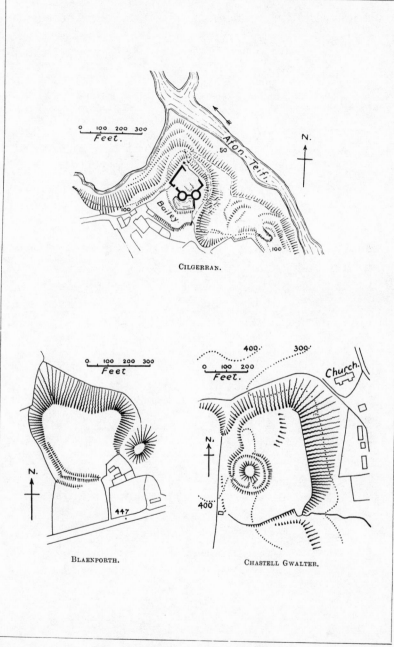

CILGERRAN.

BLAENPORTH.

CHASTELL GWALTER.

FIG. 41.—MOTTE-CASTLES OF SOUTH WALES.

[To face p. 282.

Llanbadarn Tref Eglwys, is a small hill called Hero Castell, probably the site of the keep of Dinerth Castle."[1] The O.M. shows a small motte and bailey placed between two streams.

*CAERWEDROS, or Castell Llwyndafydd, also burned by the Welsh in 1137,[2] after which it is not mentioned again. "A very large moated tumulus, with foundations of walls on the top."[3] Probably a Clare castle.

*HUMPHREY'S CASTLE, now Castle Howel, from one of its Welsh conquerors. The original name shows that it was built by a Norman, and it was restored by Roger, Earl of Clare, in 1159.[4] A moated tumulus near the river Clettwr marks the site of Humphrey's Castle.[5]

YSTRAD MEURUG, or Meyric, at the head of the valley of the Teifi, and commanding the pass leading over into Radnorshire.—Built by Gilbert de Clare when he reconquered Cardigan, and one of his most important castles.[6] Its importance is shown by the fact that it had a small stone keep, the date of which cannot now be determined, as only the foundations remain, buried under sods. There is no motte, and the bailey can only be guessed at by a portion of the ditch which still remains on the N. side, and by two platforms which appear to be artificially levelled. The castle is about three miles from the Sarn Helen or Roman road through Cardigan,

*PONT Y STUFFAN, or Stephen's Bridge, near Lampeter.—Burnt by the Welsh in 1138, and not

---

[1] Meyrick's *Hist. of Cardigan*, p. 293. Dinerth is not the same as Llanrhystyd, though Lewis (*Top. Dict. Wales*) says it is ; the two places have separate mention in *Brut*, 1157. Mr Clark mentions the motte. *M. M. A.*, i., 115.

[2] *Brut*, 1135.   [3] Meyrick's *Hist. of Cardigan*, p. 232.

[4] *Brut*, 1157.   [5] *Beauties of England and Wales*, Cardigan, p. 502.

[6] *Brut*, under 1113.

again mentioned.[1] In the outskirts of the town of Lampeter is—or was—a lofty moated tumulus (not shown on O.M.), and traces of a quadrangular court.[2] As it is also called Castell Ystuffan, it was probably built by Stephen, the Norman constable of Cardigan. There appears to be another castle mound at Lampeter itself, near the church. Lampeter was an important post on the Roman road up the valley of the Teifi.

*NANT YR ARIAN.—This castle is only mentioned once, in the partition of Cardigan and Pembroke which took place in 1216, during the most disastrous part of John's reign.[3] There are two "castellau" marked at Nant yr Arian in the N. of Cardiganshire in the O.M. ; neither of them look like mottes. This castle, as well as that of Ystrad Peithyll, seems to have been placed to defend the road from Aberystwyth to Llanidloes, which would be the chief highway between Shropshire and Ceredigion.

CASTLES OF CARMARTHENSHIRE.

RHYD Y GORS, or Rhyd Cors.—We have no hesitation in adopting the opinion of the late Mr Floyd, that this is another name for the castle of Carmarthen.[4] As it and Pembroke were the only castles which held out during the great Welsh revolt of 1096,[5] it is evident that they were the two strongest and best defended places, therefore the most important. Carmarthen also was a Roman city, and its walls were still standing in Giraldus' time ;[6] it was therefore the place where one

---

[1] In the *Rolls* edition of the *Brut* this castle is called Llanstephan, but the context makes it probable that Lampeter is meant; the *Annales Cambriæ* say "the castle of Stephen."

[2] *Beauties of England and Wales*, p. 492. [3] *Brut*, 1216.

[4] *Arch. Journ.*, xxviii., 293. [5] *Brut*, 1094. [6] *Desc. Camb.*, i., 10.

would expect to find a Norman castle. Now Carmarthen, along with Cardiff and Pembroke, continued
up till the final conquest of all Wales to be the most
important seat of English power in South Wales.
Moreover, Rhyd y Gors was a royal castle; we
are expressly told that it was built by William Fitz
Baldwin, by the command of the king of England.[1]
Carmarthen also was a royal castle, and the only
one in South Wales at that date which belonged
directly to the king. It was temporarily abandoned
after William Fitz Baldwin's death in 1096, and
afterwards Henry I. gave it into the custody of a
Welshman, who also had charge of Strath Towy; a
passage which proves that Rhyd y Gors was in that
district. It was restored by Richard Fitz Baldwin
in 1104,[2] and is mentioned for the last time in 1105.
After that the castle of Carmarthen, which has
not been mentioned before, begins to appear, and its
importance is clear from the continual references to it.
Placed as it is on a navigable river, at the entrance of
the narrower part of the vale of Towy, and on the
Roman road from Brecon to St David's, its natural
position must have marked it as a fit site for a royal
castle. The castle is now converted into a gaol, and
disfigured in the usual way; yet the ancient motte of
William Fitz Baldwin still remains, partly inside and
partly outside the walls. It is crowned with a stone
revetment which Colonel Morgan believes to have been
erected at the time of the Civil War, to form a platform

---

[1] *Brut*, 1094.

[2] *Ibid.*, p. 110. There is a farmhouse called Rhyd y Gors about a mile
lower down than Carmarthen, and on the opposite side are some embankments; but I am assured by Mr Spurrell of Carmarthen that these are only
river-embankments. Rhyd y Gors means the ford of the bog; there is no
ford at this spot, but there was one at Carmarthen.

for guns.[1] The bailey is rectangular and covers about 2 acres. The motte is placed at one corner of it, on the line of the walls. On the outside it is now built over with poor cottages; but the site of the ditch can still be traced.

*LLANDOVERY, or Llanymdyfri, or the castle of Cantrebohhan.—It is referred to in the *Pipe Rolls* of 1159-1160 by the latter name, which is only a Norman way of spelling Cantref Bychan, the little cantref or hundred, of which this castle was the head.[2] It was then in royal custody, and Henry II. spent nearly £60 on its works. But it had originally belonged to Richard Fitz Pons, one of the barons of Bernard de Neufmarché, and the fact that he held the key of this cantref goes to prove that it was from Brecknock that the Normans advanced into northern Carmarthenshire. The castle is first mentioned in the *Brut* in 1115, when Griffith ap Rhys burnt the bailey, but could not take the keep on the motte.[3] It does not appear to have been long in English hands after 1159, but its alternations were many. The 25-inch O.M. shows an oval motte, carrying some fragments of masonry, to which is attached a roughly quadrangular bailey. This was one of the many castles by which the Normans held Strath Towy.

LLANSTEPHAN.[4]—This castle stands in a splendid situation at the mouth of the Towy, and was doubtless built to secure a maritime base for Carmarthen. The motte is of unusual size, semicircular in shape, one side

---

[1] See *Arch. Camb.*, 1907, pp. 237-8.

[2] See Round's *Ancient Charters*, p. 9, *Pipe Roll* Series, vol. x.

[3] *Brut*, 1113.

[4] The first mention of the castle of Llanstephan is in the *Brut*, 1147, if, as has been assumed above, the mention in 1136 refers to Stephen's castle at Lampeter, as the *Annales Cambriæ* say.

being on the edge of the cliff; it measures 300 feet by 200 in the centre of the arc.[1] Such a size allowed all the important parts of the castle to be built on the motte; but there was a rectangular bailey attached, which is only imperfectly shown on the O.M.; the scarp is in reality well marked on all sides, and the ditch separating it from the motte is a very deep one. [H. W.] The towers that now crown the motte are not earlier than the year 1256, when the castle was destroyed by Llywelyn.[2]

DINEVOR, or Dinweiler.—Most Welsh writers associate Dinevor with the ancient residence of the kings of South Wales, but there appears to be some doubt about this, as the place is not mentioned before the 12th century.[3] Anyhow the castle was certainly the work of Earl Gilbert, as the *Brut* itself tells us so.[4] In 1162 it was taken by Rhys ap Griffith, the able prince who attempted the consolidation of South Wales, and who was made Justiciar of that province by Henry II. It continued in Welsh hands, sometimes hostile, sometimes allied, till it was finally taken by the English in 1277. The existing ruins are entirely of the 13th century, but the plan certainly suggests a previous motte and bailey, the motte having probably been lowered to form the present smaller ward, whose walls and towers appear to

---

[1] The motte of Conisburgh in Yorkshire is a very similar case known to the writer; it measures 280 × 150 feet. Such very large mottes could rarely be artificial, but were formed by entrenching and scarping a natural hill.

[2] *Brut*, 1256. See *Arch. Camb.*, 1907, p. 214, for Col. Morgan's remarks on this castle.

[3] The name *Gueith tineuur* is found in the *Book of Llandaff*, p. 78 (Life of St Dubricius), but it seems doubtful whether this should be taken to prove the existence of some "work" at Dinevor in the 6th century. See Wade-Evans, *Welsh Mediæval Law*, p. 337-8.

[4] *Brut*, 1145. "Cadell ap Griffith took the castle of Dinweiler, which had been erected by Earl Gilbert."

be of Edward I.'s reign. The small bailey attached to this ward is separated from it by a ditch cut through the headland on which the castle stands.

KIDWELLY (Cydweli).—This castle, though in Carmarthen, was not founded by the conquerors from Brecknock, but by Normans from Glamorgan or Gower. Kidwelly was first built by William de Londres, in 1094.[1] The present castle shows no trace of this early origin, but is a fine specimen of the keepless pattern introduced into England in the 13th century.[2] There is no motte.

LAUGHARNE, or Talycharne.—Also called Abercorran, being at the point where the little river Corran flows into the estuary of the Taff. In 1113 this castle belonged to a Norman named Robert Courtmain.[3] The ancient features of the plan have been obliterated by transformation first into an Edwardian castle, then into a modern house. There is of course no motte. [H. W.]

*YSTRAD CYNGEN.—This must, we think, be the same as ST CLEARS, which stands in the Cynen valley, near its junction with the Taff. Welsh writers identify St Clears with the castle of Mabudrud, the name of the *commot* in which it stands. First mentioned in 1154.[4] There is no notice of its origin, but the fact that a Cluniac priory existed in the village, which was a cell of St Martin des Champs at Paris, points to a Norman founder, and renders an 11th century date probable. It

[1] *Gwentian Chronicle.*

[2] The statement of Donovan (*Excursions Through South Wales*), that the castle stands on an artificial mount is quite incorrect.

[3] The *Rolls* edition of the *Brut* gives the corrupt reading Aber Cavwy for the castle of "Robert the Crook-handed," but a variant MS. gives Aber Korram, and it is clear from the *Gwentian Chronicle* and Powell (p. 145) that Abercorran is meant.

[4] *Brut,* 1152.

was a motte-and-bailey castle, of which the earthworks remain.[1]

*NEWCASTLE EMLYN.—This castle does not appear to have received the name of "the new castle of Emlyn" till after Edward I.'s conquest.[2]   The new castle, which is quite Edwardian, was probably built on a different site to the old, as "on the other side of the bridge is a considerable mount, of a military character, which must have commanded the river.   It may have been the original strong post occupied by the Normans."[3]   In the 12th century *Pipe Rolls* compensation is paid to William FitzGerald for many years "as long as Rhys ap Griffith holds the castle of Emlyn," which points to Gerald, the Seneschal of Pembroke, or his family, as its founders.   It is on the very border of Carmarthenshire and Cardiganshire, defending the main road from Carmarthen to Cardigan.

LLANEGWAD.—This castle is only once mentioned, in the *Brut*, under the year 1203, when it was taken by the Welsh.   A small motte, called locally Pen y Knap, with an earthen breastwork round the top, is still standing about a mile from the church of Llanegwad, and is all that is left of this castle.   The position commands a fine view over the Towy valley, and it is noteworthy that it stands very near the supposed Roman road from Brecon to Carmarthen.   [H. W.]

*LLANGADOG.—This castle also does not appear till 1203 ; it was razed or burnt at least thrice in five years.[4] A mound of earth on the banks of the Sawddwy River, near where the Roman road from Brecon is supposed to

[1] See paper by Mr D. C. Evans, *Arch. Camb.*, 1907, p. 224.

[2] The first mention known to the writer is in 1285.

[3] *Arch. Camb.*, 3rd ser., v., 346.

[4] *Annales Cambriæ*, 1205 ; *Brut*, 1207, 1208.   The *Annales* call it the castle of Luchewein.

have reached the Towy valley, is all that remains of it.[1] Lewis says that it stands in a large oval entrenchment, and that the motte is of natural rock, scarped conically, and deeply moated.

CASTLES IN BRECKNOCKSHIRE.

BRECON, or Aberhonddu, the seat of Bernard de Neufmarché himself.—A charter of Bernard's mentions the castle.[2] It seems to have been a particularly strong place, as we do not hear of its having been burnt more than once. The newer castle of Brecon is evidently of the time of Edward I., but across the road the old motte of Bernard is still standing, and carries the ruins of a shell wall, with a gatehouse tower.[3] A portion of the bank and ditch of the bailey remains; the whole is now in a private garden. The situation is a strong one, between the Usk and the Honddu. Brecon of course was a burgus, and part of the bank which fortified it remains.

BUILTH, on the upper Wye, *alias* Buallt (Fig. 42).— A remarkably fine motte and bailey, presenting some peculiarities of plan. It is not mentioned till 1210,[4] but it has been conjectured with great probability that it was one of the castles built by Bernard de Neufmarché

---

[1] *Beauties of England and Wales*, "Caermarthen," pp. 192, 309.

[2] *Mon. Ang.*, iii., 244.

[3] This motte is mentioned in a charter of Roger, Earl of Hereford, Bernard's grandson, in which he confirms to the monks of St John "molendinum meum situm super Hodeni sub pede mote castelli." *Arch. Camb.*, 1883, p. 144.

[4] The dates in the *Brut* are now one year too early. Under 1209 it says, "Gelart seneschal of Gloucester fortified (cadarnhaaod) the castle of Builth." We can never be certain whether the word which is translated *fortified*, whether from the Welsh or from the Latin *firmare*, means built originally or rebuilt.

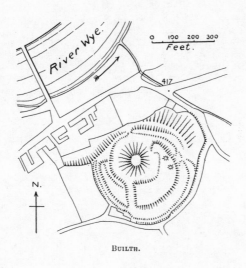

BUILTH.

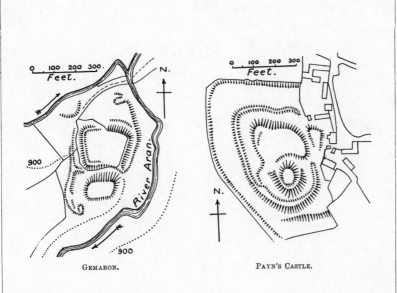

GEMARON.

PAYN'S CASTLE.

FIG. 42.—MOTTE-CASTLES OF SOUTH WALES.

[To face p 290.

when he conquered Brecknock.[1] It was refortified by
John Mortimer in 1242,[2] probably in stone, as in the
account of its destruction by Llywelyn in 1260 it is said
that "not one stone was left on another."[3]   Nevertheless
when Edward I. rebuilt it the towers on the outer wall
appear to have been of wood.[4] Mr Clark states that
there are traces of masonry foundations and small
portions of a wing wall. The bailey of this castle
consists of a rather narrow platform, divided into two
unequal portions by a cross ditch which connects the
ditch of the motte with that of the bailey. The ditch
round the motte is of unusual breadth, being 120 feet
broad in the widest part. The whole work is encircled
by an outer ditch of varying breadth, being 100 feet
wide on the weakest side of the work, and by a counterscarp bank which appears to be still perfect. The
entrance is defended by four small mounds which
probably cover the remains of towers.[5] The area of
the two baileys together is only 1 acre. [D. H. M.]

   *HAY, or Tregelli.—The earliest mention of this
castle is in a charter of Henry I.[6] The present castle
of Hay is of late date, but Leland tells us that "not
far from the Paroche Chirch is a great round Hille of
Yerth cast up by Men's Hondes."[7] It is shown on the
25-inch O.M., and so is the line of the borough walls.

---

[1] *Beauties of England and Wales*, "Brecknockshire," p. 153.
[2] *Brut*, in *anno*. The Mortimers were the heirs of the De Braoses and
the Neufmarchés.
[3] *Annales Cambriæ*, 1260. This may, however, be merely a figure of
speech.
[4] Order to cause Roger Mortimer, so soon as the castle of Built shall
be closed with a wall, whereby it will be necessary to remove the bretasches,
to have the best bretasche of the king's gift. *Cal. of Close Rolls*,
Ed. I., i., 527.
[5] See Clark, *M. M. A.,* i., 307.
[6] Round, *Ancient Charters*, No. 6.   *Itin.*, v., 74.

*Talgarth.—Mentioned in a charter of Roger, Earl of Hereford, not later than 1156.[1] A 13th-century tower on a small motte is still standing, and can be seen from the railway between Brecon and Hereford.

Castles of Radnorshire.

*Radnor, or Maes Hyvaidd.—Though this castle is not mentioned in the *Brut* till 1196, when it was burnt by Rhys ap Griffith, it must have been built by the Normans at a very early period. The English had penetrated into the Radnor district even before the Norman Conquest,[2] and the Normans were not slow to follow them. A charter of Philip de Braose is granted at "Raddenoam" not later than 1096.[3] There are mottes both at Old and New Radnor, towns three miles distant from each other, so that it is impossible to say which was the Maes Hyvaidd of the *Brut*. Both may have been originally De Braose castles, but New Radnor evidently became the more important place, and has massive remains in masonry. The town was a *burgus*.

*Gemaron, or Cwm Aron (Fig. 42).—Near Llandewi-Ystrad-denny. The *Brut* mentions its repair by Hugh Mortimer in 1145.[4] The 6-inch O.M. shows a square central bailey of 1 acre, containing some remains of masonry, lying between an oblong motte in the S. and an outer enclosure on the N., the whole being further defended by a high counterscarp bank on the W. It

[1] *Arch. Camb.*, N. S., v., 23-28.
[2] "Wales and the Coming of the Normans," by Professor Lloyd, in *Cymmrodorion Transactions*, 1899.
[3] Marchegay, *Chartes du Prieurie de Monmouth*, cited by Professor Lloyd, as above.
[4] *Brut*, 1143.

commands a ford over the river Aran. There is no village attached to it.

*Maud's Castle, otherwise Colwyn or Clun.[1]—A ditched motte with square bailey on the left bank of the river Edwy, near the village of Forest Colwyn. The statement that this castle was *repaired* in 1145 shows that it must have been older than the time of Maude de Braose, from whom it is generally supposed to have taken its name. It was rebuilt by Henry III. in 1231.[2]

*Payn's Castle, otherwise "the castle of Elvael." —First mentioned in 1196, when it was taken by Rhys ap Griffith. This is also a motte-castle (and an exceptionally fine one), placed on a road leading from Kington in Hereford to Builth. Rebuilt *in stone* by Henry III. in 1231.[3] (Fig. 42.)

*Knighton, in Welsh Trefclawdd.—First mentioned in the *Pipe Roll* of 1181. The motte still remains, near the church. There is another motte just outside the village, called Bryn y Castell. It may be a siege castle.

*Norton.—First mentioned in the *Pipe Roll* of 1191. A motte remains close to the church, and two sides of a bailey which ran down to the Norton brook.

*Bleddfa, the Bledewach of the *Pipe Roll* of 1195-1196, when £5 was given to Hugh de Saye *ad firmandum castellum*, an expression which may mean either building or repairing. An oval motte, and traces of a bailey, are marked in the 6-inch O.M.

Tynboeth, *alias* Dyneneboth, Tinbech,[4] and Llan-

---

[1] Not to be confounded with the castle of Clun in Shropshire.

[2] *Annales Cambriæ* and *Annales de Margam*. See plan in *Arch. Camb.*, 4th ser., vi., 251.

[3] *Annales Cambriæ*.

[4] Really Ty-yn-yr Bwlch, the house in the pass. Not to be confounded with Tenby in Pembrokeshire.

anno.—First mentioned in *Pipe Roll* of 1196-1197. There is a fine large motte in a commanding situation, and a crescent-shaped bailey, now marked only by a scarp. There are some remains of masonry, and the castle was evidently an important one. It is first mentioned in the *Pipe Roll* of 1196, and it occurs in lists of the Mortimer castles in the 14th century.[1] It is not far from two fords of the river Ithon. [H. W.]

These four castles are not mentioned in the *Brut y Tywysogion*, though the *Annales Cambriæ* mentions the capture of Bleddfa, Knighton, and Norton by the Welsh in 1262. They all command important roads. Knighton and Norton were boroughs.

CASTLES OF GLAMORGANSHIRE.

CARDIFF (Fig. 43).—The first castle of Cardiff was certainly a wooden one; its lofty mound still remains. It is placed inside a Roman station, and the south and west walls of the castle bailey rest on Roman foundations, "but do not entirely coincide with those foundations." [2] The Roman fort was probably ruinous when Robert Fitz Hamon placed his first castle there, as on the N. and E. sides the bailey is defended by an earthbank, in which the remains of a Roman wall have been found buried. The area of the Roman castrum was about $8\frac{1}{4}$ acres, and evidently the Normans found this too large, as they divided it by a cross wall, which reduces the inner fort to about 2 acres. The motte has its own ditch. The position of Cardiff was a very important base, not only as a port near Bristol, but as a point on

[1] *Cal. of Close Rolls*, Ed. II., iii., 415, 643.
[2] See "Cardiff Castle : its Roman Origin," by John Ward, *Archæologia*, lvii., 335.

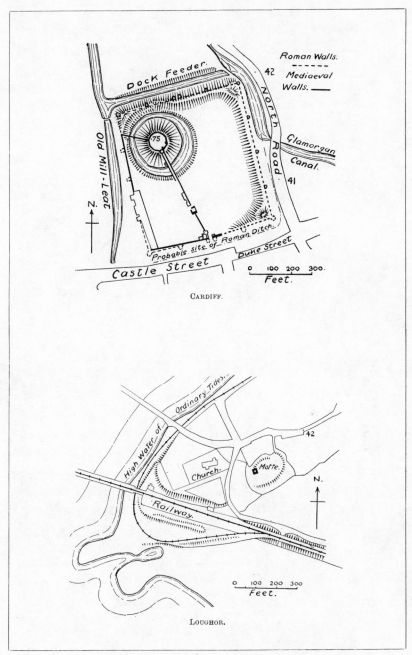

Roman Walls. ---- -- --

Mediaeval Walls. _____

Dock Feeder.

42

North Road.

Glamorgan Canal.

41

75

Old Mill-Leat.

N

Probable site of Roman Ditch.

Castle Street

Duke Street

0   100   200   300.
Feet.

CARDIFF.

High water of Ordinary Tides.

42

Church.

Motte.

N.

Railway.

0   100   200   300
Feet.

LOUGHOR.

FIG. 43.—MOTTE-CASTLES OF SOUTH WALES.

[To face p. 294.

the probably Roman road which connected Gloucester
with Carmarthen and beyond.[1]

The lands of Robert Fitz Hamon, in the next
generation, passed into the hands of Robert, the great
Earl of Gloucester, Henry I.'s illegitimate son. He was
a great castle-builder, and it is probable that the first
masonry of Cardiff Castle was his work.[2]

NEWCASTLE BRIDGEND.—This castle and the three
which follow are all situated on or near the "Roman"
road from Cardiff to St David's, of which we have already
spoken. There were two castles at Bridgend, the Old
Castle and the New Castle, from which the town takes
its name. The site of the former is now too much cut
up for any definite conclusions about it; the site of the
latter has been converted into market gardens, but a
motte is still standing in one corner with the ruins of a
tower upon it. [H. W.] This castle is not noticed either
by the *Brut* or the Aberpergwm version; the earliest
mention known to us is in the *Pipe Roll* of 1184, at a
time when the castles of the Earl of Gloucester were in
royal custody, and this appears to have been one of
them.

KENFIG.—This castle is close to the "Roman" road.
The Aberpergwm *Brut* says that it was one of the castles
of Robert Fitz Hamon, and states that in 1092 it was
rebuilt "stronger than ever before, for castles prior to
that were built of wood." This is a good specimen of
the mixture of truth and error to be found in this 16th
century MS. There is little doubt that all the first

[1] See "Cardiff Castle: its Roman Origin," by John Ward, *Archæologia*,
lvii., 335.

[2] Mr Clark thought the shell wall on the motte was Norman, and the
tower Perp. But the wall of the shell has some undoubtedly Perp. windows.
The *Gwentian Chronicle* says that Robert of Gloucester surrounded the *town*
of Cardiff with a wall, anno 1111.

castles of the Normans in Wales were built of wood; but it is extremely unlikely that any wooden keep was replaced by a stone one as early as 1092. The town and castle of Kenfig are now almost entirely buried in sand-drifts, but the top of the motte, with some fragments of masonry upon it, is still visible. [H. W.][1] The note in the *Pipe Rolls* of the repair of the *palicium* of this castle shows that the bailey wall at any rate was still of wood in 1183. Even as late as 1232 the keep was only defended by a ditch and hedge; yet it withstood an assault from Llywelyn ap Jorwerth.[2] The bailey is said to contain 11 acres, a most unusual size. Kenfig was a borough in Norman times, and it is possible that this large bailey was the original borough, afterwards enlarged in mediæval times. There is evidence that there were burgage tenements within the bailey.[3]

ABERAVON.—The Aberpergwm MS. says that Fitz Hamon gave Aberavon to the son of the Welsh traitor who had called him into Glamorgan. At a later period, however, we find it in Norman hands. The site of the castle has been entirely cleared away, but it had a motte, which is still remembered by the older inhabitants. [H. W.][4] It is not mentioned in the *Brut* before 1152, when it was attacked and burnt by Rhys ap Griffith.

*NEATH.—The site of the first castle of Neath was given by Richard de Granville, its owner, to the abbey of Neath, which he had founded.[5] About the year 1111,

---

[1] See Gray's *Buried City of Kenfig*, where there are interesting photographs. The remains appear to be those of a shell.

[2] *Annales de Margam*, 1232.

[3] Gray's *Buried City of Kenfig*, pp. 59, 150.

[4] This information is confirmed by Mr Tennant, town clerk of Aberavon.

[5] See Francis' *Neath and its Abbey*, where the charter of De Granville is given. It is only preserved in an Inspeximus of 1468.

according to the Aberpergwm *Brut*, Richard returned
from the Holy Land, bringing with him a Syrian
architect, well skilled in the building of monasteries,
churches, and castles, and by him we may presume, a
new castle was built on the other side of the river,
though the present castle on that site is clearly of much
later date.   The monks of course destroyed all vestiges
of the first (probably wooden) castle.

*REMMI, or Remni.—Of this castle there is only one
solitary mention, in the *Pipe Roll* of 1184.   The name
seems to indicate the river Rhymney, which is the
boundary between Glamorgan and Monmouth.   We are
unable to find any castle site so near the Rhymney as
Ruperra, where Clark mentions a fine motte.[1]   But we
do not venture on this identification without further
information.[2]

CASTLES OF GOWER.

*SWANSEA, or Abertawy.—This was the castle of
Henry Beaumont, the conqueror of Gower.   The
present castle is comparatively modern.   It is inside the
town ; but there used to be a moated mound outside the
town, which was only removed in 1804.   It seems
probable to us that this was the original castle of
Beaumont.[3]   That this first castle had a motte is

[1] *M. M. A.*, i., 112.

[2] Ruperra is not quite one mile from the river Rhymney.   There is
another site which may possibly be that of Castle Remni : Castleton, which
is nearly 2 miles from the river, but is on the main road from Cardiff to
Newport.   "It was formerly a place of strength and was probably built or
occupied by the Normans for the purpose of retaining their conquest of
Wentlwg.   The only remains are a barrow in the garden of Mr Philipps,
which is supposed to have been the site of the citadel, and a stone barn,
once a chapel."   Coxe's *Monmouthshire*, i., 63.

[3] It is right to say that Colonel Morgan in his admirable *Survey of East
Gower* (a model of what an antiquarian survey ought to be) does not con-

suggested by the narrative in the *Brut* which tells how Griffith ap Rhys burnt the outworks in 1115, but was unable to get at the tower.[1]

*LOUGHOR, or Aberllychor (Fig. 43).—Also built by Henry Beaumont. The mound of the castle still remains, with a small square keep on top. There was formerly a shell wall also. The place of a bailey was supplied by a terrace 15 feet wide.[2] The four castles last mentioned are all at the mouths of rivers, as well as on an ancient (if not Roman) coast road.

*LLANDEILO TALYBONT, or Castell Hu. — Only mentioned once in the *Brut*, under 1215, as the castle of Hugh de Miles. A moated mound with a square bailey and no masonry still remains.[3] It commands the river Loughor, which is still navigable up to that point at high tides.[4] On the opposite side of the river is another motte and bailey, called Ystum Enlle. Possibly there was a ford or ferry at this point, which these castles were placed to defend.[5]

OYSTERMOUTH, a corruption of Ystum Llwynarth.— First mentioned in the older *Brut* in 1215, when it was burnt by Rhys Grug. The later version says it was built by Beaumont in 1099. The castle stands on a natural height, fortified artificially by a motte, which is of great size. There is a small bailey below to the N.E., and a curious small oval embankment thrown out in the rear of the castle towards the N.W. The

nect this mound with the old castle which is mentioned, as well as the new castle, in Cromwell's Survey of Gower. But even the old castle seems to have been Edwardian (see the plan, p. 85), so it is quite possible there were three successive castles in Swansea.

[1] *Brut*, 1113.   [2] Morgan's *Survey of East Gower*, p. 24.
[3] Colonel Morgan's *Survey of East Gower*.
[4] Lewis's *Topographical Dictionary*.
[5] The passage of the river Lune in Lancashire is similarly defended by the mottes of Melling and Arkholme.

architecture of this magnificent castle is all of the
Edwardian style, and as the castle was burnt down by
Rhys ap Meredith in 1287, it is probable that only
wooden structures stood on this site until after that date.
The castle is in a fine situation overlooking the Bay of
Swansea. [H. W.]

We have now completed our list of the Norman
castles built in Wales which are known to history. It
must not be supposed, however, that we imagine this to
be a complete list of all the Norman castles which were
ever erected in Wales. The fact that several in our
catalogue are only once mentioned in the records makes
it probable that there were many others which have
never been mentioned at all. In this way we may
account for the many mottes which remain in Wales
about which history is entirely silent. As there was
scarcely a corner in Wales into which the Normans did
not penetrate at some time or other, it is not surprising
if we find them in districts which are generally reckoned
to be entirely Welsh. But there is another way of
accounting for them; some of them may have been
built by the Welsh themselves, in imitation of the
Normans. As the feudal system and feudal ideas
penetrated more and more into Wales, and the Welsh
princes themselves became feudal homagers of the kings
of England, it was natural that the feudal castle should
also become a Welsh institution, especially as it was
soon found to be a great addition to the chieftain's
personal strength. The following castles are stated in
the *Brut* to have been built by the Welsh.[1]

   1113. *CYMMER, in Merioneth.—Built by Uchtred ap

[1] The dates given are those of the *Brut*, and probably two years too early.

Edwin, whose name, as we have already remarked, suggests an English descent. Near Cymmer Abbey the motte or *tomen* remains.

*CYNFAEL, in Merioneth, near Towyn.—Built by Cadwalader, son of Griffith ap Cynan, on whose behalf Henry II. undertook his first expedition into Wales, and who was at that time a protégé of the Anglo-Normans. Clark gives a plan of this motte-castle in *Arch. Camb.*, 4th ser., vi., 66.

1148. *YALE, in Denbigh = Llanarmon. — Said to have been built by Owen Gwynedd, but here, as we have said, an earlier Norman foundation seems probable (see p. 272).

1148. LLANRHYSTYD, in Cardigan.—Also built by Cadwalader, who was then establishing himself in Cardigan. Probably the motte and bailey called Penrhos, or Castell Rhos, to the east of Llanrhystyd village. [H. W.]

1155. ABERDOVEY.—Built by Rhys ap Griffith to defend Cardigan against Owen, Prince of Gwynedd. It must therefore have been on the Cardigan shore of the Dovey, and not at the present town of Aberdovey, which is on the Merioneth shore. And in fact, on the Cardigan shore of the estuary, about two miles west of Glandovey Castle, there is a tumulus called Domenlas (the green tump), which was very likely the site of this castle of Rhys.[1]

1155. CAEREINION.—Built by Madoc of Powys, who was then a homager of Henry II. Remains of a motte near the church ; the churchyard itself appears to be the former bailey. About a mile off is a British camp called Pen y Voel, which *may* have been the seat of the son of Cunedda, who is said to have settled here. [H. W.]

---

[1] Meyrick's *History of Cardigan*, p. 146.

*WALWERN, or Tafolwern, near Llanbrynmair, in
Montgomery, may have been a Welsh castle. It is first
mentioned in 1163, when Howel ap Jeuav took it from
Owen Gwynedd, who may have been its builder. The
motte is marked in the O.M. on a narrow peninsula at
the junction of two streams.

1169. *ABEREINON, in Cardigan.—Built by Rhys ap
Griffith, Henry II.'s Justiciar of South Wales. "A
circular moated tumulus, now called Cil y Craig."[1] (It
is marked on the 25-inch O.M.)

1177. *RHAIDR GWY.—Also built by Rhys ap Griffith,
no doubt as a menace to Powys, as this castle was
afterwards sorely contested.. It is a motte-and-bailey
castle, the motte being known as Tower Mount.[2]

All these castles are of the motte-and-bailey type, and
prove the adoption by the Welsh of Norman customs.[3]
It will be noticed that in the first instances they were
built by men who were specially under Norman influences.
But probably the fashion was soon more widely followed,
although these are the only recorded cases.

The contribution made by the castles of Wales to
the general theory of the origin of mottes in these
islands is very important. Leaving out the seven
castles attributed to the Welsh, we find that out of
seventy-one castles built by the Normans, fifty-three, or
very nearly three-fourths, still have mottes ; while in the
remaining eighteen, either the sites have been so altered
as to destroy the original plan, or there is a probability
that a motte has formerly existed.

[1] Meyrick's *History of Cardigan*, p. 146.
[2] Lewis's *Topographical Dictionary*.
[3] We do not include the castles which the Welsh rebuilt. Thus in 1194
we are told that Rhys built the castle of Kidwelly, which he certainly only
rebuilt.

CHAPTER X

MOTTE-CASTLES IN SCOTLAND

THE Scottish historians of the 19th century have amply recognised the Anglo-Norman occupation of Scotland, which took place in the 11th and 12th centuries, ever since its extent and importance were demonstrated by Chalmers in his *Caledonia*. Occupation is not too strong a word to use, although it was an occupation about which history is strangely silent, and which seems to have provoked little resistance except in the Keltic parts of the country. But it meant the transformation of Scotland from a tribal Keltic kingdom into an organised feudal state, and in the accomplishment of this transformation the greater part of the best lands in Scotland passed into the hands of English refugees or Norman and Flemish adventurers.

The movement began in the days of Malcolm Canmore, when his English queen, the sainted Margaret, undoubtedly favoured the reception of English refugees of noble birth, some of whom were her own relations.[1] Very soon, the English refugees were followed by Norman refugees, who had either fallen under the displeasure of the king of England, like the Mont-

---

[1] Malcolm Canmore himself had passed nearly fourteen years in England. Fordun, iv., 45.

gomeries, or were the cadets of some Norman family, wishful to carve out fresh fortunes for themselves, like the Fitz Alans, the ancestors of the Stuarts. The immigration continued during the reign of the sons of Margaret, but seems to have reached its culminating point under David I. (1124-1153).

David, as Burton remarks, had lived for sixteen years as an affluent Anglo-Norman noble, before his accession to the Scottish crown, being Earl of Huntingdon in right of his wife, the daughter of Simon de Senlis, and granddaughter, through her mother, of Earl Waltheof. David's tastes and sympathies were Norman, but it was not taste alone which impelled him to build up in Scotland a monarchy of the Anglo-Norman feudal type. He had a distinct policy to accomplish; he wished to do for Scotland what Edward I. sought to do for the whole island, to unite its various nationalities under one government, and he saw that men of the Anglo-Norman type would be the best instruments of this policy.[1] It mattered little to him from what nation he chose his followers, if they were men who accepted his ideas. Norman, English, Flemish, or Norse adventurers were all received at his court, and endowed with lands in Scotland, if they were men suitable for working the system which he knew to be the only one available for the accomplishment of his policy. And that system was the feudal system. He saw that feudalism meant a higher state of civilisation than the tribalism of Keltic Scotland, and that only by the complete organisation of feudalism could he carry out the unification of Scotland, and the

[1] Burton remarks: "To the Lowland Scot, as well as to the Saxon, the Norman was what a clever man, highly educated and trained in the great world of politics, is to the same man who has spent his days in a village." *History of Scotland*, i., 353.

subjugation of the wild Keltic tribes of the north and west.[1]

The policy was successful, though it was not completely carried out until Alexander III. purchased the kingdom of the Isles from the King of Norway in 1266. The sons of David, Malcolm IV., and William the Lion were strong men who doughtily continued the subjugation of the Keltic parts of Scotland, and distributed the lands of the conquered among their Norman or Normanised followers. The struggle was a severe one ; again and again did the North rebel against the yoke of the House of Malcolm. In Moray the Keltic inhabitants were actually driven out by Malcolm IV., and the country colonised by Normans or Flemings.[2] The same Malcolm led no less than three expeditions against Galloway, where in spite of extensive Norse settlements on the coast, the mass of the inhabitants appear to have been Keltic.[3]

We know very little about the details of this remarkable revolution, because Scotland had no voice in the

[1] Dr Round has brought to light the significant fact that King David took his chancellor straight from the English chancery, where he had been a clerk. This first chancellor of Scotland was the founder of the great Comyn family. *The Ancestor*, 10, 108.

[2] Fordun, *Annalia*, vol. iv.

[3] It is tempting to connect the extraordinary preponderance of mottes, as shown by Dr Christison's map, in the shires which made up ancient Galloway, Wigton, Kirkcudbright, and Dumfries, with the savage resistance offered by Galloway, which may have made it necessary for all the Norman under-tenants to fortify themselves, each in his own motte-castle. It is wiser, however, to delay such speculations until we have the more exact information as to the number of mottes in Scotland, which it is hoped will be furnished when the Royal Commission on Historical Monuments has finished its work. But this work will not be complete unless special attention is paid to the earthworks which now form part of stone castles, and which are too often overlooked, even by antiquaries. The *New Statistical Account* certainly raises the suspicion that there are many more mottes north of the Forth than are recognised in the map alluded to. In one district we are told that "almost every farm had its *knap*." "Forfarshire," p. 326.

12th century, none of her chroniclers being earlier than the end of the 14th century. As regards the subject which concerns this book, the building of castles, there are only one or two passages which lift the veil. A contemporary English chronicler, Ailred of Rievaulx, in his panegyric of David I., says that David decorated Scotland with castles and cities.[1] In like manner Benedict of Peterborough tells us that when William the Lion was captured by Henry II.'s forces in 1174, the men of Galloway took the opportunity to destroy all the castles which the king had built in their country, expelling his seneschals and guards, and killing all the English and French whom they could catch.[2] Fordun casually mentions the building of two castles in Ross by William the Lion; and once he gives us an anecdote which is a chance revelation of what must have been going on everywhere. A certain English knight, Robert, son of Godwin, whose Norman name shows that he was one of the Normanised English, tarried with the king's leave on an estate which King Edgar had given him in Lothian, *and while he was seeking to build a castle there*, he was attacked by the men of Bishop Ranulf of Durham, who objected to a castle being built so near the English frontier.[3]

But even if historians had been entirely silent about the building of castles in Scotland, we should have been certain that it must have happened, as an inevitable part of the Norman settlement. Robertson remarks that the Scots in the time of David I. were still a pastoral and in some respects a migratory people, their

---

[1] Cited by Fordun, v., 43.

[2] Benedict of Peterborough, i., 68, R. S.

[3] Fordun, v., 26. Bower in one of his interpolations to Fordun's Annals, tells how a Highlander named Gillescop burnt certain wooden castles (*quasdam munitiones ligneas*) in Moray. Skene's Fordun, ii., 435.

magnates not residing like great feudal nobles in their
own castles, but moving about from place to place, and
quartering themselves upon the dependent population.
There is in fact no reason for supposing that the Keltic
chiefs of Scotland built castles, any more than those of
Wales or Ireland.[1]   But the feudal system must very
soon have covered Scotland with castles.

The absence of any stone castles of Norman type
has puzzled Scottish historians, whose ideas of castles
were associated with buildings in stone.[2]   In 1898 Dr
Christison published his valuable researches into the
Early Fortifications of Scotland, in which for the first
time an estimate was attempted of the distribution of
Scottish *motes*,[3] and their Norman origin almost, if not
quite, suspected.   His book was quickly followed by
Mr George Neilson's noteworthy paper on the "Motes
in Norman Scotland,"[4] in which he showed that the
wooden castle is the key which unlocks the historians'
puzzle, and that the motes of Scotland are nothing but
the evidence of the Norman feudal settlement.

[1] That Fordun should speak of the *castra* and *municipia* of Macduff is
not surprising, seeing that he wrote in the 14th century, when a noble
without a castle was a thing unthinkable.

[2] Burton actually thought that the Normans built no castles in Scotland
in the 12th century.   Messrs MacGibbon and Ross remark that there is not
one example of civil or military architecture of the 12th century, while there
are so many fine specimens of ecclesiastical. *Castellated Architecture of
Scotland*, i., 63.   It is just to add that when speaking of the castles of
William the Lion, they say: "It is highly probable that these and other
castles of the 13th century were of the primeval kind, consisting of
palisaded earthen mounds and ditches." *Ibid.*, iii. 6.

[3] *Mote* is the word used in Scotland, as in the north of England,
Pembrokeshire, and Ireland, for the Norman *motte*.   As the word is still a
living word in Scotland, its original sense has been partly lost, and it seems
to be now applied to some defensive works which are not mottes at all.
But the true motes of Scotland entirely resemble the mottes of France and
England.

[4] *Scottish Review*, xxxii., 232.

Two important points urged in Mr Neilson's paper are the feudal and legal connection of these motes. He has given a list of mottes which are known to have been the site of the "chief messuages" of baronies in the 13th and 14th centuries, and has collected the names of a great number which were seats of justice, or places where "saisine" of a barony was taken, not because they were moot-hills, but because the administration of justice remained fixed in the ancient site of the baron's castle. "The doctrine of the chief messuage, which became of large importance in peerage law, made it at times of moment to have on distinct record the nomination of what the chief messuage was, often for the imperative function of taking *sasine*. In many instances the *caput baroniæ*, or the court or place for the ceremonial entry to possession, is the 'moit,' the 'mothill,' the 'auld castell,' the 'auld wark,' the 'castellsteid,' the 'auld castellsteid,' the 'courthill,' or in Latin *mons placiti, mons viridis*, or *mons castri.*" [1] In certain places where two mottes are to be found, he was able to prove that two baronies had once had their seats. Another point which Mr Neilson worked out is the relation of bordlands to mottes. Bordland or borland, though an English word, is not pre-Conquest; it refers to "that species of demesne which the lord reserves for the supply of his own table." It is constantly found in the near proximity of mottes.[2]

The following is a list of thirty-eight Anglo-Norman or Normanised adventurers settled in Scotland, on whose lands mottes are to be found. The list must be regarded as a tentative one, for had all the names given by Chalmers been included, it would have been more than doubled. But the difficulties of obtain-

---

[1] *Scottish Review*, xxxii., 232.   [2] *Ibid.*, p. 236.

ing topographical information were so great that it has been judged expedient to give only the names of those families who are known to have held lands, and in most cases to have had their principal residences, in places where mottes are or formerly were existing.[1]

ANSTRUTHER.—William de Candela obtained the lands of Anstruther, in Fife, from David I. His descendants took the surname of Anstruther. The "Mothlaw" of Anstruther is mentioned in 1590.[2] "At the W. end of the town there is a large mound, called the Chester Hill, in the middle of which is a fine well." (N. S. A., 1845.) The well is an absolute proof that this was the site of a castle.

AVENEL.—Walter de Avenel held Abercorn Castle and estate, in Linlithgow, in the middle of the 12th century. The castle stood on a green mound (N. S. A.) which is clearly marked in the O.M.

BALLIOL.—The De Bailleul family had their seat at Barnard Castle, in Durham, after the Conquest. They obtained lands in Galloway from David I., and had strongholds at Buittle, and Kenmure, in Kirkcudbright. At Buittle the site of the castle exists, a roughly triangular bailey with a motte at one corner;[3] and at Kenmure the O.M. clearly shows a motte, as does the picture in Grose's

---

[1] This list is mainly compiled from Chalmers' *Caledonia*, vol. i., book iv., ch. i. The letter C. refers to Dr Christison's *Early Fortifications in Scotland;* N., to Mr Neilson's paper in the *Scottish Review*, 1898 ; O.M., to the 25-inch Ordnance Map ; G., to the *Gazetteer of Scotland*. It is a matter of great regret to the writer that she has been unable to do any personal visitation of the Scottish castles, except in the cases of Roxburgh and Jedburgh. It is therefore impossible to be absolutely certain that all the hillocks mentioned in this list are true mottes, or whether all of them still exist.

[2] *Registrum Magni Sigilli*, quoted by Christison, p. 19.

[3] A plan is given by Mr Coles in "the Motes, Forts, and Doons of Kirkcudbright." *Soc. Ant. Scot.*, 1891-1892.

Antiquities of Scotland. The terraces probably date from the time when the modern house on top was built.

BARCLAY.—The De Berkeleys sprang from the De Berkeleys of England, and settled in Scotland in the 12th century. Walter de Berkeley was Chamberlain of Scotland in 1165; William the Lion gave him the manor of Inverkeilor, in Forfarshire; there he built a castle, on Lunan Bay. "An artificial mound on the west side of the bay, called the Corbie's Knowe, bears evident marks of having been a castle long previous to the erection of Redcastle." (N. S. A.) The family also had lands in what is now Aberdeenshire, and at Towie, in the parish of Auchterless, they had a castle. "Close to the church of Auchterless there is a small artificial eminence of an oval shape, surrounded by a ditch, which is now in many places filled up. It still retains the name of the Moat Head, and was formerly the seat of the baronial court." (N. S. A.; N.; C.)

BRUCE.—The De Brus held lands in North Yorkshire at the time of the Domesday Survey. David I. gave them the barony of Annan, in Dumfriesshire. The original charter of this grant still exists in the British Museum, witnessed by a galaxy of Norman names.[1] Their chief castles were at Annan and Lochmaben. At Annan, near the site of a later castle, there is still a motte about 50 feet high, with a vast ditch and some traces of a bailey (N.), called the Moat (N. S. A.). The "terras de Moit et Bailyis, intra le Northgate," are mentioned in 1582. South of the town of Lochmaben, on the N.W. side of the loch, is a fine motte called Castle Hill, with some remains of masonry, which is still pointed out as the original castle of the

[1] M'Ferlie, *Lands and Their Owners in Galloway*, ii., 47.

Bruces.[1]   (G.) The fine motte and bailey at Moffat must also have been one of their castles, as Moffat was one of their demesne lands.   (Fig. 44.)

CATHCART.—Name territorial.   Rainald de Cathcart witnesses a charter (in the Paisley Register) in 1179. Near the old castle of Cathcart, Lanark, is "an eminence called Court Knowe."   (N. S. A.)   As Mr Neilson has shown, these court knowes and court hills are generally disused mottes.   The name Rainald is clearly Norman.

CHEYNE.—This family is first known in 1258, but had then been long settled in Scotland, and were hereditary sheriffs of Banffshire.   Chalmers only mentions their manor of Inverugie, in Aberdeenshire.   Behind the ruins of Inverugie Castle rises a round flat-topped hill, which was the Castle Hill or Mote Hill of former days.   (N. S. A.)

COLVILLE.—Appears in Scotland in the reign of Malcolm IV., holding the manors of Heton and Oxnam, in Roxburgh.   About ¼ mile from Oxnam (which was a barony) is a moated mound called Galla Knowe.   (O.M., C., and N.)   Hailes identified the castle in Teviotdale, captured and burnt by Balliol in 1333, with that of Oxnam.[2]   Le Mote de Oxnam is mentioned in 1424 (N.).

CUMYN, or COMYN.—The first of this family came to Scotland as the chancellor of David I.[3]   First seated at Linton Roderick, in Roxburghshire, where there is a rising ground, surrounded formerly by a foss, the site of the original castle ; (G.) a description which seems to

---

[1] This description, taken from the *Gazetteer*, seems clear, but Mr Neilson tells me the site is more probably Woody Castle, which is styled a manor in the 15th century.   The N. S. A. says : "There is the site of an ancient castle close to the town, on a mound of considerable height, called the Castle Hill, which is surrounded by a deep moat."   "Dumfries," p. 383.

[2] *Annals*, ii., 196, cited in Douglas's *History of the Border Counties*, 173.

[3] Round, in *The Ancestor*, 10, 108.

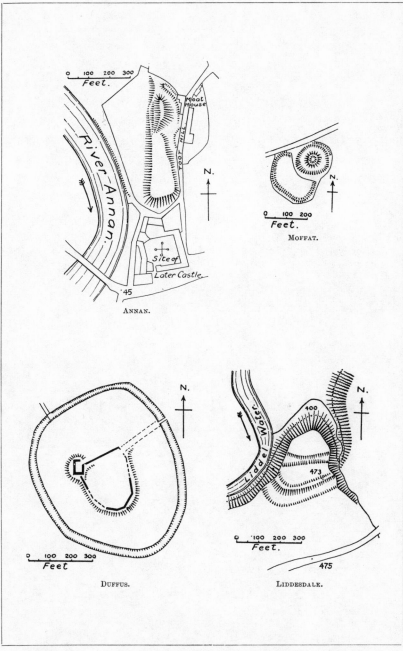

FIG. 44.—SCOTTISH MOTTE-CASTLES.

[To face p. 310.

suggest a motte. William the Lion gave the Cumyns Kirkintilloch in Dumbarton, and we afterwards find them at Dalswinton in Dumfriesshire, and Troqueer in Kirkcudbright. At Kirkintilloch the O.M. shows a square mount concentrically placed in a square enceinte. The enclosure was apparently one of the forts on the wall of Agricola, but the writer on Kirkintilloch in the N. S. A. suspected that it had been transformed into a castle by the Cumyns. At Dalswinton the O.M. shows a motte, and calls it the "site of Cumyn's Castle." At Troqueer, "directly opposite the spot on the other side the river where Cumyn's Castle formerly stood is a mote of circular form and considerable height." (N. S. A.) The Cumyn who held Kirkintilloch in 1201, was made Earl of Buchan, and held the vast district of Badenoch, or the great valley of the Spey. The N. S. A. gives many descriptions of remains in this region which are suggestive of motte-castles ; we can only name the most striking : Ruthven, "a castle reared by the Comyns on a green conical mound on the S. bank of the Spey, thought to be partly artificial," now occupied by ruined barracks ; Dunmullie, in the parish of Duthill, where "there can be traced vestiges of a motte surrounded by a ditch, on which, according to tradition, stood the castle of the early lords" ; Crimond, where Cumyn had a castle, and where there is a small round hill called Castle Hill ; and Ellon, where the Earl of Buchan had his head court, on a small hill which has now disappeared, but which was anciently known as the moot-hill of Ellon. Saisin of the earldom was given on this hill in 1476. (N. S. A.)

CUNNINGHAM. — Warnebald, who came from the north of England, was a follower of the Norman, Hugh de Morville, who gave him the lands of Cunningham, in Ayrshire, from which the family name was taken. In the parish of Kilmaurs, which is in the district of Cunningham, there is a "mote," which may have been the castle of Warnebald; at any rate the original manor place of Cunningham was in this parish. It is of course possible that this motte may have been originally a De Morville castle.

DOUGLAS. — Name territorial; progenitor was a Fleming, who received lands on the Douglas water, in Lanark, in the middle of the 12th century. In the park of Douglas, to the east of the modern castle, is a mound called Boncastle, but we are unable to state certainly that it is a motte. Lag Castle, in the parish of Dunscore, "has a moat or court hill a little to the east." (N. S. A. : shown in Grose's picture.) It must have been originally Douglas land, as in 1408 it was held by an armour-bearer of Douglas.

DURAND.—Clearly a Norman name, corrupted into Durham. The family were seated at Kirkpatrick Durham in the 13th century. There is or was a motte at Kirkpatrick.[1]

DURWARD.—This family was descended from Alan de Lundin, who was dur-ward or door-keeper to the king about 1233. They possessed a wide domain in Aberdeenshire, and had a castle at Lumphanan, where Edward I. stayed in 1296. There is a round motte in the Peel Bog at Lumphanan, surrounded by a moat, which was fed by a sluice from the neighbouring burn. There were ruins in masonry on the top some hundred years ago. The writer of the N. S. A. account of this place, with remarkable shrewdness, conjectures that a wooden castle on this mound was the ancient

---

[1] Dr Christison distinctly marks one on his map, but Mr Coles says there is no trace of one, though the name Marl Mount is preserved. *Soc. Ant. Scot.*, 1892, p. 108.

residence of the Durwards, superseded in the 15th century by a building of stone, and that it has nothing to do with Macbeth, whose burial-place is said to be a cairn in the neighbourhood.[1]

FITZ ALAN.—This is the well-known ancestor of the House of Stuart, Walter, a cadet of a great Norman family in Shropshire, who is said to have obtained lands in Scotland in Malcolm Canmore's time. Renfrew was one of his seats, and Inverwick, in Haddington, another. Renfrew Castle is entirely destroyed, but the description of the site, on a small hill, ditched round, called Castle Hill, strongly suggests a motte. The keep of Inverwick stands on a natural motte of rock.[2] Dunoon was one of their castles, near to which " stood the Tom-a-mhoid, or Hill of the court of justice " (G.), possibly an ancient motte.[3] Dunoon Castle, however, itself stands on a motte, partly artificial and partly carved out of a headland. (N.)

FLEMING.— There were many Flemings among the followers of David I., and eventually the name stuck to their descendants as a surname. Baldwin the Fleming obtained lands at Biggar, in Lanarkshire. There is a motte at the west end of the town of Biggar, 36 feet high. Biggar was the head of a barony. (N. S. A. and N.) Colban the Fleming settled at Colbantown, now Covington, Lanarkshire, where there is a motte (N.). Robert the Fleming has left a well-preserved oblong

---

[1] See the Aberdeen volume, p. 1092.

[2] See Grose's picture, which is confirmed by Dr Ross.

[3] The name Tom-a-mhoid is derived by some writers from the Gaelic *Tom*, a tumulus (Welsh Tomen) and *moid*, a meeting. Is there such a word for a meeting in Gaelic? If there is, it must be derived from Anglo-Saxon *mot* or *gemot*. But there is no need to go to Gaelic for this word, as it is clear from the *Registrum Magni Sigilli* that *moit* was a common version of *mote*, and meant a castle hill, the *mota* or *mons castri*, as it is often called.

motte at Roberton, in Lanark, which was a barony, and where the *moit* was spoken of in 1608. (N.)

GRAHAM.—Came from England under David I., and received lands in Lothian. A Graham was lord of Tarbolton, in Ayrshire, in 1335, so it is possible that the motte at that place, on which stood formerly the chief messuage of the barony of Tarbolton, was one of their castles (N. S. A.), but it may have been older.

HAMILTON.—It is not certain that the Hamiltons came to Scotland before 1272. King Robert I. gave them the barony of Cadzow, Lanark, which had originally been a royal seat. In Hamilton Park there is a mote hill, which was the site of the chief messuage of this barony (N.). It was formerly surrounded by the town of Hamilton. (N. S. A.) It is of course possible that this motte may be much older than the Hamiltons, as the site of an originally royal castle.

HAY.—First appears in the 12th century, as butler to Malcolm IV. The family first settled in Lothian, where they had lands at Lochorworth. The Borthwick family, who got this estate by marriage, obtained a license from James I. about 1430 to build a castle "on the mote of Locherwart," and to this castle they gave their own name. (N. S. A.) No doubt it was the original motte of the Hays. King William gave the Hays the manor of Errol, in Perthshire, which was made into a barony. Here is or was the mote of Errol, "a round artificial mound about 20 feet high, and 30 feet in diameter at the top; the platform at the top surrounded with a low turf wall, and the whole enclosed with a turf wall at the base, in the form of an equilateral triangle." (N. S. A.; evidently a triangular bailey.) It is called the Law Knoll, and is spoken of as a *fortalicium* in 1546. (N.)

LENNOX.—The earls of Lennox are descended from Arkel, an Englishman, who received from Malcolm Canmore lands in Dumbartonshire. At Catter, near the Earl's castle, is a large artificial mound.[1]

LOCKHART.—Stevenston, in Ayrshire, takes its name from Stephen Loccard, and Symington, in Lanark, from his son (?), Simon Loccard. At Stevenson there was formerly a castle, and there still (1845) is a Castle Hill. Stevenston was given by Richard Morville to Stephen Loccard about 1170. (N. S. A.) At Symington there was formerly a round mound, called Law Hill, at the foot of the village, but it has been levelled. (N. S. A.)

LOGAN.—A Robert Logan witnesses a charter of William the Lion, and appears later as Dominus Robertus de Logan. The name Robert shows his Norman origin. At Drumore, near Logan (parish of Kirkmaiden, Wigton), there was a castle, and there is still a court hill or mote.[2] Another mote, at Myroch, in the same parish, is mentioned by Mr Neilson as the site of the chief messuage of the barony of Logan.

LOVEL.—Settled at Hawick, Roxburghshire. The mote of Hawick, from the picture in Scott's *Border Antiquities*, seems to be a particularly fine one. Hawick was a barony, and Le Moit is mentioned in 1511. (N.)

LYLE, or LISLE.—The castle of this Norman family was at Duchal, Renfrewshire. The plan is clearly that of a motte and bailey, but the motte is of natural rock.[3]

MALE, now MELVILLE.—Settled in Haddingtonshire

[1] Chalmers, *Caledonia*, iii., 864. Sir Archibald Lawrie, however, regards it as doubtful whether Arkel was the ancestor of the earls of Lennox. *Early Scottish Charters*, p. 327.

[2] M'Ferlie, *Lands and Their Owners in Galloway*, ii., 140-141.

[3] See plan in MacGibbon and Ross, *Castellated Architecture*, iv., 341.

under David I., and called their seat Melville. Melville Castle is modern. They afterwards obtained by marriage lands on the Bervie River, in the Mearns. Dr Christison's map shows a motte near the mouth of the Bervie.

MAXWELL.—Maccus, son of Unwin[1] (evidently of Scandinavian origin), received lands on the Tweed from David I., and called his seat Maccusville, corrupted into Maxwell. There is a motte at Maxwell, near Kelso. (N.) Maxton, in Roxburghshire, takes its name from him, and there is a motte called Ringley Hall, on the Tweed, in this parish. (C. and N. S. A.)

MONTALT, or MOWAT.—Robert de Montalto (Mold, in Flintshire) witnesses a charter of David I. The family settled in Cromarty. Le Mote at Cromarty is mentioned in 1470. (N.)

MONTGOMERY.—This family is undoubtedly descended from some one of the sons of the great Earl Roger of Shrewsbury, settled in Scotland after the ruin of his family in England. Robert de Montgomerie received the manor of Eaglesham, Renfrew, from Fitz Alan, the High Steward of Scotland. The principal messuage of this manor was at Polnoon, ½ mile S.E. of Eaglesham. Here Sir John Montgomerie built the castle of Polnoon about 1388. (N. S. A.) The O.M. seems to show that the ruins of this castle stand on a motte, probably the original castle of Montgomerie.

MORVILLE.—Hugh de Morville was a Northamptonshire baron, the life-long friend of David I.[2] He founded one of the most powerful families in the south

---

[1] The name Maccus is undoubtedly the same as Magnus, a Latin adjective much affected as a proper name by the Norwegians of the 11th and 12th centuries.　　[2] Lawrie, *Early Scottish Charters*, p. 273.

of Scotland, though after three generations their lands passed to heiresses, and their chief seat is not even known by name. But Mr Neilson states that Darnhall, in Peebles, was the head of their "Black Barony," and that there is a motte there. As Hugh de Morville gave the church of Borgue to Dryburgh Abbey about 1150, it is probable that the motte at Boreland of Borgue was one of his castles. The barony of Beith, in Ayr, given by Richard de Morville to the Abbey of Kilwinning, has also a motte, which may be reckoned to be the site of a De Morville castle. Largs, in Ayr, belonged to the De Morvilles, and has a Castle Hill near the village, which appears to be a motte. (G.)

MOWBRAY.—This well-known Norman family also sent a branch to Scotland. Amongst other places, about which we have no details, they held Eckford, in Roxburghshire. In this parish, near the ancient mansion, is an artificial mount called Haughhead Kipp. (N. S. A.) This seems a possible motte, but its features are not described.

MURRAY.—Freskin the Fleming came to Scotland under David I., and received from that king lands in Moray. He built himself a castle at Duffus, in Elgin, which is on the motte-and-bailey plan.[1] The stone keep now on the motte appears to be of the 14th century. Freskin's posterity took the name of De Moravia, or Moray. (Fig. 44.)

OLIPHANT, or OLIFARD.—Cambuslang, in Lanark, belonged to Walter Olifard, Justiciary of Lothian in the time of Alexander II. About a mile E. of the church is a circular mound 20 feet high. It was here that the Oliphants' castle of Drumsagard formerly stood. (N. S. A.) Drumsagard was a barony. (N.)

---

[1] MacGibbon and Ross, i., 279.

DE QUINCY.—Obtained from William the Lion the manors of Travernant, in East Lothian, and Leuchars, in Fife. Near the village of Leuchars is a motte with some slight remains of a stone keep, a deep well in the centre, and an entrenched bailey, known as the site of the castle of Leuchars.[1]

ROSS.—Godfrey de Ros, a vassal of Richard de Morville, held of him the lands of Stewarton, in Ayr. The *caput* of the lordship was Castletown, where Le Mote is spoken of in 1451 (N. and C.). The De Ros were also the first lords of the barony of Sanquhar. A little lower down the river Nith than the later castle of Sanquhar is a mote called Ryehill, and a place anciently manorial. (N.)

SOMERVILLE.—William de Somerville was a Norman to whom David I. gave the manor of Carnwath, in Lanarkshire. There is a very perfect entrenched motte at Carnwath (N. S. A. and O.M.), and Le Moit de Carnwath is mentioned in 1599. (N.)

DE SOULIS.—Followed David I. from Northamptonshire into Scotland, and received Liddesdale, in Roxburghshire, from him. The motte and bailey of his original castle still remain, very near the more celebrated but much later Hermitage Castle.[2] (Fig. 44.)

VALOIGNES.—Philip de Valoignes and his son William were each successively chamberlains of Scotland.[3] One of their estates was Easter Kilbride, in Lanarkshire, where they had a castle. In this parish is an artificial mount of earth, with an oval area on top, about ¼ mile from the present house of Torrance. (N. S. A.)

[1] *Proceedings of Soc. Ant. Scotland*, xxxi., and N. S. A.
[2] See Armstrong's *History of Liddesdale*, cited by MacGibbon and Ross, i., 523.
[3] Round, *The Ancestor*, No. 11, 130.

VAUX, or DE VALLIBUS.—Settled in Scotland under William the Lion. Held the manors of Dirleton and Golyn, in East Lothian. Dirleton has been transformed into an Edwardian castle, but from the pictures it appears to stand on a natural motte of rock. But about 3 miles from Dirleton the O.M. shows a large motte called Castle Hill, which may possibly be the original castle of the De Vaux.

WALLACE, or WALLENSIS.—Richard Walensis was the first of this family, and acquired lands in Ayrshire in David I.'s time. He named his seat Riccardton, after himself, and the remains of his motte are still there, a small oval motte called Castle Hill, on which the church of Riccarton now stands, but which is recognised as having been a "mote hill." (G.)

To this list must be added a number of royal castles known to have been built in the 12th century, which, as they were built on mottes, must in the first instance have been wooden castles.

BANFF.—It seems clear that Banff Castle had a motte, because the doggerel rhymes of Arthur Johnstone in 1642 say :

> A place was near which was a field until
> Our ancestors did raise it to a hill ;
> A stately castle also on it stood.

The *Gazetteer* says : "The citadel occupied a mount, originally at the end though now near the middle of the town." The site is still called Castle Hill. (N. S. A.)

CRAIL, Fife.—The O.M. does not show a motte here. The N. S. A. says "there was a royal residence here, upon an eminence overlooking the harbour." That this "eminence" was a motte seems clear from the *Register of the Great Seal*, quoted by Mr Neilson, which speaks of " Le Moitt olim castrum " in 1573.

CUPAR.—There seem to be two mottes here, both raised on a natural "esker"; the one formerly called the Castle Hill is now called the School Hill, the school having been built upon it. The other and higher hill is called the Moot Hill, and is said to be the place where the earls of Fife used to dispense justice. (N. S. A.) Mr Neilson states that both are mentioned in the *Registrum.*

DUMFRIES.—Here there were two mottes, one being now the site of a church, the other, called Castle Dykes, a short distance S. of the town, on the opposite side of the river. Both no doubt were royal castles, and Mr Neilson has suggested that as an *old castlestead* is spoken of in a charter of William the Lion, it implies that a new castle had recently been built, possibly after the great destruction of the royal castles in Galloway in 1174.[1] The Castle Dykes appears to be the later castle, as it is spoken of in the 16th century. (N.)

DUNSKEATH, Cromarty.—Built by William the Lion in 1179. The castle is built on a small *moat* overhanging the sea. (G.)

ELGIN.—Built by William the Lion on a small green hill called Lady Hill, with conical and precipitous sides. (N. S. A. and G.)

FORFAR.—"The castle stood on a round hill to the N. of the town, and must have been surrounded by water." (N. S. A.) It was destroyed in 1307. It is called Gallow Hill in the O.M., and is now occupied by gasworks.

[1] *Benedict of Peterborough,* i., 67. See Mr Neilson's papers in the *Dumfries Standard,* June 28, 1899. Mr Neilson remarks : "It may well be that the original castle of Dumfries was one of Malcolm IV.'s forts, and that the mote of Troqueer, at the other side of a ford of the river, was the first little strength of the series by which the Norman grip of the province was sought to be maintained."

FORRES.—The plan in Chalmers' *Caledonia* clearly shows a motte, to which the town appears to have formed a bailey.

INVERNESS.—Built by David I. when he annexed Moray. The site is now occupied by a gaol, but the O.M. shows it to have been a motte, which is clearly depicted in old engravings.

INNERMESSAN.—As the lands here appear to have been royal property as late as the time of David II., the large round motte here may have been an early royal castle, a conjecture which finds some confirmation in the name " Boreland of Kingston," which Pont places in the same parish. (N. S. A.)

JEDBURGH.—Probably built by David I. The site, which is still called Castle Hill, has been levelled and completely obliterated by the building of a gaol. Yet an old plan of the town in 1762, in the possession of the late Mr Laidlaw of Jedburgh, shows the outline of the castle to have been exactly that of a motte and bailey, though, as no hachures are given, it is not absolutely convincing.

KINCLEVEN, Perth.—The O.M. shows no earthworks connected with the present castle, but on the opposite side of the river it places a motte called Castle Hill, which may very likely be the site of the original castle.

KIRKCUDBRIGHT.—Dr Christison marks a motte here, to the W. of the town. The place is called Castle Dykes. Mr Coles says it has an oblong central mound and a much larger entrenched area.[1]

LANARK.—Ascribed traditionally to David I. " On a small artificially shaped hill between the town and the river, at the foot of the street called Castle Gate, and

---

[1] "Mottes, Forts, and Doons of Kirkcudbright," *Soc. Ant. Scot.*, xxv., 1890.

still bearing the name of Castle Hill, there stood in former times beyond all doubt a royal castle." (N. S. A.) Mr Neilson says, " It certainly bears out its reputation as an artificial mound."

ROSEMARKIE, Cromarty.—Was made a royal burgh by Alexander II., so the castle must have been originally royal. "Immediately above the town is a mound of nearly circular form, and level on the top, which seems to be artificial, and has always been called the Court Hill." (N. S. A.)

Even if we had no other evidence that motte-castles were of Norman construction, this list would be very significant. But taken in connection with the evidence for the Norman origin of the English, Welsh, and Irish mottes, it supplies ample proof that in Scotland, as elsewhere, the Norman and feudal settlement had its material guarantees in the castles which were planted all over the land, and that these castles were the simple structures of earth and wood, whose earthen remains have been the cause of so much mystification.

CHAPTER XI

MOTTE-CASTLES IN IRELAND

In the year 1169, when the first Norman invaders landed in Ireland, the private castle had been in existence in England for more than a hundred years, and had it been suited to the social organisation of the Irish people, there had been plenty of time for its introduction into Ireland. Nor are we in a position to deny that some chieftain with a leaning towards foreign fashions *may* have built for himself a castle in the Anglo-Norman style; all we can say is that there is not the slightest evidence of such a thing.[1] We have two contemporary accounts of the Norman settlement in Ireland, the one given by Giraldus in his *Expugnatio Hibernica,* and the Anglo-Norman poem, edited by Mr Goddard H. Orpen, under the title of the "Song of Dermot and the Earl."[2] Now Giraldus expressly tells us that the Irish did not

---

[1] The *Annals of the Four Masters* mention the building of three castles (caisteol) in Connaught in 1125, and the *Annals of Ulster* say that Tirlagh O'Connor built a castle (caislen) at Athlone in 1129. What the nature of these castles was it is now impossible to say, but there are no mottes at the three places mentioned in Connaught (Dunlo, Galway, and Coloony). The *caislen* at Athlone was not recognised by the Normans as a castle of their sort, as John built his castle on a new site, on land obtained from the church. *Sweetman's Cal.,* p. 80.

[2] The meagre entries in the various *Irish Annals* may often come from contemporary sources, but as none of their MSS. are older than the 14th century, they do not stand on the same level as the two authorities above mentioned.

use castles, but preferred to take refuge in their forests
and bogs.[1] The statement is a remarkable one, since
Ireland abounds with defensive works of a very ancient
character ; are we to suppose that these were only used
in the prehistoric period ? But if castles of the Norman
kind had been in general use in Ireland in the 12th
century, we should certainly hear of their having been
a serious hindrance to the invaders. The history of the
invasion, however, completely confirms the statement of
Giraldus ; we never once hear of the Irish defending
themselves in a castle. When they do stand a siege, it
is in a walled town, and a town which has been walled,
not by themselves, but by the Danes, to whom Giraldus
expressly attributes these walls. Moreover, the repeated
insistence of Giraldus on the necessity of systematic
incastellation of the whole country [2] is proof enough that
no such incastellation existed.

It is true that in some of the earliest Irish literature
we hear of the *dun*, *lis*, or *rath* (the words are inter-
changeable), which encircled the chieftain's house.

---

[1] "Hibernicus enim populus castella non curat ; silvis namque pro
castris, paludibus utitur pro fossatis." *Top. Hib.*, 182, R. S., vol. v. In
the same passage he speaks of the "fossa infinita, alta nimis, rotunda
quoque, et pleraque triplicia ; castella etiam murata, et adhuc integra,
vacua tamen et deserta," which he ascribes to the Northmen. This passage
has been gravely adduced as an argument in favour of the prehistoric existence of mottes ! as though a round *ditch* necessarily implied a round *hill*
within it ! Giraldus was probably alluding to the round embankments or
raths, of which such immense numbers are still to be found in Ireland. By
the "walled castles" he probably meant the stone enclosures or *cashels*
which are also so numerous in Ireland. In the time of Giraldus the word
castellum, though it had become the proper word for a private castle, had
not quite lost its original sense of a fortified enclosure of any kind, as we
know from the phrases "the castle and tower" or "the castle and motte"
not infrequent in documents of the 12th century (see Round's *Geoffrey de
Mandeville*, Appendix O, p. 328). We may add that Giraldus' attribution
of these prehistoric remains to Thorgils, the Norwegian, only shows that
their origin was unknown in his day.

[2] See *Expug. Hib.*, 383, 397, 398.

Many descriptions of royal abodes in Irish poems are evidently purely fanciful, but underneath the poetical adornments we can discern the features of the great wooden hall which appears to have been the residence of the tribal chieftain, whether Keltic, Norse, or Saxon, throughout the whole north of Europe in early times.[1] The thousands of earthen rings, generally called *raths*, which are still scattered over Ireland, are believed to be the enclosures of these kings' or chieftains' homesteads. Were they intended for serious military defence? We are not in a position to answer this question categorically, but the plans of a number of them which we have examined do not suggest anything but a very slight fortification, sufficient to keep off wolves. At all events we never hear of these raths or duns standing a siege; the conquering raider comes, sees, and burns.[2] We are therefore justified in concluding that they did not at all correspond to what we mean by a private castle. And most certainly the motte-castle, with its very small citadel, and its limited accommodation for the flocks and herds of a tribe, was utterly unsuited to the requirements of the tribal system.

A good deal of light is thrown on the way in which Irish chieftains regarded private castles at the time of the invasion by the well-known story of one who refused a castle offered him by the invaders, saying that he preferred a castle of bones to a castle of stones. Whether legendary or not, it represents the natural feeling of a man who had been accustomed to sleep trustfully in the midst of men of his own blood, tied to him by the bonds of the clan. The clan system in

---

[1] I am informed that the "Crith Gablach," which gives a minute description of one of these halls, is a very late document, and by no means to be trusted.

[2] *Vide* the *Irish Annals*, passim.

Ireland undoubtedly led to great misery through the absence of a central authority to check the raids of one clan upon another ; but though we occasionally hear of a chieftain being murdered "by his own," we have no reason to think that clan loyalty was not sufficient, as a rule, for the internal safety of the community. So that a popular chieftain might well refuse a fortification which had every mark of a hateful and suspicious invader.[1]

Unfortunately there is—or has been until quite recently—a strong prejudice in the minds of Irish antiquaries that works of the motte-and-bailey kind belong to the prehistoric age of Ireland. Irish scholars indeed admit that the word *mota* is not found in any Irish MS. which dates from before the Norman invasion of Ireland.[2] We must therefore bear in mind that when they tell us that such and such an ancient book mentions the "mote" at Naas or elsewhere, what they mean is that it mentions a *dun*, or *rath*, or *longport*, which they imagine to be the same as a motte. But this is begging the whole question. There is not the slightest proof that any of these words meant a motte. *Dun* is often taken to mean a hill (perhaps from its resemblance to Anglo-Saxon *dun*), but Keltic scholars are now agreed that it is cognate with the German *zaun* and Anglo-Saxon *tun*, meaning a fenced enclosure.[3] It may be applied to a fort on a hill, but it may equally well be

---

[1] There is another story, preserved in *Hanmer's Chronicle*, that the Irish chief Mac Mahon levelled two castles given to him by John de Courcy, saying he had promised to hold not stones but land.

[2] Joyce's *Irish Names of Places*, p. 290.

[3] See J. E. Lloyd, *Cymmrodor*, xi., 24 ; Skeat's *English Dictionary*, "town." In the "Dindsenchas of Erin," edited by O'Beirne Crowe, *Journ. R. S. A. I.*, 1872-1873, phrases occur, such as "the *dun* was open," "she went back into the dun," which show clearly that the *dun* was an enclosure. In several passages *dun* and *cathair* are interchanged.

applied to a fort on the flat. *Rath* is translated *fossa* in the *Book of Armagh;* Jocelin of Furness equates it with *murus*.[1] The rath of Armagh was evidently a very large enclosure in 1166, containing several streets, houses, and churches, so it was certainly not a motte.[2] It is of course not impossible that the Normans may sometimes have occupied an ancient fortified site, but we may be sure from the considerations already urged that the fortifications which they erected were of a wholly different character to the previous ones, even if they utilised a portion for their bailey.

It is of course difficult to decide in some cases (both in Ireland and elsewhere) whether a mound which stands alone without a bailey is a sepulchral tumulus or a motte. There are some mottes in England and Scotland which have no baileys attached to them, and do not appear ever to have had any. In Ireland, the country of magnificent sepulchral tumuli, it is not wonderful that the barrow and the motte have become confused in popular language. It would appear, too, that there exist in Ireland several instances of artificial tumuli which were used for the inauguration of Irish chieftains, and these have occasionally been mistaken for mottes.[3] As Mr Orpen has shown, there are generally indications in the unsuitability of the sites, in the absence of real fortification, or in the presence of sepulchral signs, to show that these tumuli did not belong to the motte class. Magh Adair, for example, which has been adduced as a motte outside the Norman boundary, is shown by Mr Orpen to be of quite a different character.

[1] Joyce, *Irish Names of Places*, p. 273.
[2] *Annals of the Four Masters*, 1166.
[3] See Orpen, "Motes and Norman Castles in Ireland," in *Journ. R. S. A. I.*, xxxvii., 143-147.

At many sites in Ireland where the Normans are known to have built castles at an early period of the invasion there are no mottes to be seen now. It is probable that where the Norman conquerors had both money and time at their disposal they built stone keeps from the first, and that the motte-castles, with their wooden towers or *bretasches*, were built in the times of stress, or were the residences of the less wealthy under-tenants. But we know from documents that even in John's reign the important royal castle of Roscrea was built with a motte and bretasche,[1] which proves that this type of castle was still so much esteemed that we may feel reasonably certain that when Giraldus speaks of "slender defences of turf and stakes" he does not mean motte - castles, but mere embankments and palisades.[2]

But there is another reason for the absence of mottes from some of the early Norman castle sites. Those who have examined the castles of Wales know that it is rare to find a motte in a castle which has undergone the complete metamorphoses of the Edwardian[3] period. These new castles had no keeps, and necessitated an entire change of plan, which led either to the destruction of the motte or the building of an entirely new castle on a different site. The removal of a motte is only a question of spade labour, and many

[1] Sweetman's *Calendar of Documents* relating to Ireland, i., 412.

[2] That a motte-castle of earth and wood seemed to Giraldus quite an adequate castle is proved by the fact that numbers of the castles which he mentions have never had any stone defences. It may be a mere coincidence, but it is worth noting, that there are no mottes now at any of the places which Giraldus mentions as *exilia municipia*, Pembroke, Dundunnolf, Down City, and Carrick.

[3] This word must not be understood to mean that this new type of castle was Edward's invention, nor even that he was the first to introduce it into Europe from Palestine ; it was used by the Hohenstauffen emperors as early as 1224. See Köhler, *Entwickelung des Kriegswesen*, iii., 475.

sites in England can be pointed out where mottes are
known to have existed formerly, but where now not a
vestige is left.[1]   There are many other cases where the
Edwardian castle shows not a trace of any former
earthworks, but where a motte and bailey a little distance off probably represents the original wooden
castle.[2]

The passion for identifying existing earthworks
with sites mentioned in ancient Irish history or
legend has been a most serious hindrance to the
progress of real archæological knowledge in Ireland.
It is not until one begins to look into this matter
that one finds out what giddy guesswork most of
these identifications of Irish place-names really are.
O'Donovan was undoubtedly a great Irish scholar,
and his editions of the *Book of Rights* and the
Annals of the Four Masters are of the highest importance.   The topographical notes to these works
are generally accepted as final.   But let us see what
his method was in this part of his labours.   In the
Book of Rights, he says very naïvely, about a place
called Ladhrann or Ardladhrann, " I cannot find any
place in Wexford according with the notices of this
place except Ardamine, on the sea-coast, where there is
a remarkable *moat*." [3]   No modern philologist, we think,
would admit that Ardamine could be descended from
Ardladhrann.   In the same way O'Donovan guessed
Treada-na-righ, " the triple-fossed fort of the kings," to
be the motte of Kilfinnane, near Kilmallock.   But this
was a pure guess, as he had previously guessed it to be
" one of the forts called Dun-g-Claire."   To the antiquaries of that day one earthwork seemed as good as

---

[1] Newcastle, Worcester, Gloucester, and Bristol are instances.
[2] Rhuddlan is an instance of this.   [3] *Book of Rights*, p. 203.

another, and differences of type were not considered important.[1]

The following list of early Norman castles in Ireland was first published in the *Antiquary* for 1906.   It is an attempt to form a complete list from contemporary historians only, that is, from Giraldus Cambrensis and the " Song of Dermot," and from the documents published in Sweetman's *Calendar*, of the Norman castles built in Ireland, up to the end of John's reign.[2]   Since then, the task has been taken up on a far more philosophical plan by Mr Goddard H. Orpen, whose exceptional knowledge of the history of the invasion and the families of the conquerors has enabled him to trace their settlements in Ireland as they have never been traced before.[3]   Nevertheless, it still seems worth while to republish this list, as though within a limited compass, consistent with the writer's limited knowledge, it furnishes an adequate test of the correctness of the Norman theory, on a perfectly sound basis.   The list has now the advantage of being corrected from Mr Orpen's papers, and of being enlarged by identifications which he has been able to make.[4]

[1] It must be admitted that in the most recent and most learned edition of the *Anglo-Saxon Chronicle* the topographical identifications are quite on a level with O'Donovan's.

[2] The *Annals* have not been used, partly because in their present form they are not contemporary, and partly because the difficulties of identifying many of the castles they mention appeared insuperable.

[3] See especially two papers on " Motes and Norman Castles in Ireland," in *English Historical Review*, vol. xxii., pp. 228, 240.   Mr Orpen has further enriched this subject by a number of papers in the *Journ. R. S. A. I.*, to which reference will be made subsequently.

[4] The only castles still unidentified are Aq'i, Kilmehal, Rokerel, and Inchleder.

*Antrim [1] (*Cal.*, i., 88).—A royal castle in 1251. Present castle modern; close to it is a large motte, marked in 25-inch O.M.

Aq'i (*Cal.*, i., 13).—Unidentified; perhaps an *alias* for one of the Limerick castles, as it was certainly in the county of Limerick.

Ardfinnan, Tipperary (*Gir.*, v., 386).—Built in 1185, immediately after John's coming to Ireland. No motte; castle is late Edwardian and partly converted into a modern house; one round tower has ogee windows. [B. T. S.]

Ardmayle, or Armolen, Tipperary (*Cal.*, i., 81).—A castle of Theobald Walter. A motte with half-moon bailey, and earthen wing walls running up its sides, exactly as stone walls do in later Norman castles. Ruins of a Perpendicular mansion close to it, and also a square tower with ogee windows. [B. T. S.] Fig. 45.

Ardnurcher, or Horseleap, King's Co. (*Song of Dermot* and *Cal.*, i., 145).—A castle of Meiler Fitz Henry's, built in 1192.[2] An oblong motte with one certain bailey, and perhaps a second. No masonry but the remains of a wall or bridge across the fosse. [B. T. S.]

Ardree, Kildare (*Gir.*, v., 356, and *Song*).—The castle built by Hugh de Lacy for Thomas the Fleming in 1182, was at Ardri, on the Barrow. There is an artificial mound at Ardree, turned into a graveyard, and near it a levelled platform above the river, on which stands Ardree House.[3] On the west bank of the

---

[1] It should be stated that the great majority of the castles in this list have been visited for the writer by Mr Basil T. Stallybrass, who has a large acquaintance with English earthworks, as well as a competent knowledge of the history of architecture. The rest have been visited by the writer herself, except in a few cases where the information given in Lewis's *Topographical Dictionary* or other sources was sufficient. The castles personally visited are initialled.

[2] *Annals of Loch Cè.*   [3] Orpen, *Eng. Hist. Rev.*, xxii., 249.

Barrow, opposite Ardree, is a low circular motte with
ditch and bank, but no bailey. A piece of Norman
pottery with green glaze was found by Mr Stallybrass,
one foot below the surface in the counterscarp bank.
Mr Orpen thinks this motte may have been the castle of
Robert de Bigarz, also mentioned by Giraldus as near
Ardree, on the opposite side of the Barrow.

ASKEATON, or HINNESKESTI, Limerick.—Built in
1199, probably by Hamo de Valoignes.[1] An excellent
instance of a motte-and-bailey castle, where the motte
is of natural rock. The splendid keep and hall are of
the 15th century, but there are two older towers, which
might date from 1199. This natural motte has been
identified with the ancient Irish fort of Gephthine
(Askeaton = Eas Gephthine), mentioned in the *Book of
Rights*. But this work does not mention any *fort* at
Gephthine, only the place, in a list which is clearly one
of lands (perhaps mensal lands), not of forts, as it
contains many names of plains, and of tribes, as well as
the three isles of Arran.[2]

*ASKELON, or ESCLUEN (*Cal.*, i., 91).—Castle *restored
to* Richard de Burgh in 1215; the site is placed by Mr
Orpen at Carrigogunell, which is in the parish of
Kilkeedy, Limerick.[3] Carrigogunell has the ruins of a
castle on a natural motte of rock.

[1] Orpen, *Eng. Hist. Rev.*, xxii., 450, citing from MS. *Annals of Innisfallen.*
[2] The poetical list enumerates the places which were "of the right of
Cashel in its power." The prose version, which may be assumed to be
later, is entitled "Do phortaibh righ Caisil," which O'Donovan translates
"of the seats of the king of Cashel." But can one small king have had sixty-
one different abodes? Professor Bury says "The *Book of Rights* still awaits
a critical investigation." *Life of St Patrick*, p. 69.
[3] *Ibid.*, p. 449. See Westropp, *Trans. R. I. A.*, xxvi. (c), p. 146. Mr
Orpen informs me that the *Black Book of Limerick* contains a charter of
William de Burgo which mentions "Ecclesia de Escluana alias Kilkyde."
No. cxxxv.

*ATHLONE, Roscommon (*Cal.*, i., 80).—Built in 1210 by the Justiciar, John de Gray. The keep is placed on a lofty motte, which has been revetted with masonry. Turlough O'Connor built a *caislen* at Athlone in 1129, but it was not even on the site of the Norman castle, for which John obtained land from the church, as already stated.

BAGINBUN (*Gir.*, i., 13; *Song*, 1406).—Mr Orpen has proved that this was the spot where Raymond le Gros landed and entrenched himself for four months.[1] It is a headland on the sea-coast, and headland castles seldom have mottes, as they were not needed on a promontory washed on three sides by the sea. Moreover, Baginbun was of the nature of a temporary fort rather than a residential castle, and it is to be noted that Giraldus calls it "a poor sort of a castle of stakes and sods." Still, the small inner area, ditched off with a double ditch, and the large area, also ditched, roughly correspond to the motte-and-bailey plan. [B. T. S.]

BALIMORE EUSTACE, Kildare (*Cal.*, i., 28).—A castle of the Archbishop of Dublin. A motte, with a remarkable platform attached to one side (*cf.* Wigmore Castle). No bailey now; no stone castle. [B. T. S.]

CAHERCONLISH (Karkinlis, Kakaulis, *Cal.*, i., 81).— Castle of Theobald Fitz Walter. There is nothing left above ground but a chimney of late date. A few yards from it is a hillock, which has very much the appearance of a mutilated motte. [E. S. A.] Mr Orpen, however, thinks that Theobald's castle may have been at Knockatancashlane, "the hill of the old castle," a townland a little to the north of Caherconlish.[2]

CARBURY, Kildare.—The *Song* says Meiler Fitz

---

[1] *Journ. R. S. A. I.*, 1898, 155 ; and 1904, 354.
[2] *Eng. Hist. Rev.*, xxii., 452.

Henry first got Carbury, so the castle was probably his. It is a motte with two baileys, one of imperfect outline, the other a curious little half-circle. A 15th-century castle is built against the side of the motte. [B. T. S.]

CARLINGFORD, Louth (*Cal.*, i., 95).—Apparently a royal castle (*Cal.*, i., 156), first mentioned in 1215. It stands on a rock, which might possibly have been a former motte. There certainly has been a former castle, for the present ruin is Edwardian in plan and in every detail. [E. S. A.]

CARRICK, Wexford (*Gir.*, v., 245).—This again seems to be one of the temporary forts built by the first invaders (in this case Fitz Stephen), in a strong natural situation, and Giraldus applies to it the same contemptuous language as to Baginbun. There is no motte, but an oval area of 45 yards by 25 is ditched and banked ; a modern imitation of a round tower stands within the enclosure. [B. T. S.]

CARRICKFERGUS, Antrim (*Cal.*, i., 107).—This was probably one of the castles built by John de Courcy, the conqueror of Ulster. The gatehouse and mural towers are late, but the keep may well be of De Courcy's time, and furnishes an excellent instance of a castle on the keep-and-bailey plan, built by the Normans in stone from the beginning. [E. S. A.]

CASTLETOWN DELVIN, Westmeath [*Gir.*, v., 356].— Castle of Gilbert de Nungent. A motte, with a garden at base, which *may* have been the bailey ; near it the stone castle, a keep with round towers at the angles, probably not as early as John's reign. [B. T. S.]

CLONARD, Meath (*Gir.*, v., 356).—Built by Hugh de Lacy about 1182. A motte, with broad ditch and curious little oblong bailey ; no remains in masonry. [B. T. S.]

CLONMACNOISE, King's Co. (*Cal.*, i., 94).—First contemporary mention 1215 ; the *Annals of Loch Cè* say it
was built in 1214 "by the foreigners." A royal castle.
A large motte with bailey attached ; the wing walls of
the bailey run up the motte. The importance of the
castle is shown by the fact that a stone keep was added
not very long after it was built. [B. T. S.]

*COLLACHT (*Gir.*, v., 355).—Castle of John of Hereford. Collacht appears to be a scribal error for Tullaght,
now Tullow, Carlow.[1] The site of the castle is marked
on the 6-inch O.M. ; it has been visited by Mr G. H.
Orpen, who found very clear indications of a motte and
bailey. (See Appendix L.)

CROMETH (*Cal.*, i., 91).—Castle of Maurice FitzGerald.
Supposed to be Croom, Limerick, though the identification is by no means certain.[2] There are the ruins of
an Edwardian castle at Croom ; no motte. [E. S. A.]

DOWNPATRICK, Down (*Gir.*, v., 345).—The traveller
approaching Downpatrick sees a number of small hills
which no doubt have once been islands rising out of
the swamps of the Quoyle. On one of these hills stands
the town and its cathedral ; on another, to the east, but
separated from the town by a very steep descent and a
brook, stands a motte and bailey of the usual Norman
type. It occupies the whole summit of the small hill, so
that the banks of the bailey are at a great height above
the outer ditch, which is carried round the base of the
hill (compare Skipsea). The motte, which is not a very
large one, has had an earthen breastwork round the top,
now much broken away. Its ditch falls into the ditch
of the bailey, but at a higher level. The bailey is semilunar, extending round about three-quarters of the

[1] Butler's *Notices of the Castle of Trim*, p. 13.
[2] *Eng. Hist. Rev.*, xxii., 458.

circumference of the motte.   There is not the slightest
sign of masonry.   As the size of this work has been
greatly exaggerated, it is as well to say that when
measured on the 25-inch O.M. with a planimeter, its
area proves to be 3.9 acres ; the area of the motte and
its ditch .9, leaving 3 acres for the bailey.   [E. S. A.]
Fig. 45.

This thoroughly Norman-French castle, which was
formerly called a Danish fort, has lately been baptised
as Rathceltchair, and supposed to be the work of a
mythical hero of the 1st century A.D.   Mr Orpen,
however, has disposed of this fancy by showing that the
name Rathceltchair belonged in pre-Norman times to
the enclosure of the ancient church and monastery which
stood on the *other* hill.[1]   We may therefore unhesitat-
ingly ascribe this motte-castle to John de Courcy, who
first put up a slender fortification within the town walls
to defend himself against temporary attack,[2] but afterwards built a regular castle, for which this island offered
a most favourable site.[3]   A stone castle was built inside
the town at a later period ; it is now entirely destroyed.

DROGHEDA, Louth (*Cal.*, i., 93).—First mention
1203, but Mr Orpen thinks it probable that it was one
of the castles built by Hugh de Lacy, who died in 1186.
A high motte, with a round and a square bailey, just
outside the town walls ;[4] called the Mill Mount in the
time of Cromwell, who occupied it ; he mentions that it
had a good ditch, strongly palisadoed.[5]   No stone

[1] *Eng. Hist. Rev.*, xxii., 441.
[2] "Exile municipium," *Giraldus*, 345.   See *Eng. Hist. Rev.*, xx., 717.
[3] *Annals of Ulster*, 1177.
[4] See Orpen, "Motes and Castles in County Louth," *Journ. R. S. A. I.*,
xxxviii., 249.   The town walls are later than the castle, and were built up
to it.
[5] Cited by Westropp, *Journ. R. S. A. I.*, 1904, paper on "Irish Motes
and Early Norman Castles."

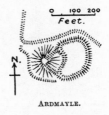

ARDMAYLE.

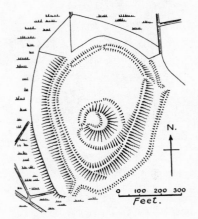

DOWNPATRICK.

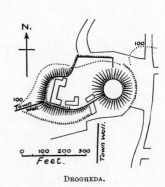

DROGHEDA.

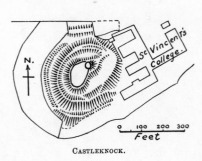

CASTLEKNOCK.

FIG. 45.—IRISH MOTTE-CASTLES.

[*To face p.* 336.

castle, though much of the bailey wall remains ; a late
martello tower on top of motte. [B. T. S.] Fig. 45.

DULEEK, Meath (the castrum Duvelescense of
Giraldus, v., 313).—Probably first built by Hugh de
Lacy ; restored by Raymond le Gros in 1173. The
motte is destroyed, but an old weaver living in the
village in 1906 says that it existed in the time of his
father, who used to roll stones down it in his youth. It
was in the angle between two streams, and there is still
a slight trace of it. No stone castle. [B. T. S.]

DUNAMASE, Queen's Co. (Dumath, *Cal.*, i., 100).—
First mentioned in 1215 as a castle of William
Marshall's, which makes it not unlikely that it was
originally built by Strongbow. The plan of this castle
is the motte-and-bailey plan, but the place of the motte
is taken by a natural rock, isolated by a ditch. There
are three baileys, descending the hill. The stone keep
on the summit is of the 15th or 16th century. [B. T. S.]

DUNGARVAN, Waterford (*Cal.*, i., 89).—Granted to
Thomas Fitz Antony in 1215. To the west of the town
is a motte called Gallowshill ; it has no bailey, but some
trace of a circumvallation. The castle east of the river
is not earlier than the 14th or 15th century. [B. T. S.]

*DURROW, King's Co. (*Gir.*, v., 387).—A castle of
Hugh de Lacy's ; he was murdered while he was building it, because he had chosen the enclosure of the
church for his bailey.[1] A plan in *Journ. R. S. A. I.*,
xxix., 227, shows clearly the motte and bailey, though
the writer mistakes for separate mounds what are clearly
broken portions of the vallum. It is possible that the
bailey may have followed the line of the ancient *rath* of
the church, but it would almost certainly be a much
stronger affair.

[1] *Annals of Ulster*, 1186.

*FAVORIE = FORE, Westmeath.—I owe this identification to Mr Orpen. As Hugh de Lacy founded or endowed the monastery at Fore,[1] this was probably one of his castles, but the first mention is in 1215 (*Cal.*, i., 95). Mr Westropp mentions the oval motte of Fore with its bailey in his list of "complex motes."[2]

FERNS, Wexford (*Gir.*, v., 326).—A castle was built by Walter the German *near* Ferns. Ferns is spoken of as a city in the time of King Dermot. There is no motte at Ferns; the stone castle has a keep, which is certainly not earlier than the time of Henry III. [B. T. S.]

*FOTHERET ONOLAN, castle of Raymond le Gros (*Gir.*, v., 355).—Mr Orpen identifies this with Castlemore, near Tullow, Co. Carlow. There is an oval motte, and a rectangular bailey with indications of masonry.[3]

GALTRIM, Meath.—Identified by Mr Orpen with the castle of Hugh de Hose, or Hussey, mentioned in the "Song of Dermot." Destroyed in 1176; no stone castle. An oval motte; bailey indistinctly traceable. [B. T. S.]

GEASHILL, King's Co. (*Cal.*, i., 30).—Mentioned in 1203 as a castle of William, Earl Marshall. There are remains of a motte, on which stands a 14th-century keep; but the whole site has been so pulled about in making a modern house, drive, and gardens, that nothing more can be made of the plan. The motte, however, is plain, though mutilated. [E. S. A.]

GRANARD, Longford (*Cal.*, i., 95).—Built by Richard Tuit in 1199.[4] A magnificent motte, with a very wide

---

[1] Round, *Cal. of Doc.* preserved in France, i., 105, 107.

[2] "On the Ancient Forts of Ireland," *Trans. R. I. A.*, 1902.

[3] Orpen, "The Castle of Raymond le Gros at Fodredunolan," *Journ. R. S. A. I.*, 1906.

[4] *Annals of Innisfallen.*

ditch, and a small fan-shaped bailey. Foundations of
a shell wall round the top of the motte, and of a small
round tower in the centre. [B. T. S.]

*HINCHELEDER, or INCHELEFYRE (*Cal.*, i., 95).—Said
by Butler (*Notices of Trim Castle*, 12) to be Inchleffer,
Meath, a castle of Hugh de Lacy. No further information.

JOHN DE CLAHULL'S CASTLE.—Mr Orpen believes this
to be Killeshin, Queen's Co., as it corresponds to the
description in the *Song*, "entre Eboy et Lethelyn."
There is a motte there, and traditions of a town.

*KARAKITEL, or CARRICKITTLE, Limerick (*Cal.*, i., 14).
—Castle of William de Naas in 1199. There was a
remarkable natural motte of rock here, with the foundations of a castle upon it, now destroyed.[1]

*KILLAMLUN (*Cal.*, i., 53).—Identified by Mr Orpen
with Killallon, Meath, where there is a large motte.
There is a stone passage into this motte, but no
evidence has been brought forward to prove that it is
of the same nature as the prehistoric *souterrains* so
common in Ireland.[2] In England there is a remarkable
instance at Oxford of a well-chamber built inside a
motte.

KILLARE, Westmeath (*Gir.*, v., 356).—A castle of
Hugh de Lacy, built in 1184;[3] burnt in 1187. A good
motte, with ditch and well-preserved bank on counterscarp; no bailey. No stone castle. [B. T. S.]

KILBIXIE, Westmeath.—Identified by Mr Orpen

---

[1] Orpen, *Eng. Hist. Rev.*, xxii., 449.
[2] "On some Caves in the Slieve na Cailliagh District," by E. C.
Rotheram, *Proc. R. I. A.*, 3rd ser., vol. iii. Mr Rotheram remarks that
the passages in the motte of Killallon, and that of Moat near Oldcastle,
seem as if they were not built by the same people as those who constructed
the passages at Slieve na Cailliagh.
[3] *Annals of Ulster.*

with Kelbery, given to Geoffrey de Constantin (*Song*, 3154); the castle is mentioned in a charter of Walter de Lacy, as well as in the *Annals of Loch Cè*, which state that it was built in 1192. A motte, with a broad ditch, and no bailey; but on the W. side the counterscarp bank of the ditch widens out into a sort of narrow half-moon terrace. This peculiarity may be noted in several other Irish castles. Foundations of an oblong shell on top of motte, and of a small square tower in the centre of this ward. [B. T. S.]

*KILFEAKLE, Tipperary (*Cal.*, i., 29).—A castle of William de Burgh. Built in 1193.[1] A motte and bailey ; trace of a stone wing wall down the motte.[2]

*KILMEHAL (*Cal.*, i., 44).—Mr Orpen regards the identification of this castle with Kilmallock as extremely doubtful.

*KILMORE (*Cal.*, i., 95).—Restored to Walter de Lacy in 1215. Identified with Kilmore, near Lough Oughter, Cavan.[3] Mr Westropp mentions the motte at this place, which is outside the Anglo-Norman area. The castle was wrecked in 1225 or 1226, and no more is heard of it. The Anglo-Norman advance in this direction failed.

*KILSANTAN, Londonderry (*Cal.*, i., 70).—Built by John de Courcy in 1197.[4] Now called Kilsandal, or Mount Sandal, a large motte on the Bann, not far from Coleraine. The castle of Coleraine, inside the town, was built in 1214, apparently of stone,[5] and probably superseded the castle of Kilsandal.

KILTINAN, Tipperary (*Cal.*, i., 94).—Castle of Philip of Worcester in 1215. No motte ; a headland castle

---

[1] *Annals of Loch Cè.*
[2] Orpen, *Eng. Hist. Rev.*, xxii., 448.   [3] *Ibid.*, p. 242.
[4] *Annals of Ulster.*   See Orpen, *Eng. Hist. Rev.*, xxii., 443.
[5] *Annals of Ulster.*

overhanging a river valley. The castle has not only undergone a late Edwardian transformation, but has been cut up to make a modern mansion and farm buildings. No fosses or earthworks remain. [E. S. A.]

KNOCK, or CASTLEKNOCK, Dublin (*Cal.*, i., 81).— Castle of Hugh Tyrrel. An oval motte, walled round the top, carrying on its edge a smaller motte (with traces of a ditch) on which stand the ruins of an octagonal keep. No other bailey; ditch and bank double for more than half the circumference. [B. T. S.] Fig. 45.

*KNOCKGRAFFAN, Tipperary (*Cal.*, i., 27).—Castle of William de Braose in 1202. One of the finest mottes to be seen anywhere. Built in 1192, at the same time as the castle of Kilfeakle.[1] The motte is 55 feet high, has a wide ditch and high counterscarp bank, which is also carried round the ditch of the "hatchet-shaped" bailey, in proper Norman fashion. "There are indications of a rectangular stone building on the flat summit of the mote, and there are extensive stone foundations in the bailey."[2]

*LAGELACHON (*Cal.*, i., 95).—Probably Loughan or Castlekieran, in which parish is the great motte of Derver.[3]

LEA, Queen's Co. (*Cal.*, i., 30).—Castle of William, Earl Marshall, in 1203. A motte with two baileys; motte entirely occupied, and partly mutilated by a 13th-century keep, with two large roundels. [B. T. S.]

LEIGHLIN, Carlow.—Mr Orpen has shown that the fine motte of Ballyknockan answers to the description

---

[1] *Annals of the Four Masters*, vol. iii. See Orpen, *Journ. R. S. A. I.*, vol. xxxix., 1909.

[2] Orpen, *Eng. Hist. Rev.*, xxii., 448. A place called Graffan is mentioned in the *Book of Rights*, and on the strength of this mere mention it has been argued that the motte is a prehistoric work. *Trans. R. I. A.*, vol. xxxi., 1902.   [3] Mr Orpen.

given by Giraldus of the site of the castle of Lechlin built by Hugh de Lacy.[1] There is a trace of a possible bailey. The stone castle called Black Castle at Leighlin Bridge is of very late date. Those who believe that we have authentic history of Ireland in the 3rd century B.C. will be able to believe with Dr Joyce that the description of the annalists identifies this motte with the site of the ancient palace of Dinn Righ, burnt by the chieftain Maen at that date! [B. T. S.]

LISMORE, Waterford (*Gir.*, i., 386).—About a quarter of a mile from Lismore, above a ford of the river, is an excellent specimen of a Norman motte and bailey, called the Round Hill. The name of the prehistoric fort of Dunsginne has lately been applied to it, but purely by guesswork.[2] The *Song* says that Henry II. intended to build a castle at Lismore, and that it knows not why he put it off. Possibly he may have placed these earth-works here, and never added the wooden castle, or else this is the site of the castle which was built by his son John in 1185. The castle inside the town is certainly later than the time of John, as although much modern-ised it is clearly Edwardian in plan. The Norman fragments incorporated in the walls probably belonged to the abbey of St Carthagh, on the site of which the town castle is said to have been built. The so-called King John's Tower is only a mural tower, not a keep. [B. T. S.]

*LOUTH, or LUVETH (*Cal.*, i., 30).—A royal castle in 1204, but it must have been in existence as early as 1196, when the town and castle of Louth were burnt by

[1] Giraldus' words are : "Castrum Lechliniæ, super nobilem Beruæ fluvium, a latere Ossiriæ, trans Odronam in loco natura munito." V., 352. See *Eng. Hist. Rev.*, xxii., 245.

[2] See Orpen, *Eng. Hist. Rev.*, xxii., 456, and *Journ. R. S. A. I.*, xxxvii., 140.

Niall MacMahon.[1] This was probably the "Fairy Mount" at Louth, of which a plan is given in Wright's *Louthiana*. This plan shows "the old town trench," starting from opposite sides of the motte, so that the castle stood on the line of the town banks. The motte was ditched and banked round, but the plan does not show any bailey or any entrance.

*LOSKE (*Cal.*, i., 30).—Mr Orpen has pointed out to the writer that this cannot be Lusk, which was a castle of the Archbishop of Dublin, while Loske belonged to Theobald Walter, and is not yet identified.

*LOXHINDY (*Cal.*, i., 95).—Mr Orpen identifies this name with Loughsendy, or Ballymore Loughsendy, Westmeath, where there is a motte.[2]

NAAS, Kildare (*Gir.*, v., 100).—The *dun* of Naas is mentioned in the *Book of Rights*, p. 251, and in the *Tripartite Life of St Patrick*. By the *Dindsenchas* it is attributed to the lengendary Princess Tuiltinn in 277 A.D. On this "evidence" the motte at Naas has been classed as prehistoric. But as we have seen, a *dun* does not mean a motte, or even a hill, but an enclosure. Naas was part of the share which fell to the famous Anglo-Norman leader, Maurice FitzGerald, and the earthworks are quite of the Norman pattern;[3] a good motte, ditched and banked, with trace of a small bailey attached. The terrace round the flank of the motte may be no older than the modern buildings on the summit.[4] [B. T. S.]

[1] Orpen, "Motes and Norman Castles in County Louth," *Journ. R. S. A. I.*, xxxviii., 241, from which paper the notice above is largely taken. [2] *Eng. Hist. Rev.*, xxii., 242.

The castle is casually mentioned by Giraldus, v., 100, and the date of its erection is not given.

[4] As far as the writer's experience goes, terraces are only found on mottes which have at some time been incorporated in private gardens or grounds.

NAVAN, Meath.—The *Song* says Navan was given to Jocelin de Nangle, and it is known that the castle of the Nangles was at Navan. A lofty motte, with a very small semilunar platform below, formed by broadening out a part of the counterscarp bank of the ditch. (Compare Kilbixie.) [B. T. S.]

NOBBER, Meath (*Cal.*, i., 104).—A castle of Hugh de Lacy. A motte, with traces of a breastwork round the top, and wing banks running down to what remains of the bailey on the S. Two curious little terraces on the N. side of the motte. No masonry. [B. T. S.]

RATH' (*Cal.*, i., 95).—This castle, evidently one of the most important in Ulster, but hitherto unidentified, has been shown by Mr Orpen to be the famous castle of Dundrum, Down.[1] This castle is situated on a natural motte of rock, no doubt scarped by art, with a deep ditch cut through the rock, and a bailey attached. The top of the motte contains a small ward fortified in stone, and a round keep. It is very doubtful whether this keep is as old as the time of John de Courcy, to whom the castle is popularly attributed ; for the round keep without buttresses hardly appears in England before the reign of Henry III. [E. S. A.]

RATHWIRE, Meath.—Rathwire was the portion of Robert de Lacy (*Song*, 3150), and a castle was built here by Hugh de Lacy.[2] There is a motte and bailey, with considerable remains of foundations in the bailey, and one wing bank going up the motte. [B. T. S.]

*RATOUTH, Meath, now RATOATH (*Cal.*, i., 110).—A castle of Hugh de Lacy. There is "a conspicuous mount" near the church, about which there is a legend

---

[1] *Journ. R. S. A. I.*, vol. xxxix., 1909.
[2] Piers, *Collect. de Rebus Hib.*, cited by Orpen.

that Malachy, first king of all Ireland, held a convention of states (Lewis). It is marked in the map.

*ROKEREL (*Cal.*, i., 81).—Unidentified.

ROSCREA, Tipperary (*Cal.*, i., 81).—A motte and bretasche were built here in King John's reign, as is recorded in an inquisition of 29 Henry III. (*Cal.*, i., 412). There is no motte now at Roscrea, but an Edwardian castle with mural towers and no keep; a 14th-century gatehouse tower. Here we have a proved instance of a motte completely swept away by an Edwardian transformation.[1] [E. S. A.]

SKREEN, Meath.—Giraldus mentions the castle of Adam de Futepoi, and as Skreen was his barony, his castle must have been at Skreen. In the grounds of the modern castellated house at Skreen there is a motte, 11 feet high (probably lowered), with a terrace round its flank; some slight traces of a bailey. [B. T. S.]

SLANE, Meath.—The *Song* relates the erection of a motte by Richard the Fleming: "un mot fist cil jeter pur ses enemis grever."[2] It also tells of its destruction by the Irish, but does not give its name, which is supplied by the *Annals of Ulster*. Probably Richard the Fleming restored his motte after its destruction, for there is still a motte on the hill of Slane, with a large annular bailey,[3] quite large enough for the "100 foreigners, besides women and children and horses," who were in it when it was taken. The motte has still a slight breastwork round the top. The modern castle of

---

[1] Mr Orpen says: "The castle was 'constructed anew' in the sixth and seventh years of Edward I., when £700 was expended." *Irish Pipe Rolls*, 8 Edward I., cited in *Eng. Hist. Rev.*, xxii., 454.

[2] Line 3178.

[3] The annular bailey, with the motte in the centre, is a most unusual arrangement, and certainly suggests the idea that the motte was placed in an existing Irish rath.

the Marquis of Conyngham, below, incorporates half a round tower of 13th-century work, belonging no doubt to the stone castle which succeeded the motte.[1] [B. T. S.]

THURLES, Tipperary (Dorles, *Cal.*, i., 81).—A castle of Theobald Walter. Thurles Castle has a late keep with trefoil windows, and according to Grose was built by the Earl of Ormond in 1328. From information on the spot it appears that there used to be a motte in the gardens behind the castle; mentioned also by Lewis. [B. T. S.]

TIBRAGHNY, or TIPPERAGHNY, Kilkenny (*Gir.*, i., 386; *Cal.*, i., 19).—Granted to William de Burgh in 1200; built by John in 1185.[2] A motte, with ditch and bank, and some trace of a half-moon bailey to the north. About 200 yards away is the stone castle, a late keep with ogee windows. [B. T. S.]

TIMAHOE, Queen's Co. (*Gir.*, i., 356).—Built by Hugh de Lacy for Meiler Fitz Henry. A motte, called the Rath of Ballynaclogh, half a mile west of the village. The bailey, the banks and ditches of which seem remarkably well preserved, is almost circular, but the motte is placed at its edge, not concentrically. There are wing-banks running up the motte. Near it are the ruins of a stone castle built in Elizabeth's reign (Grose). [B. T. S.]

TRIM, Meath.—The *Song* tells of the erection of this castle by Hugh de Lacy, and how in his absence the *meysun* (the keep—doubtless wooden) was burnt by the Irish, and the *mot* levelled with the ground. This express evidence that the first castle at Trim had a motte is of great value, because there is no motte there now. The castle was restored by Raymond le Gros,[3]

---

[1] See Appendix M.   [2] *Annals of Loch Cé.*
[3] *Giraldus*, v., 313.

but so quickly that the present remarkable keep can
hardly have been built at that date.[1] [B. T. S.]

*TRISTERDERMOT (*Gir.*, v., 356).—Castle of Walter
de Riddlesford. Tristerdermot is now Castledermot;
there used to be a *rath* of some kind here close to the
town. But Mr Orpen inclines to believe that the castle
Giraldus alludes to was at Kilkea, another manor of De
Riddlesford's, where there is a motte, near the modern
castle. "In the early English versions of the *Expugnatio* Kilcae is put instead of Tristerdermot as the place
where Walter de Riddlesford's castle was built."[2]

*TYPERMESAN (*Cal.*, i., 110).—Mr Orpen writes that
this name occurs again in a list of churches in the
deanery of Fore, which includes all the parish names in
the half barony of Fore, except Oldcastle and Killeagh.
He suspects that Typermesan is now known as Oldcastle
"where there is a remarkably well-preserved motte and
raised bailey."[3]

WATERFORD (*Cal.*, i., 89).—We are not told whether
Strongbow built a castle here when he took the town
from the Ostmen in 1170. The castle is not mentioned
till 1215, when it was granted by John to Thomas Fitz-
Antony. Waterford was a walled town in 1170, and
had a tower called Reginald's Tower, which seems to
have been the residence of the two Danish chieftains,
as they were taken prisoners there. Here too, Henry
II. imprisoned Fitz Stephen.[4] It is possible that this
tower, as Mr Orpen supposes,[5] may have been considered
as the castle of Waterford. But the existing "Ring

---

[1] This keep has a square turret on each of its faces instead of at the
angles. A similar plan is found at Warkworth, and Castle Rushen, Isle of
Man.

[2] Orpen, *Eng. Hist. Rev.*, xxii., 248.

[3] Figured in *The Tomb of Ollamh Fodhla*, by E. A. Conwell, 1873.

[4] *Gir.*, i., 255, 277.   [5] *Eng. Hist. Rev.*, xxii., 457.

tower" on the line of the walls, which is sometimes called Reginald's Tower, is certainly a round mural tower of the 13th century ; there are others of similar masonry on the walls. [B. T. S.]

*WEXFORD (*Gir.*, v., 314).—Probably built by Maurice Prendergast ; first mentioned when taken from his sons in 1176. Mr Orpen writes: " The site of Wexford Castle is an artificial mound. Two of the scarped sides still remain, and the other two are built up above streets. When recently laying some drainpipes, the workmen came upon no rock, but only made earth."

WICKLOW (*Gir.*, i., 298).—Existing when Henry II. left Ireland in 1173 ; he gave it to Strongbow. The Black Castle at Wicklow is a headland castle; it preserves the motte-and-bailey plan, though there is no motte, as there is a small triangular inner ward (about thirty paces each side) several feet higher than the outer bailey, from which it is separated by a very deep ditch cut through the rock. [B. T. S.]

We have here a list of seventy-two castles mentioned in the contemporary history of the Norman invasion. If the list is reduced by omitting Aq'i, Kilmehal, Loske, Rokerel, and Incheleder, which are not yet identified, and five castles of which the identification may be considered doubtful, Caherconlish, Croom, Clahull's Castle, Lagelachan, and Typermesan, sixty-two castles are left, and out of these sixty-two, fifty-two have or had mottes.[1] In five cases the place of the motte is taken by a natural rock, helped by art ; but as the idea and plan are the same it is legitimately classed as the same type.

This list might easily have been enlarged by the addition of many castles mentioned in the various Irish annals as having been built by the Normans.   But this

---

[1] In five cases the mottes are now destroyed.

would have involved the identification of a number of difficult names, a labour to which the writer's limited knowledge of Irish topography was not equal. The greater number of these sites have now been identified by Mr Orpen, and to his papers, so frequently cited above, we must refer the reader who wishes to study the fullest form of the argument sketched in these pages.

One can easily sympathise with the feelings of those who, having always looked upon these mottes as monuments of ancient Ireland, are loath to part with them to the Norman robber. Many of us have had similar feelings about the mottes of England, some of which we had been taught to regard as the work of that heroic pair, Edward the Elder and Ethelfleda. But these feelings evaporated when we came to realise that it would have been highly unpatriotic in these founders of the British empire to have built little castles for their own personal safety, instead of building cities which were "to shelter all the folk," in the words of Ethelfleda's charter to Worcester. In like manner, wretched as were the intertribal wars of Ireland, it would have been a disgrace to the Irish chieftains if they had consulted solely their own defence by building these little strongholds for their personal use.

The Irish motte-castles furnish us with interesting proof that this type of castle was commonly used, not only as late as the reign of Henry II., but also in the reigns of his sons, Richard I. and John ;[1] that is to say, at a time when castle-building in stone was receiving remarkable developments at the hands of Richard I. and Philip Augustus of France. This, however, need not surprise us, since we know that as late as 1242,

---

[1] The dates of the building of numbers of these castles are given in the *Annals of Ulster* and the *Annals of Loch Cè*.

Henry III. was building a motte and wooden castle in the Isle of Rhé, at the mouth of the Garonne.[1]   But those who imagine that the Normans built stone castles everywhere in England, Wales, and Ireland, will have to reconsider their views.

Note.—Mr Orpen's work on *Ireland under the Normans* did not appear until too late for use in this chapter.   The reader is referred to it for a more careful tracing of the history and archæology of the Norman settlements in Ireland.

[1] *Cal. of Pat. Rolls*, 1232-1247.

CHAPTER XII

STONE CASTLES OF THE NORMAN PERIOD

IT may be a surprise to some of our readers to learn how very few stone castles there are in England which can certainly be ascribed to the first period of the Norman Conquest, that is to the 11th century. When we have named the Tower of London, Colchester, the recently excavated foundations of the remarkable keep at Pevensey, and perhaps the ruined keep of Bramber, we have completed the list, as far as our present knowledge goes, though possibly future excavations may add a few others.[1]

It is obvious that so small a number of instances furnishes a very slender basis for generalisations as to the characteristics of early Norman keeps, if we ask in what respect they differed from those of the 12th century. But it is the object of this chapter to suggest research, rather than to lay down conclusions. The four early instances mentioned should be compared with the earliest keeps of France, the country where the pattern was developed. This has not yet been done in any serious way, nor does the present writer pretend to the knowledge which would be necessary for such a

---

[1] The tower at Malling was supposed to be an early Norman keep by Mr G. T. Clark (*M. M. A.*, ii., 251), but it has recently been shown that it is purely an ecclesiastical building.

comparison.[1]　But data exist, which, if they were used in the right way, would greatly add to our knowledge.

In the first place, we have a list of the castles built by Fulk Nerra, Count of Anjou, at the end of the 10th and the beginning of the 11th century, during his life-long struggle with the Counts of Blois for the possession of Touraine. This list may be regarded as authentic, as it is given by his grandson, Fulk Rechin, in the remarkable historical fragment which he has bequeathed to us.[2] The list is as follows :—*In Touraine :* Langeais, Chaumont-sur-Loire, Montrésor, St Maure. *In Poitou :* Mirabeau (N.W. of Poitiers), Montcontour, Faye-la-Vineuse, Musterolum (Montreuil-Bonnin), Passavent, Maulevrier. *In Anjou :* Baugé, Chateau-Gontier, Durtal. "Et multa alia," adds Fulk's grandson. Nine of these others are mentioned by the chroniclers : Montbazon, Semblançay, Montboyau, St Florent-le-Vieil, Chateaufort near Langeais, Chérament, Montre-vault, Montfaucon, and Mateflon. Many of these were undoubtedly wooden castles, with wooden keeps on mottes.[3] In many other cases the ancient fabric has been replaced by a building of the Renaissance period. Whether any remains of stone donjons built by Fulk Nerra exist at any of these places except at Langeais, the writer has been unable to find out; probably Langeais is the only one; but French archæologists

---

[1] The only stone castles of early date in France which the writer has been able to visit are those of Langeais, Plessis Grimoult, Breteuil, and Le Mans. The two latter are too ruinous to furnish data.

[2] Given in D'Achery's *Spicilegium,* iii., 232.

[3] This can be positively stated of Baugé, Montrichard, Montboyau, St Florent-le-Vieil, Chateaufort, and Chérament. M. de Salies thinks the motte of Bazonneau, about 500 metres from the ruins of the castle of Montbazon, is the original castle of Fulk Nerra. *Histoire de Fulk Nerra,* 57. About the other castles the writer has not been able to obtain any information.

are agreed that the ruined tower which stands on the ridge above the 15th-century castle of Langeais is the work of this count,[1] a venerable fragment of a 10th-century keep.[2]

Unfortunately only two sides of this tower and the foundations of the other sides remain. The walls are only 3 feet 6 inches thick, contrasting strikingly with the castles of the 12th and 13th centuries, where the usual thickness is 10 feet, which is often exceeded. This points to a date before any great improvement had taken place in assaulting-machinery. The masonry is what French architects call *petit appareil,* very small stones, but regularly coursed. There is no herring-bone work. The buttresses, of which there are five on the front, certainly suggest a later date, from the size of the ashlar with which they are faced, and from their considerable projection (3 feet on the entrance wall, 2 on the front). There is no sign of a forebuilding. There are only two storeys above the basement. The floors have been supported on ledges, not on vaults. The doorway, a plain round arch, with bar-holes, is on the first floor;[3] it is now only a few feet above the ground, but probably the basement has been partially filled up with rubbish. The first storey is quite windowless in the walls which remain. There are no fireplaces nor any loopholes in these two fragments. In the second storey there are three rather small windows and one very large one;[4] they are round arched, have no splay, and their voussoirs are

---

[1] See Halphen, *Comté d'Anjou au xiième Siècle,* 153.

[2] The building of Langeais was begun in 994. *Chron. St Florent,* and *Richerius,* 274.

[3] It somewhat shakes one's confidence in De Caumont's accuracy that in the sketch which he gives of this keep (*Abécédaire,* ii., 409) he altogether omits this doorway.

[4] Measurements were impossible without a ladder.

of narrow stones alternated with tiles.   In these details they resemble the Early Romanesque, which in England we call Anglo-Saxon.

The Tower of London and Colchester keep are some seventy or eighty years later than that of Langeais, and if we attempt to compare them, we must bear in mind that Langeais was the work of a noble who was always in the throes of an acute struggle with a powerful rival, whereas the Tower and Colchester Castle were built by a king who had reached a position of power and wealth beyond that of any neighbouring sovereign.[1]   Langeais is but a small affair compared with these other two keeps.   The larger area,[2] thicker walls, the angle towers with their provision of stairways, the splayed windows [of Colchester] the fireplaces, the chapels with round apses, the mural gallery [of the Tower] cannot be definitely pronounced to be instances of development unless we have other instances than Langeais to compare with them.   De Caumont mentions Chateau du Pin (Calvados), Lithaire (Manche), Beaugency-sur-Loire, Nogent-le-Rotrou (Eure et Loire), Tour de l'Islot (Seine et Oise), St Suzanne (Mayenne), and Tour de Broue (Charente Inf.), as instances of keeps of the 11th century.[3]   These should be carefully examined by the student of castle architecture, and De Caumont's statements as to their date should be verified.   Not

[1] It is well known that William the Conqueror left large treasures at his death.

[2] The keep of Colchester is immensely larger than any keep in existence. Mr Round thinks it was probably built to defend the eastern counties against Danish invasions. *Hist. of Colchester Castle*, p. 32.   Its immense size seems to show that it was intended for a large garrison.

[3] *Cours d'Antiquités Monumentales*, v., 152, and *Abécédaire*, ii., 413-431. De Caumont says of the keep of Colchester, "il me parait d'une antiquité moins certaine que celui de Guildford, et on pourrait le croire du douzième siècle" (p. 205), a remark which considerably shakes one's confidence in his architectural judgment.

having had the opportunity of doing this, we will only ask what features the keeps of Langeais, London, and Colchester have in common, which may serve as marks of an earlier date than the 12th century.[1]   The square or oblong form and the entrance on the first floor are common to all three, but also to the keeps of the first three-quarters of the 12th century.   The absence of a forebuilding is probably an early sign,[2] and so is the extensive use of tiles.[3]   The chapel with a round apse which projects externally only occurs in the keeps of London and Colchester, and in the ruins of Pevensey keep.[4]   The absence of a plinth is believed by Enlart to be an early token.[5]   But Colchester has a plinth and so has the Tower.   It is, however, very possible that in both cases the plinth is a later addition; at Colchester it is of different stone to the rest of the building, and may belong to the repairs of Henry II., who was working on this castle in 1169; while the Tower has undergone so many alterations in the course of its

[1] As only the foundations of Pevensey are left, it gives little help in determining the character of early keeps.   It had no basement entrance, and the forebuilding is evidently later than the keep.

[2] The Tower had once a forebuilding, which is clearly shown in Hollar's etching of 1646, and other ancient drawings.   Mr Harold Sands, who has made a special study of the Tower, believes it to have been a late 12th-century addition.

[3] Tiles are not used in the Tower, but some of the older arches of the arcade on the top floor have voussoirs of rag, evidently continuing the tradition of tiles.   Most of the arches at Colchester are headed with tiles.

[4] The room supposed to be the chapel in Bamborough keep has a round apse, but with no external projection, being formed in the thickness of the wall.   The keep of Pevensey has three extraordinary apse-like projections of solid masonry attached to its foundations.   See Mr Harold Sands' *Report of Excavations at Pevensey.*

[5] "In the course of the 12th century, the base of the walls was thickened into a plinth, in order better to resist the battering ram." (*Manuel d'Archæologie Française*, ii., 463.)   The keep of Pevensey has a battering plinth which is clearly original, and which throws doubt either on this theory of the plinth, or on the age of the building.

eight hundred years of existence that it is difficult to say whether the rudimentary plinth which it still possesses is original or not.

— Wide-jointed masonry is generally recognised by architectural students as a mark of the early Norman style. Even this is a test which may sometimes deceive; certain kinds of ashlar are very liable to weather at the edges, and when the wall has been pointed at a comparatively recent period, a false appearance of wide joints is produced. Moreover, there are instances of wide-jointed masonry throughout the 12th century. The use of rubble instead of ashlar is common at all dates, and depends no doubt on local conditions, the local provision of stone, or the affluence or poverty of the castle-builder. We are probably justified in laying down as a general rule that the dimensions of the ashlar stones increase as the Middle Ages advance. There is a gradual transition from the *petit appareil* of Fulk Nerra's castle to the large blocks of well-set stone which were used in the 15th century.[1] But this law is liable to many exceptions, and cannot be relied upon as a test of date unless other signs are present. The Tower of London is built of Kentish rag; Colchester keep of small cement stones (septaria), which whether they are re-used Roman stones or not, resemble very much in size the masonry of Langeais. It is of course unnecessary to say to anyone who is in the least acquainted with Norman architecture that all Norman walls of ashlar are of the core-and-facing kind, an internal and an external shell of ashlar, filled up with rubble; a technique which was inherited

---

[1] It is well known that blocks of huge size are employed in Anglo-Saxon architecture, but generally only as quoins or first courses. See Baldwin Brown, *The Arts in Early England*, ii., 326.

from Roman times in Gaul, but which was not followed by the Anglo-Saxons.[1]

The presence or absence of fireplaces and chimneys is not a test of date. Colchester is certainly an early keep,[2] but it is well provided with fireplaces which appear to be original. These fireplaces have not proper chimneys, but only holes in the wall a little above the fireplace. But this rudimentary form of chimney is found as late as Henry II.'s keep at Orford, and there is said to be documentary mention of a proper chimney as early as 816 in the monastery of St Gall.[3] The entire absence of fireplaces is no proof of early date, for in Henry II.'s keep at the Peak in Derbyshire, the walls of which are almost perfect (except for their ashlar coats) there are no fireplaces at all, nor are there any in the 13th-century keep of Pembroke. It is possible that in these cases a free standing fireplace in the middle of the room, with a chimney carried up to the roof, was used. Such a fireplace is described by the poet, Chrestien of Troyes, but no example is known to exist.[4]

But apart from details, if we look at the general plan of these four early stone castles, we shall see that it is exactly similar. It is the keep-and-bailey plan, the plan which prevailed from the 10th to the 13th century, and was not even superseded by the introduction of the keepless castle in the latter century.[5] The motte-and-

[1] Baldwin Brown, "Statistics of Saxon Churches," *Builder*, Sept. 1900.

[2] Mr Round gives ground for thinking that this keep was built between 1080 and 1085. *Colchester Castle*, p. 32.   [3] Piper's *Burgenkunde*, p. 85.

[4] Schulz, *Das Hofische Leben zur Zeit der Minnesinger*, i., 59. Grose writes of Bamborough Castle : "The only fireplace in it was a grate in the middle of a large room, where some stones in the middle of the floor are burned red." He gives no authority. *Antiquities of England and Wales*, iv., 57.

[5] "The type of castle created in the 10th century persisted till the Renascence." Enlart, *Manuel d'Archæologie*, ii., 516.

bailey type was of course only another version of the keep-and-bailey. In this primitive type of castle the all-important thing was the keep or donjon.[1] Besides the donjon there was little else but a rampart and ditch. " Until the middle of the 12th century, and in the simpler examples of the epochs which followed, the donjon may be said to constitute in itself the whole castle."[2] Piper states that up to the time of the Crusades German castles do not seem to have been furnished with mural towers.[3] Köhler, whose work treats of French and English castles as well as German, says that mural towers did not become general till the second half of the 12th century.[4] Nevertheless, as it is highly probable that the baileys of castles were defended at first with only wooden ramparts on earthen banks, even when the donjon was of stone, it is not unlikely that mural towers of wood may have existed at an earlier period than these writers suppose. It is, however, in favour of the general absence of mural towers that the word *turris*, even in 12th-century records, invariably means the keep, as though no other towers existed.[5]

That the baileys of some of the most important castles in England had only these wooden and earthen defences, even as late as the 13th century, can be amply

---

[1] See Appendix N.

[2] Enlart, *Manuel d'Archæologie*, ii., 516. "Jusqu' au milieu du xiiième siècle, et dans les exemples les plus simples des époques qui suivent, le donjon est bien près de constituer à lui seul tout le chateau."

[3] *Abriss der Burgenkunde*, 50-60.

[4] *Entwickelung des Kriegswesen*, iii., 352 and 428. No continental writers are entirely to be trusted about English castles ; they generally get their information from Clark, and it is generally wrong.

[5] This of course explains why the castle of London is always called *The Tower ;* it was originally the only tower in the fortress.

proved from the *Close Rolls.*[1] Colchester Castle had only a timber wall on the banks of its bailey as late as 1215, and in 1219 this *palicium* was blown down and an order issued for its reconstruction.[2]

The arrangements in the stone donjons were probably the same as those we have already described when writing of the wooden ones.[3] The basement was the storehouse for provisions,[4] the first floor was generally the guardhouse, the second the habitation, of the lord and lady. Where there were three or four storeys, the arrangements varied, and the finest rooms are often found on the third floor. An oratory was probably an invariable feature, though it cannot always be detected in ruined keeps. One of Mr Clark's most pronounced mistakes was his idea that these keeps were merely towers of refuge used only in time of war.[5] History abounds with evidence that they were the permanent residences of the nobles of the 11th and 12th centuries. The cooking, as a rule, was carried on in a separate building, of which there are remains in some places.[6]

Occasionally we find a variant of the keep-and-bailey type, which we may call the gatehouse keep. The most

---

[1] The *Close Rolls* mention *palicia* or stockades at the castles of Norwich, York, Devizes, Oxford, Sarum, Fotheringay, Hereford, Mountsorel, and Dover.

[2] *Close Rolls*, i., 195a and 389.

[3] See Chapter VI., p. 89, and Appendix O.

[4] Piper states that the evidence of remains proves that the lower storey was a prison. But these remains probably belong to a later date, when the donjon had been abandoned as a residence, and was becoming the *dungeon* to which prisoners were committed. The top storey of the keep was often used in early times as a prison for important offenders, such as Conan of Rouen, William, the brother of Duke Richard II., and Ranulf Flambard.

[5] See Appendix P.

[6] At Conisburgh and Orford castles there are ovens on the roofs, showing that the cooking was carried on there ; these are keeps of Henry II.'s time.

remarkable instance of this kind in England is Exeter, which appears never to have had any keep but the primitive gatehouse, undoubtedly the work of Baldwin de Moeles, the first builder of the castle. In Normandy, De Caumont gives several instances of gatehouse keeps. Plessis-Grimoult (which has been visited by the writer) has a fragment of a gatehouse tower, but has also a mural tower on the line of the walls; as the castle was ruined and abandoned in 1047, these remains must be of early date.[1] The gatehouse keep is probably an economical device for combining a citadel with the defence of the weakest part of the castle.

We must pass on to the keeps of Henry I.[2] There is only one in England which authentic history gives to his time, that of Rochester.[3] But the chronicler Robert de Torigny[4] has fortunately given us a list of the keeps and castles built by Henry in Normandy, and though many of these are now destroyed, and others in ruins, a certain number are left, which, taken along with Rochester, may give us an idea of the type of keep built in Henry I.'s time. The keeps attributed by Robert to Henry I. are Arques, Gisors, Falaise,

---

[1] De Caumont says these remains are on a motte, a strange statement, as they are only a foot or two above the surrounding level.

[2] No stone castles in England are known to have been built by William Rufus; he built Carlisle Castle, but probably only in wood. As we have seen, several Welsh castles were built in his time, but all in earth and timber.

[3] Built by Archbishop William of Corbeuil. *Gervase of Canterbury*, R. S., ii., 382.

[4] Robert de Torigny, also called Robert de Monte, was Abbot of Mont St Michael during the lifetime of Henry II., and was a favoured courtier whose means of obtaining information were specially good. French writers are in the habit of discounting his statements, because they do not recognise the almost universal precedence of a wooden castle to the stone building, which when it is recognised, completely alters the perspective of castle dates. See Appendix Q.

Argentan, Exmes, Domfront, Ambrières, Vire, Waure,
Vernon, Evreux, Alençon, St Jean, and Coutances.
How many of these survive we cannot positively say ;[1]
we can only speak of those we have seen (Falaise,
Domfront, and Gisors),[2] and of Arques, described by
M. Deville in his *Histoire du Chateau d'Arques*, by
M. Viollet le Duc in his treatise on Donjons,[3] and by
Mr G. T. Clark.[4]

Speaking under correction, as a prolonged study of
the keeps in Normandy was impossible to the writer, we
should say that there is no very striking difference to be
observed between the keeps of Henry I. and those built
by his father. The development of the forebuilding
seems to be the most important change, if indeed we
are justified in assuming that the 11th-century keeps
never had it ; its remains can be seen at Arques,
Falaise,[5] Domfront, and Rochester. At Arques and
Falaise the doorway is on the second floor, which is an
innovation, a new attempt to solve the difficulty of
defending the entrance. The first floor at Arques could

[1] The keep of Caen, which was square, was demolished in 1793. De
Caumont, *Cours d'Antiquités*, v., 231. The keep of Alençon is also
destroyed. There are fragments of castles at Argentan, Exmes, and St
Jean-le-Thomas. The keep of Vernon or Vernonnet is embedded in a
factory. *Guide Joanne*, p. 6.

[2] The writer has also visited Vire and Le Mans, but even if the walls of
the keep of Vire, of which only two sides remain, were the work of Henry I.,
the details, such as the corbelled lintel, the window benches, and the loop
in the basement for a crossbow, point to a later period. At Le Mans, to
the north of the cathedral, is a fragment of an ancient tower, built of the
rudest rubble, with small quoins of ashlar ; this may be the keep built by
William I., which Wace says was of stone and lime (p. 234, Andresen's
edition). It is difficult to examine, being built up with cottages. Domfront, like Langeais, is only a fragment, consisting of two walls and some
foundations.

[3] *Dictionnaire de l'Architecture.*   [4] *M. M. A.*, i., 186.

[5] In speaking of Falaise, of course we only mean the great square keep,
and not the Little Donjon attached to it at a later period, nor the fine round
keep added by Talbot in the 15th century.

only be entered by a trap from the second floor; at Falaise there is a stone stair from one to the other. Rochester is entered from the first floor. The basement storeys of Arques, Falaise, and Domfront are quite unlit; at the Tower the basement has had a number of loopholes, and the angular heads of those which remain suggest that they are at least copied from original lights. The main floors in Henry I.'s keeps are always of wood, but this was not because vaulting was then unknown, because the crypt, sub-crypt, and chapel of the Tower are vaulted, not to speak of many early churches.[1] The four keeps mentioned have all three storeys, thus not exceeding Colchester in height;[2] the Tower has now four storeys, but a good authority has remarked that the fourth storey has not improbably been made by dividing the third.

No marked advance is observable in the masonry of these keeps. Arques is built of *petit appareil;* Falaise of small stones in herring-bone work; Domfront of very small stones rudely coursed; Rochester of Kentish rag mixed with flint rubble. Both Falaise and Dom-front have plinths of superior masonry, but there is always the possibility that these plinths are later additions. The voussoirs of the arches at Falaise, Domfront, and Rochester are larger than the rag or tile voussoirs which are used at Colchester, the Tower, and Langeais. At Rochester and Arques provision is made for carrying the water-supply from the well in the

---

[1] Small spaces, such as the chapel, passages, and mural chambers, are vaulted in most keeps.

[2] Colchester keep has only two storeys now, but Mr Round argues that it must have had three, as a stairway leads upward from the second floor, in the N.W. tower, and some fragments of window cases remain as evidence. *Colchester Castle*, p. 92.

basement to the upper floors, a provision of which there is no trace in the older keeps.[1]

As Robert de Monte says that Henry I. built many castles in England as well as in Normandy, we naturally ask what other English keeps besides Rochester may be assigned to him. It appears to the writer that Corfe and Norwich keeps may very likely be his. Both were royal castles in his time, and both were originally wooden castles on mottes.[2] Both these castles have forebuildings, and neither of them have floors supported on vaults.[3] Corfe has very superior masonry, of larger stones than those used in the keeps known to be Henry I.'s, but wide-jointed. At Norwich only a very small piece of the original ashlar is left. Corfe is extremely severe in all its details, but quite corresponds to work of Henry I.'s reign.[4] Norwich has a great deal of decoration, more advanced in style than that to be seen at Falaise, but still consistent with the first half of the 12th century. Neither keep has the least sign of Transition Norman, such as we seldom fail to find in the keeps of Henry II. Moreover, neither of them figure in the *Pipe Rolls* of Henry II., except for repairs;

[1] The Tower and Colchester keep both have wells, which are seldom wanting in any keep. There was no appearance of a well at Langeais, but excavation might possibly reveal one.

[2] The first castle at Corfe was built by William's half-brother, Robert, Count of Mortain. The keep of Corfe is sometimes attributed to him, but when we compare its masonry with that of the early hall or chapel in the middle bailey, we shall see that this date is most unlikely. Norwich was always a royal castle.

[3] Part of the basement of Norwich keep has pillars, from which it has been assumed that it was vaulted ; but no trace of vaulting is to be seen.

[4] The only decoration at Corfe keep is in the oratory, which being at a vast height in one of the ruined walls is inaccessible to the ordinary visitor. Corfe was so much pulled about by Sir Christopher Hatton in Elizabeth's reign, and is now so ruinous, that many features are obscure. Norwich has suffered greatly from restorations, and from re-casing.

and as Stephen in his harassed reign can hardly have had any money for building stone keeps, we may with some confidence ascribe these two keeps to Henry I.

A few words should be given to the castle of Gisors, which contains in itself an epitome of castle history. The first castle, built by William Rufus in 1096, was undoubtedly a wooden castle on a motte, with a stockaded bailey below it ; certain portions of the present bailey walls rest on earthen banks, which probably belonged to the original castle, and show what a much smaller affair it was than the present one. Henry I., Robert de Monte tells us, strengthened this castle with a keep. Probably this was the shell wall which now crowns the motte ; the smallness of the masonry (stones about 5 inches high, rudely dressed and coursed) and the slight projection of the buttresses (9 inches) agree with much of the work of his time. There would be a wooden tower inside.[1] The chemise or shell wall is pierced by loopholes, a very unusual arrangement ; they are round arched, and of very rude voussoirs.[2] Inside this shell there is a decagonal tower, called the Tower of Thomas à Becket, which is almost certainly the work of Henry II.,[3] as its name would indicate ; the chapel of St Thomas

---

[1] In 1184 Henry II. paid "for re-roofing the tower of Gisors." *Rotuli Scacc. Normanniæ*, i., 72.

[2] It should be remembered that rude work is not invariably a sign of age ; it may only show haste, or poverty of resources. It should also be mentioned that in the *Exchequer Rolls of Normandy* there is an entry of £650 in 1184 for several works at Gisors, including "the wall round the motte" (murum circa motam). Possibly this may refer to a wall round the foot of the motte, which seems still to exist. The shell wall of Gisors should be compared with that of Lincoln, which is probably of the first half of the 12th century.

[3] No decagonal tower of Henry I.'s work is known to exist ; all his tower keeps are square.

is close to it. A stair turret of the 15th century has been added to this keep; its original entrance was, as usual, a door on the first floor, but a basement entrance was built afterwards, probably in the 13th century. Philip Augustus, after he had taken this castle from John, added to it one of the round keeps which had then become the fashion, and subsequent enlargements of the bailey converted it into a "concentric" castle, of which the motte now forms the centre.

There is one keep which is known to be of the reign of Stephen, though not built by him, that of Carlisle, built by David, King of Scotland, in 1136,[1] a time when he thought his hold on the four northern counties of England was secure, little reckoning on the true character of his great-nephew, Henry, son of Matilda. There is no advance to be seen in this keep on those of Henry I., except that the walls are faced with ashlar. The vaulting of the basement is pronounced by Mr Clark to be very evidently a late insertion.[2]

With the reign of Henry II. a new era opens as regards the documentary history of our ancient castles, because the *Pipe Rolls* of that king's reign have most fortunately been preserved.[3] These contain the sheriff's accounts for money spent on the building or repair of the king's castles, and are simply invaluable for the history of castle architecture. The following is a list of

---

[1] Bower, *Scotichronicon*, v., 42. This passage was first pointed out by Mr George Neilson in *Notes and Queries*, 8th ser., viii., 321. The keep of Carlisle has been so much pulled about as to obscure most of its features. The present entrance to the basement is not original.

[2] *M. M. A.*, i., 353.

[3] Unfortunately the greater part of these valuable *Rolls* is still unpublished. The Pipe Roll Society is issuing a volume every year, and this year (1910) has reached the 28th Henry II.

the keeps which the *Pipe Rolls* show to have been built
or finished by Henry II. :—

Scarborough,	built between	1157	and	1174.	Tower
Windsor,	,, ,,	1161	,,	1177.	Shell wall
Orford,	,, ,,	1165	,,	1172.	Tower
Bridgenorth,	,, ,,	1166	,,	1173.	Tower
Newcastle,	,, ,,	1167	,,	1177.	Tower
Bowes,	,, ,,	1171	,,	1187.	Tower
Richmond,	,, ,,	1171	,,	1174.	Tower
Chilham,	,, ,,	1171	,,	1173.	Tower
Peak,	,, ,,	1172	,,	1176.	Tower
Canterbury,	,, ,,	1172	,,	1174.	Tower
Arundel,	,, ,,	1176	,,	1182.	Shell wall
Tickhill,	,, ,,	1178	,,	1181.	Tower

The dates given here must be taken as only roughly
accurate, as owing to the meagreness of the entries in
the *Pipe Rolls*, it is not always certain whether the
expenses were for the great tower or for other buildings.
The list by no means includes all the work which Henry
II. did on his English castles, for he was a great builder ;
but a good deal of his work seems to have been the
substitution of stone walls with mural towers, for wooden
stockades, and our list comprises all the cases in which
it is clear that the keep was the work of this king.[1] We
confine our attention to the keeps, because though mural
towers of stone began to be added to the walls of baileys
during Henry II.'s reign (a detail which must have
greatly altered the general appearance of castles), it is
certain that the keep was still the most important part,
and the residence of the king or noble whenever he
visited the castle.

Seven out of the ten tower keeps are built on

[1] The keeps of Richmond and Bowes were only finished by Henry II.;
Richmond was begun by Earl Conan, who died in 1170, when Henry
appears to have taken up the work. Bowes was another of Earl Conan's
castles. Tickhill is now destroyed to the foundations, but it is clear that it
was a tower. The writer has examined all the keeps mentioned in this
list. It will be noticed that most of the towers took many years to build.

precisely the same plan as those of Henry I.   The chief
advance is in the masonry.   All the tower keeps of
Henry II., except Dover, Chilham, and Canterbury, are
or have been cased with good ashlar, of stones somewhat
larger in size than those used by Henry I.   The same
may be said of the shell walls (namely, Windsor and
Arundel); it is interesting to note that Henry II. still
used this elementary form of citadel, which consisted
merely of a wall round the top of a motte, with wooden
buildings inside.[1]   In three cases out of the ten tower
keeps, Newcastle, Bowes, and Richmond, the basement
storey is vaulted, which does not occur in the older
keeps.[2]   Yet such important castles as Scarborough,
Dover, and Canterbury are without this provision
against fire.   None of these keeps appear to have more
than three storeys above the basement.[3]   None of the
entrances to the keeps (except Tickhill) have any portcullis grooves,[4] nor any special contrivances for defence,
except at Canterbury, where the entrance (on the first
floor) takes two turns at right angles before reaching
the hall to which it leads.[1]   There are nearly always

[1] Henry built one shell keep of rubble and rag, that of Berkeley Castle,
which is not mentioned in the *Pipe Rolls*, having been built before his
accession.   It is noteworthy that he did not build it for himself, but for his
ally, Robert Fitz Hardinge.

[2] The basement storey of Chester keep (the only part which now remains)
is also vaulted, but this can scarcely be Henry's work, for though he spent
£102 on this castle in 1159, it must have been begun by Ranulf, Earl of
Chester, in Stephen's reign.   Moreover, it is doubtful whether the vaulting,
which is covered by whitewash, is really ancient.

[3] Leland says of Wark, "the dongeon is made of foure howses hight,"
but probably he included the basement.

[4] The earliest instance of a portcullis groove with which the writer is
acquainted is in the basement entrance of Colchester.   It is obvious to anyone who carefully examines this entrance and the great stair to the left of it
that they are additions of a later time than William's work.   The details
seem to point to Henry I.'s reign.   The keep of Rochester has also a portcullis groove which seems to be a later addition.

in the keeps of Henry II. some signs of Transition Norman in the details, such as the nook shafts at the angles of the towers of Scarborough and the Peak, certain arches at Canterbury, the Transition capitals used at Newcastle, and the filleted string round the outside of Bowes.

But we have yet to speak of three keeps of Henry II.'s reign which are on a different plan to all the others, and which point to coming changes—Chilham, Orford, and Tickhill.[2] Chilham is an octagonal tower of three storeys, with a square annexe on one side, which appears to be original. Orford is polygonal outside, round inside. Orford indeed is one of the most extraordinary keeps to be seen anywhere, and we must regard it as an experiment, and an experiment which appears never to have been repeated.[3] Instead of the usual Norman buttresses, this polygonal keep has three buttress towers, placed between every four of the outer faces, 22 feet wide, and 12 feet in projection.[4] Tickhill, however, the last keep he built, is decagonal. The object of the polygonal tower was to deflect the missiles thrown from siege engines, and the round tower was evidently considered

---

[1] King, paper on Canterbury Castle in *Archæologia*, vi., 298. We have not observed in any English keeps (except in this single instance) any of the elaborate plans to entrap the enemy which M. Viollet le Duc describes in his article on Donjons. He was an imaginative writer, and many of his statements should not be accepted without reserve.

[2] Wark was also an octagonal keep, but there is considerable doubt whether this octagonal building was the work of Henry II., as Lord Dacre wrote to Wolsey in 1519 concerning Wark that "the dongeon is clerely finished," and mentions that all the storeys but one were vaulted with stone. This makes it almost certain that the castle of Wark was entirely rebuilt at this time, after having been demolished by the Scots in 1460. It is now an utter ruin, and even the foundations of the keep are buried.

[3] At Thorne, near Doncaster, where the great earls Warenne had a castle, there are the foundations, on a motte, of a keep which seems to resemble that of Orford ; it ought to be thoroughly excavated.

[4] These measurements are from Grose, *Antiquities*, v., 74.

an improvement on the polygonal for this purpose, as it subsequently supplanted the polygonal type. It is therefore rather remarkable that Henry II. built both these keeps in the second decade of his reign, and afterwards went on building square keeps like his predecessors. We have seen, however, that he built at least one polygonal tower in Normandy, that of Gisors. We must bear in mind that the Norman and Angevine frontier was the theatre of the continuous struggle of Henry II. with the French kings, Louis VII. and Philip Augustus, and that it is here that we must expect the greatest developments in military architecture.

Speaking generally, we may say that just as there was comparatively little change in armour during the 12th century until the end of Henry II.'s reign, so there was comparatively little change in military architecture during the same period. But great changes took place towards the end of the 12th century. One of these changes was a great improvement in missile engines; the trébuchet was one of the most important of these. It could throw much heavier stones than the largest catapult, and could take a more accurate aim.[1] These new engines were useful for defence as well as attack, and this affected the architecture of castles, because flat roofs covered with lead, on which machines could be placed, were now substituted for the former sloping roofs.[2] There are several payments for lead for roofing castles in the *Pipe Rolls* of Henry II., the earliest being in 1166. In the reigns of John and Henry III.

[1] See Payne Gallwey, *The Crossbow*, 309; Köhler, *Kriegswesen*, iii., 192. The trébuchet is first mentioned at the siege of Piacenza in 1199.

[2] As far as we can tell, the tops of keeps having generally been ruined or altered, the common arrangement was either a simple gable, or two gables resting on a cross wall, such as all the larger keeps possessed.

the mention of lead for roofing becomes much more frequent.[1]

Hitherto, in the defence of keeps, reliance had mainly been placed upon their passive strength, though not so entirely as has been commonly assumed, since it was always the practice to shoot with arrows from the battlements round the roof of the tower. But not only was the fighting strength of the keep increased by the trébuchet, but the introduction of the crossbow gave it a defensive arm of the greatest importance. The crossbow had been known to the Romans, and was used in the early part of the 12th century, but it was forbidden by the second Lateran Council in 1139 as a weapon hateful to God.[2] This prohibition seems actually to have been effective, as William the Breton says expressly that the crossbow was unknown to the French before the wars of Richard I. and Philip Augustus.[3] Richard learned the use of it in the third crusade.[4] But to use the crossbow in the defence of buildings it was necessary to construct special loopholes for shooting, splayed downwards externally, so that it was possible to aim from them. Up till this time the loopholes of castles had been purely for light and not for shooting; anyone

---

[1] Another consequence of the introduction of an engine of longer range was the widening of castle ditches. We frequently find works on ditches mentioned in John's accounts.

[2] Payne Gallwey, *The Crossbow*, p. 3. We find it used by Louis VI. of France, before 1137. Suger's *Gesta Ludovici*, 10 (ed. Molinier). Ten balistarii are mentioned in Domesday Book, but they may have been engineers of the great balista, a siege machine. There is no representation of a crossbow in the Bayeux Tapestry. There are entries in the *Pipe Rolls* of 6, 8, and 9 Henry II. of payments for arbelast', but these also may refer to the great balista.

[3] *Guill. Brit. Armorici Philippides*, Bouquet xvii., line 315.

[4] The bow brought by Richard from Palestine is believed to have been an improved form of crossbow, made of horn and yew, "light, elastic, and far more powerful than a bow of solid wood." Payne Gallwey, *The Crossbow*.

may see that it is impossible to take aim through an immensely thick wall unless there is a downward splay to increase the field of vision. William the Breton tells us that Richard built windows for crossbows to his towers, and this is the first mention we have of them.[1]

From this time defensive loopholes become common in castles, and take various fanciful forms, as well as the commoner ones of the circle, square, or triangle at the base of the loop. The *cross loophole*, which does not appear till the latter quarter of the 13th century, is explained by Viollet le Duc as an ingenious way of allowing three or four archers to fire in a volley.[2] But up to the present time very little study has been given to this subject, and we must be content to leave the question for future observation to settle.[3]

The crossbowmen not only required splayed loopholes, but also niches, large enough to accommodate at least three men, so that a continuous discharge of darts (quarrells) might be kept up. Any defensive loop which really means work will have a niche like this behind it. These niches had the defect of seriously weakening the wall.

Another innovation introduced by Richard I. was

[1] "Fenestris arcubalistaribus," Bouquet xvii., 75. The writer has never found a single defensive loophole in any of the keeps of Henry I. or Henry II. Köhler remarks that the loopholes up to this period do not seem to be intended for shooting (*Entwickelung des Kriegswesen*, iii., 409), and Clark has some similar observations.

[2] *Dictionnaire de l'Architecture*, art. "Meurtrière."

[3] Meyrick in his *Ancient Armour* quotes a charter of 1239, in which the French king grants a castle to the Count de Montfort on condition "quod non possumus habere in eodem archeriam nec arbalisteriam," which Meyrick audaciously translates "any perpendicular loophole for archers, nor any cruciform loophole for crossbowmen." The quotation is unfortunately given by Sir R. Payne Gallwey without the Latin original. It is at any rate probable that the cruciform loophole was for *archers;* it does not appear till the time of the long-bow, which was improved and developed by Edward I., who made it the most formidable weapon of English warfare.

that of stone machicolations, or *hurdicia*.[1]   Whether
wooden galleries round the tops of walls, with holes for
dropping down stones, boiling-water, or pitch on the
heads of the besiegers had not been used from the
earliest times, is regarded by Köhler as extremely doubtful.[2]   They were certainly used by the Romans, and
may even be seen clearly figured on the Assyrian
monuments.   In the Bayeux Tapestry, the picture of
Bayeux Castle shows the stockade on top of the motte
crested with something extremely like hurdicia.   Yet
the writer has found no authentic mention of them
before the end of the 12th century.[3]   The stone machicolations built by Richard round his keep of Chateau
Gaillard are of an unusual type, which was only rarely
imitated.[4]   But from this time wooden hurdicia became
universal, to judge from the numerous orders for timber
for *hoarding* castles and town walls in the *Close Rolls*
of the first half of the 13th century.   Towards the
middle of the 13th century stone brackets for the support
of wooden hurdicia began to be used ; they may still
be seen in the great keep of Coucy, which was begun
in 1230.   But machicolations entirely of stone, supported
on double or triple rows of brackets, do not become
common till the 14th century.[5]

[1] See Appendix H.

[2] *Entwickelung des Kriegswesen,* iii., 417.

[3] In 1186, the Duke of Burgundy caused the towers and walls of his
castle of Chatillon to be "hoarded" (hordiari).   This duke had been a
companion of Richard's on the third crusade.   William le Breton, *Philippides,*
line 600.   Richard's *hurdicia* at Chateau Gaillard were two years earlier.

[4] See Dieulafoy, *Le Chateau Gaillard et l'Architecture Militaire au
Treizième Siècle,* p. 13.

[5] The best French and German authorities are agreed about this.   The
holes in which the wooden beams supporting the hurdicia were placed may
still be seen in many English castles, and so may the remains of the stone
brackets.   They would be good indications of date, were it not that hurdicia
could so easily be added to a much older building.

The greatest architectural change witnessed at the end of the 12th century was the victory of the round keep over the square. Round towers were built by the Romans as mural towers, but the universal type of mediæval keep appears to have been the square or oblong, until towards the end of the 12th century.[1] The polygonal keep was probably a transitional form ; we have seen that Henry II.'s polygonal keep at Orford was begun as early as 1165. Many experiments seem to have been made at the end of the 12th century, such as the addition of a stone prow to the weakest side of a keep, to enable it better to resist showers of missiles. Richard I.'s keep at Chateau Gaillard is a round keep with a solid prow of this kind. Five-sided keeps are said to be not uncommon on the left bank of the Rhine and in Nassau ; this type was simply the addition of a prow to a square keep. The only English instance known to the writer is that of Mitford, Northumberland, but this is merely a five-sided keep, the prow is not solid, as at Chateau Gaillard. The castle of Étampes, whose plan is a quatrefoil, is assigned by French archæologists to this period of experiment.[2] But the round keep was eventually the type preferred. Philip II. thought it necessary to add a round keep to the castle of Gisors, after he had taken it from John, and he adopted the round keep for all his new castles, of which the Louvre was one.[3]

Along with the round keep, ground entrances became

[1] Köhler gives the reign of Frederic Barbarossa (1155-1191) as the time of the first appearance of the round keep in Germany.

[2] In spite of this, I cannot feel satisfied that the keep of Étampes is of so early a date. The decorative features appear early, but the second and third storeys are both vaulted, which is a late sign. The keep called Clifford's Tower at York, built by Henry III. 1245 to 1259, is on the same plan as Étampes.

[3] This keep has been long destroyed.

common.[1] Viollet le Duc states that when the French soldiers broke into the inner ward at Chateau Gaillard the defenders had no time to escape into the keep by the narrow stair which led to the first floor, and consequently this proud tower was surrendered without a blow; and that this event so impressed on Philip's mind the danger of difficult entrances that he abandoned the old fashion. This may be true, but it is a pure guess of Le Duc's, as there is nothing whatever to justify it in William the Breton's circumstantial narrative. It is, however, certain that Philip adopted the ground entrance to all his keeps. In England we find ground entrances to many round keeps of the 13th century, as at Pembroke; but the older fashion was sometimes retained; Conisburgh, one of the finest keeps in England, has its entrance on the first floor.[2]

After the introduction of the trébuchet, we might expect that the walls of keeps would be made very much thicker, and such seems to have been the case in France,[3] but we do not find that it was the rule in England.[4] The lower storeys were now generally instead of occasionally vaulted. In the course of the 13th century it became common to vault all the storeys. But in spite of the military advantages of the round keep, in its avoidance of angles favourable to the battering-ram, and

[1] Ground entrances occur in several much earlier keeps, as at Colchester (almost certainly an addition of Henry I.'s time), Bamborough (probably Henry II.'s reign), and Richmond, where Earl Conan seems to have used a former entrance gateway to make the basement entrance of his keep. See Milward, *Arch. Journ.*, vol. v.

[2] Built by Earl Hamelin, half-brother of Henry II., who died in 1201.

[3] Viollet le Duc, art. "Donjon."

[4] The walls of the Tower are from 12 to 15 feet thick at the base; those of Norwich 13; the four walls of Dover respectively, 17, 18, 19, and 21 feet; Carlisle, 15 feet on two sides. (Clark.) William of Worcester tells us that Bristol keep was 25 feet thick at the base! *Itin.*, p. 260.

its deflection of missiles, the square keep continued to be built in various parts of both France and England till quite late in the Middle Ages.[1] On the Scottish border, square towers of the ancient type, with quite Norman decorations, were built as late as the 15th century.[2] The advantage of the square tower was that it was more roomy inside, and was therefore preferred when the tower was intended for habitation.

We come now to the greatest of all the changes introduced in the 13th century : the keepless castle, in which the keep is done away with altogether, and the castle consists of a square or oblong court surrounded by a strong wall with massive towers at the angles, and in large castles, in the curtain also.[3] Usually this inner quadrangle is encircled with an outer quadrangle of walls and towers, so that this type of castle is frequently called the *concentric*. But the castles of the keepless kind are not invariably concentric; those built by Edward I. at Conway, Carnarvon, and Flint are not so.[4] Instead of a dark and comfortless keep, the royal or noble owner is provided in this type of castle with a palatial house. In England this house is frequently attached to the gateway, forming what we may call a gatehouse palace; good examples may be seen at Beaumaris, Harlech, and Tonbridge.[5] The gate-

---

[1] See Enlart, *Manuel d'Archæologie Française*, ii., 526.

[2] MacGibbon and Ross, *Castellated Architecture of Scotland*, p. 159.

[3] This type of castle was probably borrowed from the fortifications of Greek cities, which the Crusaders had observed in the East.

[4] Conway and Carnarvon consist of two adjoining courts, without any external enclosure but a moat. Flint has a great tower outside the quadrangle, which is sometimes mistakenly called a keep, but its internal arrangements show that it was not so, and it is doubtful whether it was ever roofed over. It was simply a tower to protect the entrance, taking the place of the 13th-century barbican.

[5] Köhler states that the gatehouse palace is peculiar to England: "only at Perpignan is there anything like it." *Entwickelung des Kriegswesen*, iii., 480.

way itself is always defended by a pair of massive towers.

Edward I. is generally credited with the introduction of this type of castle into England, but until the *Pipe Rolls* of Henry III.'s reign have been carefully examined, we cannot be certain that it was not introduced earlier. It was certainly known in Germany fifty years before Edward's accession to the throne, and in France as early as 1231.[1]

It is always supposed that this type of castle was introduced by the Crusaders from Syria. But when did it make its first appearance in Syria? This is a point which, we venture to think, has not been yet sufficiently investigated. We do not believe that it can have existed in Syria at the time of the third crusade, otherwise Richard I., who is universally acknowledged to have been a first-class military architect, would have brought the idea home with him.[2] Yet his favourite castle of Chateau Gaillard, built in accordance with the latest military science, is in the main a castle of the keep-and-bailey type, and has even a reminiscence of the motte, in the scarped rock on which the keep and inner ward are placed.

---

[1] Köhler mentions the castle of Neu Leiningen as the first example in Germany, built in 1224. *Kriegswesen*, iii., 475. Frederic II.'s castles were of this type. The castle of Boulogne, finished in 1231, is one of the oldest examples of the keepless type in France. Enlart, *Archæologie Française*, ii., 534. The Bastille of Paris was a castle of this kind. According to Hartshorne, Barnwell Castle, in Northants, is of the keepless kind, and as the *Hundred Rolls* state that it was built in 1264, we seem to have here a positive instance of a keepless castle in Henry III.'s reign. *Arch. Inst. Newcastle*, vol. 1852. And it appears to be certain that Gilbert de Clare, Earl of Gloucester, built the keepless castle of Caerphilly before Edward came to the throne. See Little's *Mediæval Wales*, p. 87.

[2] French archæologists are enthusiastic over the keep of Chateau Gaillard, the scientific construction of the towers of the curtain, the avoidance of "dead angles," the continuous flanking, etc. See Viollet le Duc, art. "Chateau," and Dieulafoy, *Le Chateau Gaillard*.

The new type of keepless castle never entirely displaced the old keep-and-bailey type. We have already seen that keeps of the old sort continued to be built till the end of the Middle Ages. Hawarden Castle has a good example of a 14th-century round keep; Warkworth a most remarkable specimen of the 15th, the plan being a square tower with polygonal turrets set on each face.[1] In France and Germany also the old type appears to have persisted.[2]

We have already trespassed beyond the limits of our subject; but as we offer this chapter more as a programme of work than as a categorical outline, we trust it may not be without use to the student who may feel disposed to take up this much-neglected subject.

A few words must yet be said about the state of the law relating to castles. Nothing explicit has come down to us on this subject from the 11th century in England, but it is clear that the feudal system which William introduced, and which required that all lands should revert to the king on the death of the holder, forbade the building of any castle without the king's license, and, further, allowed only a life tenure in each case. The Council of Lillebonne in 1080 had laid it down in express terms that no one should build a castle in Normandy without the permission of the duke;[3]

---

[1] This type is extremely rare: Trim, in Ireland, and Castle Rushen, in the Isle of Man, are the only other instances known to the writer. Trim is a square tower with square turrets in the middle of each face; Castle Rushen is on the same plan, but the central part appears to have been an open court.

[2] Enlart, *Archæologie Française*, ii., 516.

[3] *Martène's Thesaurus Anecdotorum*, iv., 118. "Nulli licuit in Normannia fossatum facere in planam terram, nisi tale quod de fundo potuisset terram jactare superius sine scabello. Et ibi nulli licuit facere palicium, nisi in una regula ; et id sine propugnaculis et alatoriis. Et in rupe et in insula nulli licuit facere fortitudinem, et nulli licuit in Normannia castellum facere."

and William, after his great victory over his revolted barons, had enforced the right of garrisoning their castles. He was not able to do this in England, while he must have desired to check the building of private castles as far as possible. On the other hand, he had to face the dilemma that no Norman land-holder would be safe in his usurped estates without the shelter of a castle. In this situation we have the elements of the civil strife which burst forth in Stephen's reign, and which was ended by what we may call the anti-castle policy of Henry II.[1]

The rights secured by this able king were often recklessly sold by his successors, but in the reign of Henry III. it was evidently illegal even to fortify an ordinary house with a ditch and stockade without royal permission.[2]

Feudalism was an inevitable phase in the evolution of the Western nations, and it ought neither to be idealised nor execrated. After the break-up of the tribal system the nations of Europe sought refuge in the forms of imperialism which were devised Charlemagne, and even the small and distant island of England strove to move in the same direction. But the times were not ripe for centralisation on so great a scale, and when the system of the Carlovingian Empire gave way under the inrush of Northmen and Huns, European society would have fallen into ruin had it not been for the institutions of feudalism. These offered,

---

[1] The document which calls itself *Leges Henrici Primi*, x., I, declares the "castellatio trium scannorum" to be a right of the king. *Scannorum* is clearly *scamnorum*, banks. It is noteworthy that a motte-and-bailey castle is actually a fortification with three banks : one round the top of the motte, one round the edge of the bailey, one on the counterscarp of the ditch.

[2] See the case of Benhall, *Close Rolls*, ii., 52b (1225).

in place of the old blood bond of the tribe, a social compact which, though itself artificial, was so admirably adapted to the general need that it was speedily adopted by all the progressive nations of Europe. The great merit of feudalism was that it replaced the collective responsibility of the tribe by the individual responsibility of the man to his lord, and of the lord to his man. In an age when the decay of mutual trust was the worst evil of society it laid stress on individual loyalty, and insisted that personal honour should consist in the fulfilment of obligations. Being a system so wholly personal, its usefulness depended largely on the nature of the person in power, and it was therefore liable to great abuses.

But it is probable that feudalism worked better on the whole in England than in any other part of Western Europe. The worst evils of French feudalism never appeared in this country, except during the short and disastrous reign of Stephen. The strong kings of the Norman and Plantagenet Houses held in check the turbulence of the barons; and private war was never allowed to become here, as it was on the Continent, a standing evil. To follow out this subject would lead us beyond the limits of this book, but it is interesting to remember that not only the picturesque ruins of our castles, but also the neglected green hillocks of which we have treated in this work, while they point to the skilful machinery by which the Norman Conquest was riveted on the land, bear witness also to something still more important. They tell of a period of discipline and education through which the English people passed, when in spite of much oppression and sometimes even cruelty, seeds of many noble and useful things were sown, from which succeeding generations have garnered the enduring fruit.

APPENDICES

APPENDIX A

PRIMITIVE FOLK-MOOTS

THE popular meetings of the Anglo-Saxons, those of the hundred and the shire, were held in the open air. Since many of those who attended them had to travel far, some sign was necessary to mark out the place of meeting, and some striking feature, such as a hillock, or a particular tree, or an ancient · barrow, was chosen. Thus we have the Shire Oak, near Leeds, which gives its name to the wapentake of Skyrack; and in a charter of Edgar we find the *mot-beorh* mentioned, and translated *Congressionis Collem* = the meeting barrow. (*M. A.*, ii., 324.) It does not appear that a hillock was an essential feature of these meeting-places, though this is popularly supposed to be the case, because the "Thing-wall" in Iceland and the "Tynwald" in the Isle of Man have hillocks from which laws were proclaimed. The Thingwall, or field of meeting in Iceland had a natural rock just above it, isolated by a stream, and though proclamations were made from this rock, deliberations took place on the level. (Gomme's *Primitive Folk-Moots*, 31.)

The Tynwald Hill, in the Isle of Man, which is also still used for the proclamation of new laws, was probably an ancient barrow, as there are other barrows in the immediate neighbourhood. (Kermode and Herdman, *Illustrated Notes on Manx Antiquities*, pp. 23 and 61.) At Thingwall, near Liverpool, and Thingwall in Wirral, both probably Norse settlements, there is no hillock.

In Scotland, the use of a former motte as a meeting-place for the baronial court appears to have been much more common than in England. Mr George Neilson's explanation of this fact is referred to in Chapter X., p. 307.

881

APPENDIX B

WATLING STREET AND THE DANELAGH

IT has been pointed out by Schmid (*Gesetze der Angelsachsen*, xxxviii.) that the document called *Alfred and Guthrum's Peace* cannot belong to the year of Guthrum's baptism at Wedmore; and Mr J. R. Green (*Conquest of England*, p. 151) goes further, and doubts whether the boundaries laid down in this deed refer to anything except to the East Anglian kingdom of Guthrum. But Mr Green gives no adequate reason for rejecting the generally accepted conclusion that the Watling Street was the boundary between English and Danish Mercia, which is borne out by the following facts: (1) the Danish confederacy of the five boroughs, Lincoln, Stamford, Leicester, Nottingham, and Derby, pretty well covers the part of Mercia north of Watling Street, especially when Chester is added, as it sometimes is, to the list; (2) the division into wapentakes instead of hundreds, now believed to be of Danish origin, is found in Lincolnshire, Notts, Derbyshire, Rutland, Leicestershire, and Northamptonshire. Staffordshire, it is true, is not divided into wapentakes, but it was apparently won by conquest when Ethelfleda fortified the town. Chester was occupied by her husband in 908. Watling Street furnishes such a well-defined line that it was natural to fix upon it as a frontier.

APPENDIX C

THE MILITARY ORIGIN OF ALFRED'S BOROUGHS

KEUTGEN (*Untersuchungen über den Ursprung der Deutschen Stadtverfassung*, 1895) appears to have been the first to notice the military origin of the Old Saxon boroughs; and Professor Maitland saw the applicability of the theory to the boroughs of Alfred and Edward the Elder. (*Domesday Book and Beyond.*)

The *Anglo-Saxon Chronicle*, in 894, speaks of "the men whose duty it was to defend the towns"; this proves that Alfred had made some special arrangement for the defence of the towns; and this arrangement must have been something quite apart from the ordinary service of the *fyrd* or militia, which was only due for a short time. It must have been something permanent, with an adequate economic basis, such as we have in Henry the Fowler's plan.

APPENDIX D

THE WORDS "CASTRUM" AND "CASTELLUM"

IF we take the chroniclers of the reign of Charlemagne and his successors in the 9th century, we find the word *castrum* constantly used for places such as Avignon, Dijon, Macon, Rheims, Chalons, Cologne, Andernach, Bonn, Coblenz, etc., all of which are known to have been Roman *castra*, when there can be no doubt that the *city* is meant. Take, for instance, the *Annales Mettenses* (Pertz, i., 326), 737 : Karl Martel hears that the Saracens have taken "castrum munitissimum Avinionem" (Avignon); he marches against them, and "*predictam urbem* obsidione circumdat." But these cities are not only called *castra*, they are also called *castella*. Thus the chronicle ascribed to Hincmar calls Macon both *castrum* and *castellum* in the same breath. (*Migne*, 125, 1298.) The fortifications built by Charlemagne against the Saxons are called *castra*, *castella*, and *civitates*. (*Chron. Moissiacense*, Pertz, i., 308. *Ann. Einhardi*, ibid., 196, 204.) The camps of the Northmen, which as we have seen, were of great size, are also called not only *castra*, but *civitates*, *castella*, *munitiones*, *oppida*. (*Annales Fuldenses*, Pertz, i., 397.) The camp built by Charles the Bald at Pistes in 868 is called a *castellum*, though it was evidently an enclosure of great size, as he measured out quarters in it for his nobles, and formed an elaborate scheme for its maintenance. (Hincmar, *Migne*, 125, 1242, 1244.) Coming to the 10th century, the following passage from Flodoard will show the vagueness of the words in common use for fortifications: "Heribertus Ansellum Bosonis subditum, qui prædictum custodiebat *castrum* (Vitry), cum ipso *castello* recipit, et Codiacum S. Remigii *municipium* illi cum alia terra concedit. Nec longum, Bosonis fideles *oppidanorum* proditione Victoriacum (Vitry) recipiunt, et Mosonum fraude pervadunt. At Heribertus, a quibusdam Mosomensibus evocatus, supervenit insperatus, et entrans *oppidum*, porta latenter a *civibus* aperta, milites Bosonis, qui ad custodiam loci residebant, ibidem omnes capit." (*Migne*, 135, 297.) Here it is clear that *castrum*, *castellum*, *municipium*, and *oppidum* all mean the same thing, and the one word *civibus* betrays that it is a *city* which is meant. Undoubtedly the chronicler thinks it elegant to change his words as often as he can. *Munitio* is another word frequently used; in classical Latin it means a bulwark, a wall or bank; in the chroniclers of the 10th century it is used indifferently for a town or castle, though certain passages, such as "subversis multarum munitionibus urbium" (Flodoard, i., vi.), show that the right sense is not far from the mind of the writer. The numerous passages in which we are told of monasteries being enclosed with walls and converted into *castella*, show that the *enclosure* is the chief idea which the chroniclers associate with this word. The citations made above are not exceptional, but typical, and could be paralleled by countless others.

Since the above was written, I have read Keutgen's *Untersuchungen über den Ursprung der Deutschen Stadtverfassung*. He remarks that the Latin words for a town (in the 10th and 11th century writers) are *urbs, castellum, civitas*, sometimes *arx ;* for a village, *villa, oppidum, vicus*. This absolutely agrees with what I have observed in these writers, except that I have certainly found *oppidum* used for a town, as in the passage from Flodoard cited above.

APPENDIX E

THE BURGHAL HIDAGE

THE *Burghal Hidage* has been printed by Birch, *Cartularium*, iii., 671. The manuscript is very corrupt, and several of the places cannot be identified. Those which can be identified are: Hastings, Lewes, Burpham (near Arundel), Chichester, Porchester, Southampton, Winchester, Wilton, Tisbury, Shaftesbury, Twineham, Wareham, Bridport, Exeter, Halwell, Lidford, Pilton, Barnstaple, Watchet, Axbridge, Lyng (near Athelney), Langport, Bath, Malmesbury, Cricklade, Oxford, Wallingford, Buckingham, Eashing (near Guildford), and Southwark. The list thus seems to give an outline of Alfred's kingdom as it was at his death, or at the beginning of the reign of his son. Dr Liebermann refers it to the latter date. (*Leges Anglorum*, 9.)

APPENDIX F

THELWALL

A WRITER in the *Manchester Guardian* a few years ago suggested a new solution of the name Thelwall. He believes that the Thelwall raised by Edward was a boundary wall of timber, stretching from Thelwall to Runcorn. The Mersey, he argues, above Thelwall formerly broadened out into a series of swamps which would effectually defend the frontier towards the east. But westward from Thelwall there were no such obstacles, and it is assumed that Edward made a timber wall from Thelwall to Ethelfleda's fortress at Runcorn. Some support to this hypothesis is given in the names of places between Thelwall and Runcorn: Stockton, Walton (twice), Stockham, Walford, Wallmore, and Wall-hes. Further, when the bed of the Mersey was delved for the Ship Canal, discovery was made of "a remarkable series of submerged piles, 9 feet long, arranged in two parallel ranks which were 30 feet apart. The intervals between the piles varied, but seem to have averaged 5 to 6 feet. Between the ranks were diagonal rows of upright stakes, each stake about 5 feet long, extending from either rank chevron-wise to the middle and there overlapping, so that the ground-plan of them makes a kind of herring-bone pattern. By this plan, anyone passing through would have to make a zigzag course. In some places sticks and sedges were found interwoven horizontally with the stakes, a condition of things which probably obtained throughout the whole series. The tops of the tallest piles were 10 feet below the present surface of the ground, which fact goes far toward precluding the possibility that this elaborate work may have been a fish-weir. The disposition of the stakes points to a military origin. So arranged, the advantage they offered to defending forces was enormous." I think it worth while to reproduce this account, especially because of the place-names, but those who are learned in the construction of fish-weirs may perhaps think that the description will apply to a work of that kind.

APPENDIX G

THE WORD "BRETASCHE"

THIS word, which also appears as bretagium, britagium, or bristega, evidently means a tower, as is clear from the following passages: Order from King John to erect a *mota et bretagium* at Roscrea, in Ireland (Sweetman's *Calendar*, i., 412); Order by Henry III. to the dwellers in the Valley of Montgomery "quod sine dilatione motas suas bonis bretaschiis firmari faciant" (*Close Rolls*, ii., 42); Order that the timber and bretasche of Nafferton Castle be carried to Newcastle, and the bretasche to be placed at the gate of the drawbridge *in place of the little tower* which fell through defect in its foundations (*Close Rolls*, i., 549b).

The word is also expressly defined by William the Breton as a wooden castle : " Circuibat castrum ex omni parte, et fabricavit brestachias duplices per septem loca, *castella videlicet lignea munitissima.*" (Bouquet, xvii., 78.)

See also Wright, " Illustrations of Domestic Architecture," *Arch. Journ.*, i., 212 and 301. In these papers it is clear that " breteske " means a tower, as there are several pictures of it. At a later period it seems to have been used for a wooden balcony made for the purpose of shooting, in the same sense as the word "hurdicium "; but I have not met with any instance of this before the 14th century.

APPENDIX H

THE WORDS "HURDICIUM" AND "HORDIARI"

THESE words refer to the wooden galleries carried round the tops of walls, to enable the defenders to throw down big stones or other missiles on those who were attempting to attack the foot of the walls. " Hurdicia quæ muros tutos reddebant." (*Philippidos*, vii., 201 ; Bouquet, xvii.) The word "alures" is sometimes used in the same sense. See a mandamus of Henry III., cited by Turner, *History of Domestic Architecture*, i., 198 : " To make on the same tower [of London] on the south side, at the top, deep alures of good and strong timber, entirely and well covered with lead, through which people can look even to the foot of the tower, and better defend it, if need may be." The alures of the castle of Norwich are spoken of as early as 1187, but this mention, and one of the alures round the castle of Winchester in 1193, are the only ones I find in the 12th century in England.

APPENDIX I

"HERICIO, ERICIO, HERITO, HERISSON"

THIS is derived from the French word *hérisson*, a hedgehog, and should mean something bristling, perhaps with thorns or osiers. Several passages show that it was a defence on the counterscarp of the ditch, and it may sometimes have been a hedge. Cohausen, *Befestigungen der Vorzeit*, shows that hedges were frequently used in early fortifications (pp. 8-13). The following passages seem to show clearly that it was on the counterscarp of the ditch : "[Montreuil] il a bien clos, esforce e ferme de pel e *hericon*." (Wace, 107.) " Reparato exterioris Ardensis munitionis valli fossato et amplificato, et sepibus et ericiis consepto et constipato." (Lambert of Ardres, 623, *circa* 1117.) The French poem of Jordan Fantosme, describing the siege of Wark by the Scots in 1174, says the Scots attacked and carried the *hericon*, and got into the ditch, but they could not take the bayle, *i.e.*, they could not get over the palicium.

APPENDIX K

THE CASTLE OF YALE

IN the year 1693, the antiquary Edward Llwyd was sitting on the motte of Tomen y Rhoddwy engaged in making a very bad plan of the castle [published in *Arch. Camb.*, N.S., ii., 57]. His guide told him that he had heard his grandfather say that two earls used to live there. Llwyd called the guide an ignorant fellow. Modern traditions are generally the work of some antiquary who has succeeded in planting his theories locally ; but here we have a tradition of much earlier date than the time when antiquaries began to sow tares, and such traditions have usually a shred of truth in them. Is it possible that this castle of Tomen y Rhoddwy and the neighbouring one of Llanarmon were built by the earls of Chester and Shrewsbury, who certainly went on expeditions together against Wales, and appear to have divided their conquests? It is to be noted that the township is called *Bodigre yr Yarll*, the township of the earls.

APPENDIX L

THE CASTLE OF TULLOW OR "COLLACHT," p. 335

THIS information is kindly supplied by Mr Goddard H. Orpen, who writes to me: "I visited Tullow lately, and asked myself where would a Norman erect a mote, and I had no difficulty in answering: on the high ground near where the Protestant church stands. When I got up there the first thing that I noticed was that the church stood on a platform of earth 10 to 14 feet higher than the road, and that this platform was held in position by a strong retaining wall, well battered towards the bottom on one side. I then found on enquiry that the hill on which it stood and the place to the N.W. of it was called the 'Castle Hill.' On going round to the N.W. of the church I found a horseshoe-shaped space, scarped all round to a height of 6 to 10 feet, and rising to about 16 feet above the adjoining fields. There is no doubt that this was the site of the castle, and that it was artificially raised. To my mind there was further little doubt that it represented an earlier mote. In a field adjoining on the W. I could detect a platform of about 50 to 70 paces, with traces of a fosse round the three outer sides. . . . This was certainly the Castellum de Tulach mentioned in the deeds concerning Raymond le Gros' grant to the Abbey of St Thomas.—*Dublin Reg. St Thomas*, pp. 111, 113."

APPENDIX M

THE CASTLE OF SLANE

MR WESTROPP says that the "great earthworks and fosses" on the Hill of Slane are mentioned in the "Life of St Patrick" (*Journ. R. S. A. I.*, 1904, p. 313). What the *Life* really says is : "They came to Ferta Fer Fiecc," which is translated "the graves of Fiacc's men"; and the notes of Muirchu Maccu-Machtheni add, "which, as fables say, were dug by the slaves of Feccol Ferchertni, one of the nine Wizards" (*Tripartite Life*, p. 278). It does not mention any fort, or even a hill, and though Ferta Fer Fiecc is identified with Slane, there is nothing to show what part of Slane it was.

APPENDIX N

THE WORD "DONJON"

PROFESSOR SKEAT and *The New English Dictionary* derive this word from the Low Latin, *dominionem*, acc. of *dominio*, lordship. Leland frequently speaks of the keep as the dungeon, which of course is the same word. Its modern use for a subterranean prison seems to have arisen when the keeps were abandoned for more spacious and comfortable habitations by the noble owners, and were chiefly used as prisons. The word *dunio*, which, as we have seen, Lambert of Ardres used for a motte, probably comes from a different root, cognate with the Anglo-Saxon *dun*, a hill, and used in Flanders for the numerous sandhills of that coast.

APPENDIX O

THE ARRANGEMENTS IN EARLY KEEPS

WE get a glimpse of these in a story given in the "Gesta Ambasiensium Dominorum," D'Archery, *Spicilegium*, 278. Sulpicius the Treasurer of the Abbey of St Martin at Tours, an important personage, built a stone keep at Amboise in 1015 (*Chron. Turonense Magnum*), in place of the "wooden house" which his brother had held. In the time of Fulk Rechin (1066-1106), this keep was in the hands of the adherents of the counts of Blois. Hugh, son of Sulpicius, with two other men, hid themselves by night in the basement, which was used as a storehouse; it must therefore have had an entrance from outside. With the help of ropes, they climbed up a sewer into the bedchamber, which was above the cellar, and evidently had no stair communicating with the cellar. Here they found the lady of the house and two maids sleeping, and a watchman who was also asleep. While one of the men held these in terror with a drawn sword, the other two climbed up a ladder and through a trap-door up to the roof of the tower, where they unfurled the banner of Hugh. Here we see a very simple keep, which has only one storey above the basement; this may have been divided into two or more apartments, but it was thought a fitting residence for a lady of rank. It had no stairs, but all the communications were by trap-doors and ladders. We may be quite sure that the people of rank of the 11th and 12th centuries were content with much rougher accommodation than Mr Clark imagined. Even Richard I.'s much admired keep of Chateau Gaillard appears to have had no communication but ladders between the floors.

APPENDIX P

KEEPS AS RESIDENCES

THE description of a keep which we have already given from Lambert of Ardres (Chap. VI.) is sufficient to prove that even wooden keeps in the 12th century were used as permanent residences, and this is confirmed by many scattered notices in the various chronicles of France and England. It was not till late in the 13th century that the desire for more comfortable rooms led to the building of chambers in the courtyard.

APPENDIX Q

CASTLES BUILT BY HENRY I.

THE castles, which according to Robert de Monte, Henry I. built altogether [*ex integro*] were Drincourt, Chateauneuf-sur-Epte, Verneuil, Nonancourt, Bonmoulins, Colmemont, Pontorson, St Denis-en-Lyons, and Vaudreuil. Many of these may have been wooden castles; Chateauneuf-sur-Epte almost certainly was; it has now a *round* donjon on a motte. The "Tour Grise" at Verneuil is certainly not the work of Henry I., but belongs to the 13th century.

APPENDIX R

THE SO-CALLED SHELL KEEP

WE have three accounts of motte-castles from the 12th century: that of Alexander Neckham, in the treatise *De Utensilibus;* that of Laurence of Durham, cited in Chapter VII., p. 147; and the well-known description of the castle of Marchem, also cited in Chapter VI., p. 88. All these three describe the top of the motte as surrounded by a wall (of course of wood), within which is built a wooden tower. The account of Marchem says that it was built in the middle of the area. This supports the conjecture in the text. Mr H. E. Malden has shown (*Surrey Archæolog. Collections*, xvi., 28) that the keep of Guildford is of later date than the stone wall round the top of the motte. Remove this tower, and there would be what is commonly called a shell keep. It would appear, therefore, that it was a common practice to change the bank or stockade round the top of the motte into a stone wall (no doubt as a defence against fire), leaving the keep inside still of wood. Four of the pictures from the Bayeux Tapestry (see Frontispiece) all give the idea of a wooden tower inside a stockade on a motte.

APPENDIX S

PROFESSOR LLOYD'S "HISTORY OF WALES"

I REGRET that this valuable work did not appear until too late for me to make use of it in my chapter on Welsh Castles. It is worth while to note the following points in which Professor Lloyd's conclusions differ from or confirm those which I have been led to adopt.

Aberystwyth and Aberrheiddiol.—"After the destruction of the last Aberystwyth Castle of the older situation in 1143, the chief stronghold of the district was moved to the mouth of the Rheiddiol, a position which it ever afterwards retained, though people still insisted on calling it Aberystwyth" (514). "The original castle of Aberystwyth crowned the slight eminence at the back of the farm of Tan y Castell, which lies in the Ystwyth valley 1½ miles S. of the town. There is the further evidence of the name, and the earthworks still visible on the summit" (426, *note*).

Carreghova.—I ought perhaps to have included this castle in my list, though on the actual map its site is within the English border; but as there are absolutely no remains of it [D. H. M.] it does not affect the question I am discussing.

Cardigan and Cilgerran.—"Dingeraint cannot be Cilgerran, because Cilgerran is derived from *Cerran*, with the feminine inflection, not from *Geraint;* nor is Cilgerran 'close to the fall of the Teifi into the sea,' as the chronicler says Dingeraint was. The castle built by Earl Roger was probably Cardigan" (401). Professor Lloyd afterwards identifies Cilgerran with the castle of Emlyn (661). This seems to me questionable, as the "New Castle of Emlyn," first mentioned in Edward I.'s reign, pre-supposes an older castle, and as I have stated, a mound answering to the older castle still exists not far from the stone castle.

Carmarthen.—Professor Lloyd thinks this castle stood at the present farm of Rhyd y Gors, about a mile below the town; but I see no reason to alter the conclusion to which I was led by Mr Floyd's paper, that the Rhyd y Gors of the castle was a ford at Carmarthen itself. The fact that Henry I. founded a cell to Battle Abbey at Carmarthen (431) seems to me an additional piece of evidence that the castle was there; castle and abbey nearly always went together.

Dinweiler. — Professor Lloyd assumes Dinweiler to be the same as the castle in Mabudryd built by Earl Gilbert, and to be situated at or near Pencader (501). It should be noted, however, that Dinweiler reads Dinefor in MS. B. of the *Brut*, in 1158. I am in error in supposing St Clair to be the castle of Mabudryd (following a writer in *Archæologia Cambrensis*), as St Clair is not in that commote. Professor Lloyd's map of the *cantrefs* and *commotes* differs widely from that of previous writers.

Llangadoc.—"Luchewein" should not be identified with this castle; Professor Lloyd thinks it may refer to a castle at Llwch

Owain, a lake in the parish of Llanarthney, where there is an entrenchment known as Castell y Garreg.

Maud's Castle.—Camden identified " Matildis castrum " with Colewent or Colwyn, but Professor Lloyd is of opinion that "a careful collation of the English and Welsh authorities for the events of the years 1198 and 1231 will make it clear that Payne's Castle and Maud's Castle are the same." This of course does not affect what is said about Colwyn Castle in the text.

Montgomery.—Professor Lloyd deems that the emphasis laid (especially in the *Charter Rolls*, i., 101) on the fact that the building of Henry III.'s reign was New Montgomery, leaves no doubt that the former town and castle stood elsewhere, probably at Hên Domen. This, if true, would greatly strengthen my case, as Hên Domen is an admirable motte and bailey.

SCHEDULE OF ENGLISH CASTLES KNOWN TO DATE FROM THE ELEVENTH CENTURY [1]

IN TOWNS

No.	Name of Castle.	Type.[2]	Head of District T. R. E.	Whole Area of Enceinte or Bailey.	Value.
1.	Arundel	M. and B., O.	...	Whole area 4½ acres	Risen.
2.	Bamborough	K. and B.	...	4¾ acres	Not given T. R. E.
3.	Barnstaple	M. and B.	...	Bailey 1⅛ acres	...
4.	Bristol	M. and B., O.	...	Whole area nearly 4 acres	Not given T. R. E.
5.	Buckingham	M. and B.	...	?	Risen.
6.	Caerleon	M. and B., O.	...	Bailey 4¾ acres	Risen.
7.	Cambridge	M. and B.	...	4¼ acres	Not given T. R. W.
8.	Canterbury (Dungeon Hill)	M. and B., O.	...	Whole area 3 acres	Risen.
9.	Carlisle	K. and B., O.	...	", 4 acres	...
10.	Chester	M. and B., O.	...	First ward ¾ acre	Risen.
11.	Colchester	K. and B.	...	Inner ward and keep about 2 acres / Inner castle about 6 acres	Risen.
12.	Dover	K. and B.	...		Risen.
13.	Durham	M. and B., O.	...	Bailey 1 acre	Fallen, but rising.
14.	Ely	M. and B., O.	...	", 2½ acres	...
15.	Exeter	B. only now.	...	2 acres	Risen.
16.	Gloucester	M. and B., O.	...	?	Fallen, but rising.
17.	Hastings	M. and B., O.	...	?	Risen.
18.	Hereford	M. and B., O.	...	Bailey 5½ acres	Stationary.
19.	Huntingdon	M. and B.	...	Inner bailey 2½ acres	Risen.
20.	Lewes	M. and B.	...	Bailey 3 acres	Risen.
21.	Lincoln	K. and B.	...	", 5¾ acres	Risen.
22.	Monmouth	M. and B.	...	", 1¾ acres	Not given T. R. E.
23.	Newcastle	M. and B., O.	...	Whole area 3 acres 1 rood	...
24.	Norwich	M. and B., O.	...	Inner bailey 3¼ acres	Risen.

25.	Nottingham	M. and B., O.	...	Bailey $1\frac{2}{3}$ acres	Risen.
26.	Oxford	M. and B., O.	...	,, 3 acres	Risen.
27.	Pevensey	K. and B.	...	,, 1 acre	Risen.
28.	Quatford	M. and B., probably O.	...	,, 1 acre	...
29.	Rochester (Boley Hill)	M. and B., O.	...	Whole area about 3 acres	Risen.
30.	Old Sarum	M. and B.	...	Inner ward $1\frac{3}{4}$ acres	Risen.
31.	Shrewsbury	M. and B., O.	...	Bailey $\frac{4}{5}$ of an acre	Risen.
32.	Stafford	M. and B., O.	...	,, $1\frac{3}{5}$ acres	Risen.
33.	Stamford	M. and B.	...	,, $1\frac{3}{4}$ acres	Risen.
34.	Tamworth	M. and B., probably O.	...	,, 1 acre	Not given.
35.	Totnes	M. and B., O.	...	,, $\frac{3}{4}$ of an acre	Risen.
36.	Tower of London	K. and B.	...	Originally ?	Not given.
37.	Wallingford	M. and B.	...	Bailey $4\frac{1}{2}$ acres	Risen.
38.	Warwick	M. and B., O.	...	,, $2\frac{1}{2}$ acres	Risen.
39.	Winchester	M. and B., O.	...	Whole area $4\frac{1}{2}$ acres	Not given.
40.	Worcester	M. and B., O.	...	,, between 3 and 4 acres	Risen.
41.	York	M. and B., O.	...	,, formerly about 3 acres	Risen.
42.	The Baile Hill, York	M. and B., O.	...	,, $2\frac{3}{4}$ acres.	...

[1] Aldreth and Burton are omitted from this list.

[2] M. and B. stand for Motte and Bailey; K. and B. for Keep and Bailey; O. for Outside the Town.

SCHEDULE OF ENGLISH CASTLES KNOWN TO DATE FROM THE ELEVENTH CENTURY—Continued.

IN MANORS

No.	Name of Castle.	Type.	Head of District T. R. E.	Whole Area of Enceinte or Bailey.	Value.
43.	Abergavenny	M. and B.	...	Bailey 1 acre	...
44.	Belvoir	M. and B.?	No	?	Risen.
45.	Berkeley or Ness	M. and B.	Yes	1½ acres	Risen.
46.	Berkhampstead	M. and B.	Yes	3 acres	Fallen.
47.	Bishop's Stortford	M. and B.	No	2½ acres	Risen.
48.	Bourn	M. and B.	Yes	3 acres	Risen.
49.	Bramber	M. and B.	No	3 acres	Risen.
50.	Carisbrooke	M. and B.	No	2¾ acres	Risen.
51.	Castle Acre	K. and B.	No	2 acres	Risen.
52.	Chepstow	M. and B.	No	Whole area 1⅜ acres	Risen.
53.	Clifford	M. and B.	No	Bailey 2¼ acres	Risen.
54.	Clitheroe	M. and B.	No	1 acre	Fallen.
55.	Corfe	M. and B.	No	1½ acres	Risen.
56.	Dudley	M. and B.	No	1¾ acres	Fallen.
57.	Dunster	M. and B.	No	1¾ acres	Risen.
58.	Ewias	M. and B.	?	2⅘ acres	Not given T. R. E.
59.	Eye	M. and B.	No	2 acres	Risen.
60.	Launceston	M. and B.	No	3 acres	Fallen.
61.	Montacute	M. and B.	No	?	Not given T. R. E.
62.	Morpeth	M. and B.	?	?	
63.	Norham	M. and B.	?	Bailey 2 acres	...
64.	Okehampton	M. and B.	No	½ an acre	Risen.
65.	Oswestry	M. and B.	No	?	Risen.
66.	Peak Castle	K. and B.	No	1 acre	Risen.
67.	Penwortham	M. and B.	No	?	Risen.
68.	Peterborough	Motte only now	Probably	?	
69.	Pontefract	M. and B.		2½ acres	Fallen.

No.						
70.	Preston Capes	.	M. and B.	No	Bailey ⅔ acre .	Risen.
71.	Rayleigh	.	M. and B.	Yes	,, ⅔ acre .	Risen.
72.	Richard's Castle	.	M. and B.	No	,, 2½ acres .	Stationary. ?
73.	Richmond	.	K. and B.	No	,, 2½ acres .	?
74.	Rockingham	.	M. and B.	No	First bailey 3 acres .	Risen.
75.	Skipsea	.	M. and B.	No	Bailey 8¼ acres .	Fallen.
76.	Stanton Holgate	.	M. and B.	No	?	Risen.
77.	Tickhill	.	M. and B.	No	,, 2 acres .	Risen.
78.	Tonbridge	.	M. and B.	No	,, 1½ acres .	Stationary.
79.	Trematon	.	M. and B.	No	,, 1 acre .	Fallen.
80.	Tutbury	.	M. and B.	No	,, 2½ acres .	Not given T. R. E.
81.	Tynemouth	.	?	No	,, 1 acre .	?
82.	Wigmore	.	M. and B.	No	,, 1 acre .	Risen.
83.	Windsor	.	M. and B.	No	Upper bailey 6½ acres .	Fallen, but rising.
84.	Wisbeach	.	M. and B.	No	Whole area 4 acres .	Fallen.

It has been thought best to tabulate the *chief* defensible area of each castle. The total area, including ditches and scarps, is liable to great variation owing to the nature of the ground.

INDEX